P9-DWK-888

BREAKERS

OTHER NOVELS BY MARTIN WALSER

TRANSLATED BY
LEILA VENNEWITZ

PUBLISHED BY
HENRY HOLT AND COMPANY

Runaway Horse
The Swan Villa
The Inner Man
Letter to Lord Liszt

A NOVEL BY MARTIN WALSER

Translated from the German by LEILA VENNEWITZ

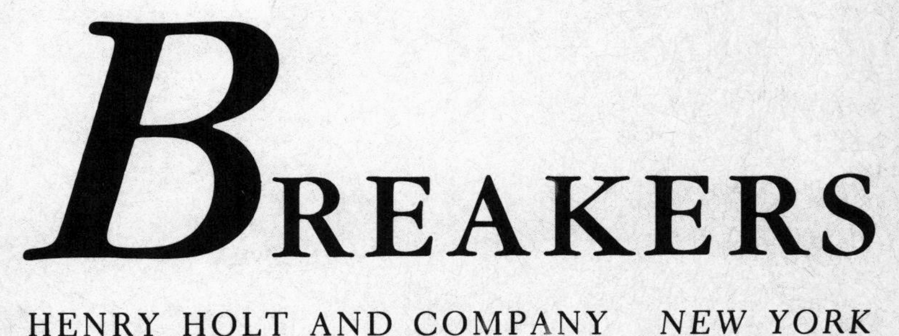

HENRY HOLT AND COMPANY *NEW YORK*

Published in the United States by
Henry Holt and Company, Inc., 521 Fifth Avenue,
New York, New York 10175.
Published in Canada by Fitzhenry & Whiteside Limited,
195 Allstate Parkway, Markham, Ontario L3R 4T8.
Originally published in the Federal Republic of Germany
under the title *Brandung*.

Library of Congress Cataloging in Publication Data
Walser, Martin, 1927–
Breakers.
Translation of: Brandung.
I. Title.
PT2685.A48B713 1987 833'.914 87–126
ISBN 0-8050-0415-7

First American Edition

Design by Kate Nichols
Printed in the United States of America
1 2 3 4 5 6 7 8 9 10

ISBN 0-8050-0415-7

Grateful acknowledgment is made for permission to reprint
the following material:

"Young Girl," lyrics by Jerry Fuller, copyright © 1968 by Warner-Tamerlane
Publishing Corporation. All rights reserved. Used by permission.

"Honey Hungry," lyrics by Moe Lytle, courtesy of Power Play Music/BMI.

"The Panther," in *Selected Poems of Rainer Maria Rilke*,
A Translation from the German and Commentary by Robert Bly,
copyright © 1981 by Robert Bly. Reprinted by permission of
Harper & Row, Publishers, Inc.

TRANSLATOR'S ACKNOWLEDGMENT

My husband William has given me the utmost in patient and knowledgeable help in the work of this translation, and I am deeply grateful to him.

Leila Vennewitz

BREAKERS

1

HALM STOOD FACING THE bathroom mirror. He had finished shaving but couldn't stop contemplating his face with an indissoluble blend of dislike and satisfaction. Even during school vacation, Halm woke up as if he had to go off to school, but once he was up he enjoyed the freedom of letting all his movements slacken a bit. When the phone call came from California, it was just after eight: on a school day it would not have reached him. It was reasonable to assume that a phone call at that hour would be from one of Sabina's relatives. Her mother had been taken to the hospital three days ago and operated on yesterday. Besides, nine out of ten calls were for Sabina. While the children had still been living at home hardly a single call had been for him.

He could tell at once from Sabina's voice that the call was an unusual one. She wasn't speaking, she was shouting. She shouted that she would call her husband to the phone. The voice, not all that remote—Sabina had been shouting simply because California was so far away—belonged to Rainer Mersjohann. Halm could visualize him instantly. In Tübingen. In more than one situation. Rainer Mersjohann was a giant. But not clumsy. A refined giant, so to speak. His hands, which he had a habit of uplifting, were almost priestly. Rainer Mersjohann had never been quite of this world. In an intimidating way. He may have known this, perhaps even intended it. Halm had revered him, as it were. And Mersjohann, the blond, refined giant from Münster, had not minded this reverence.

What time was it in Stuttgart, asked Mersjohann? In Oakland it was shortly after eleven at night. He was calling because someone had just let him down, a young fellow from Austin, Texas. He was supposed to have started on August 26 in Oakland, California, and had been there during the past week to settle in. On Saturday Mersjohann had taken him along to a skat evening, and the next day the fellow had disappeared. Two days later a telegram from the Midwest announcing that the young man had decided not to accept the position: the skat evening had shown him that he wasn't the right person for the job. Would Helmut try and understand that in the U.S. there were some two hundred applicants for every vacant university job, and three hundred for every California one. And that fellow turns it down after one skat evening! Needless to say, the fellow had had references such as Mersjohann had never laid eyes on even in this part of the world, a tropical zone for references. So: today was July 21. . . .

"Over here it's already the twenty-second!" Halm exclaimed, thereby disrupting the flow of the conversation. The great distance noticeably separates the voice from the speaker. You still hear the person in California when he has already stopped speaking, whereas he doesn't hear you yet although you are already speaking, so he starts to speak and only then, while speaking, realizes that on this side of the globe the person has started to speak so both speak at once and the one with the stronger nerves carries on while the other stops.

It was already July 21—Halm now said nothing—and it was too late to arrange for a new appointment before the start of the fall term, that was why he was phoning Helmut Halm. In his opinion, it was unworthy of their former relationship to remain in touch on the level of the Christmas-card industry. Either Helmut would come to Oakland for the fall semester to teach two German courses, or they should release each other from the seasonal mail routine and eventually go to their deaths without ever hearing from one another again.

Halm's ear still remembered Mersjohann's Westphalian lilt from the Tübingen days. At the time he had cultivated a nasal drawl that carried over from sentence to sentence. Rainer Mersjohann was a poet. He was the young genius needed in every college milieu to torment the mass of knowledge-seekers with his example. Professor B., dedicated to the highest requirements of purity, had read aloud in a seminar the flawless sonnets of the twenty-year-old Mersjohann as published in literary magazines. Enraptured and reproachful. Why don't you all produce such sonnets! Of course, Mersjohann had been younger than all the others. It is always one of the attributes of genius that it can produce something at an unconscionably early age.

Halm did not hear that nasal tone over the phone. Evidently Mersjohann now opened his mouth when speaking. In the old days he could only open the middle third of his mouth; the corners of his mouth seemed to have grown together or been sewn together. Those who didn't like him found him irritating. Halm liked him. His gently fluttering, gently fanning, delicately rotating hands compensated for the movement denied to his mouth. And then this man, the best qualified for this course of studies, had taken off, no one knew where to. Ten years later he had surfaced again. Letters from America started arriving at Halm's home address. Then came postcards, then greeting cards. Halm would have liked to ask whether the sleeves of Mersjohann's jackets were still too short. In an apostle play put on by students, Mersjohann had taken the part of Saint John and then retained the jacket style of his Saint John's costume.

"You'll come, won't you?" asked Mersjohann.

"This is the second day of our school vacation," Halm replied. Whereupon Mersjohann: "So you'll come." Halm: he'd have to discuss it with his wife. "Sure, sure," said Mersjohann somewhat sarcastically. He had, he said, been chairman for four years, was now starting his fifth, and he wouldn't want to take on the job again that soon, or ever, so this was an opportunity that would never come again. Halm asked for time to think it over. Forty-eight hours. But he found it exceedingly kind of Mersjohann to have thought of him. Mersjohann did too.

No sooner had he replaced the phone when the next call came. Sabina's father. He asked Sabina to drive to the hospital, the specialist wanted to discuss the results but he wasn't feeling well. Sabina didn't ask why her father hadn't phoned either Elmar or Franz, her two brothers; she merely said: "Yes, of course." "To California in August," said Halm. "To Saint Mary's Hospital at one-thirty," said Sabina. At four-thirty she returned. The usual thing. Opened up, immediately closed again. Sabina had already told her father, who had raised his eyebrows and not lowered them again. She had visited her mother, congratulated her on the successful operation, and her mother had said: "For once you're wearing a pretty dress." "And I," said Sabina, "had been worrying whether this jumble of gold and green stripes wasn't a bit much for the hospital." But her mother had kept reverting to the dress. She asked how much it had cost, she wanted to pay for it because she was so glad that for once Sabina was wearing a pretty dress. Halm said: "That's the Gutöhrlein blood showing up. A Gutöhrlein can never believe that a schoolteacher can clothe and feed a wife."

Sabina telephoned a clinic in the Allgäu region that promised to help cancer patients with liver extracts. Halm said: "To California in August." Sabina said her father was apparently totally unprepared. That was why she had immediately said they must explore every avenue. She had heard of a clinic in Oberstaufen. Helmut could no longer bring up the subject of California. That evening Sabina didn't utter a single word that didn't relate to her mother. And when she said nothing it was obvious what she was thinking about. He couldn't go up to his study and, unseen by Sabina, think about the invitation to California. He had to sit near her and wait for her next sentence and answer it. Sabina had become impervious; she seemed immune to anything that was less important than death.

Not until Halm lay beside her in the dark and could tell from her breathing that she was asleep was he able to think about Mersjohann's phone call. His colleagues would be impressed, the principal annoyed. Four months of not having to go into the staff room! What would the vice-principal remark on if he could no longer remark on Helmut's entrance into the staff room? Halm must accept. He accepted without having discussed it with Sabina. Fortunately Sabina had already left the house when Mersjohann made his second call.

Halm then telephoned the principal. Mrs. Rimmele told him reproachfully that her husband had already left, her tone of voice implying: Now that you've been at my husband's school for eleven years you should know that on the first day of vacation he starts off on one of his famous Rimmele hikes that begin outside the front door in Degerloch, lead up into the Alb hills, and end exactly four weeks later back at the Degerloch front door. Rimmele does not preach hiking, but he acquaints his colleagues with everything he has rediscovered and experienced on his annual four-week excursion. The remainder of the vacation is devoted to the preparation of the circular letter that each staff member will find in his box on the first day of school. At first it had been assumed that Rimmele's dogma of limiting one's vacations to places that are accessible on foot was merely a product of his stinginess. But Rimmele's second dogma, that a person should spend at least one tenth of his life on his own feet was finding more and more disciples. The third Rimmele dogma, that a person must spend one tenth of all his nights sleeping in the open, was prompting fewer and fewer smiles but put into practice by almost nobody except Rimmele.

From the school board office Halm learned that a request for a leave of absence must be accompanied by a statement from the school. So: get in touch with the vice-principal. According to Miss Gebauer, also known as the Spanish Fly, he was available only on

Mondays and Wednesdays from four to six. Halm said: "Thank you." The Fly said: "Not at all." Halm groaned. This was the first sacrifice he had been required to make for California: phoning the Spanish Fly, whom otherwise he wouldn't have had either to see or speak to for forty-six vacation days. She managed to inject a tone of deepest personal injury even into information that could be supplied with but a single word. When she said "Not at all," one was left with a guilty conscience.

Should he call Kiderlen at his home? He admitted to himself that he didn't dare. He should have stayed on at the school down in the city. But the new school was only fifteen minutes away. And he hadn't been able to get along all that well with his colleagues down there. With Rimmele he could have. But then Kiderlen had appeared who, as vice-principal, wanted to raise Stauffenberg School above all other schools in the region, especially above those with a venerable reputation. And since Kiderlen knew that Halm had come from one of those fine old traditional establishments, Halm had from the very beginning been a target for Kiderlen's wit. Or had Halm been the first to make snide remarks? In any case Halm had shrunk from the aggressive I-can-take-on-anyone manner of this superman.

Kiderlen had gradually taken over most of the principal's duties from Rimmele who, despite his extended hikes, was aging rapidly. Kiderlen was the real principal. He wasted no time on protracted hikes. He did 180 push-ups every day and, he used to say with a smile, would do a few more if it weren't for the bother of counting. He was working, he said, toward a rhythmical method so that he could do ten push-ups without counting them. This meant he only had to count eighteen but would have done 180. The world record was held by a Swiss with 1,611. He mentioned this to minimize his own achievement. Ridiculous, a mere 180 push-ups. But then, of course, he was writing textbooks. That was his most important sideline.

During the past year he had filled the staff room with his complaints about the new minister. This new minister of education, actually two years younger than Kiderlen and obviously of the same stamp, was constantly issuing new guidelines, with the result that Kiderlen had to revise for the third time the textbook he happened to be working on. And at this point he would direct the attention of his listeners to his wife, the psychologist, who wrote three to five books in the time it took him to produce one. These books were available from him at a 40 percent discount. The most recent one, dealing with twelve- to fourteen-year-old drug addicts from low-income families, was still being widely discussed.

Halm commanded himself to phone Kiderlen. He couldn't. On a Saturday! The Kiderlens were also famed for all the things that went on in their glorious old house. Unthinkable for him to drive there, ring the bell, and say he was asking for endorsement of his application. Probably no one had as poor a relationship with Kiderlen as Halm. Halm was forced gradually to admit that Kiderlen was admirable in every possible respect. Starting with his outward appearance! Those double-breasted jackets, pinstripes, material always old, faded, but of the best quality. Who aged them for Kiderlen? The material was not worn, merely faded. Consequently, in spite of their excellent cut and their excellent material, the jackets never had the look of a men's fashion magazine. Halm admired Kiderlen. Only he wasn't capable of letting him know it. No doubt he came from a sensitive family, an only son, raised with endless patience and enthusiasm plus constant adulation. Several aunts, who had denied themselves children for his sake, must have taken their turn, day and night, kissing and caressing and praising him. And then there was his wife, the psychologist! Equally tall, equally slim. As blond as he was dark. When Halm was introduced to her at a school function he took her for a doctor. She: That must be because her father was a doctor, a professor. . . . While she spoke, reeling off family details that her husband must have known for years, Kiderlen positively hung on her lips. His eyes shone like those of a child who has received the very presents he had hoped for.

This fellow Kiderlen had never once worn a tie. Not even when the minister of education came to address an assembly. We never know whether we understand our real motive when we believe we do understand our real motive. Perhaps we are merely deceived by a different backdrop that we have shifted in front of the true scenario because the latter would be intolerable for our so-called self-perception. The fact that Kiderlen never wore a tie was by no means the sore point. The really sore point was that Halm despised himself for still consistently wearing a tie. Every morning when he knotted his tie in front of the mirror he reproached himself for not liberating himself from this noose. What he really wanted to wear were lurid scarves, and necklaces made of gold or jade, or even amber. For as long as he could remember. But he had never had the courage. He didn't feel he looked like a person who could wear such jewelry. Then along comes that Kiderlen and proves to him every day that there is nothing easier than to discard a tie and wear scarves and jewelry.

Meanwhile Halm had come to be regarded in the staff room as a stronghold of opposition. Kiderlen was practically on friendly terms with the new minister in spite of the flood of new directives; indeed, he saw to it that these directives were strictly carried out although, in the opinion of many of his colleagues, they served merely to discipline the teaching staff. Of late it was no longer necessary to give advance notice of an inspection visit. At any time any teacher could be surprised by the school administration or by the school board. Just before school vacation, Halm had spoken at a faculty meeting on behalf of a colleague who had received a surprise visit while he was handing back exam papers. Halm's argument had been that an inspection visit was justified while a teacher was teaching but not while he was handing back exam papers. Halm had made some pointed comments on the new practice and implied that Kiderlen was solely responsible for it. Halm had heard himself speaking and not liked what he heard. What concern of his was all this? It was up to his young colleague to speak for himself. Everyone must speak for himself. What Halm would have liked to say was: Some other mock battles, if you please!

But now it was Kiderlen's turn. Our blackener of power, Kiderlen had said, our beatifier of impotence! Machiavelli would have been burned at the stake if Halm had had anything to say at that time, not to mention Ignatius Loyola and Lenin! Kiderlen was rewarded by a burst of laughter, which he waved away.

Until Mersjohann had phoned him, Halm hadn't realized how necessary it was for him to get away from here. He had never allowed himself to admit this because there had been no prospect of it. Now that it was possible there was no suppressing the idea. Just as glowing embers, suddenly fanned by a breeze, will flare up, now the idea flared up in him. He had to get away from here.

Sabina was asleep. Or wasn't she? Each had learned to breathe in such a way that the other would think one was asleep. As long as one could hear that the other was still awake, it was impossible to fall asleep. The next morning there was a friendly argument as to which of them had successfully deceived the other and who had actually fallen asleep first. Each of them invariably wanted to have been the last to fall asleep.

When Sabina returned from her third visit to Oberstaufen, she collapsed onto the garden bench beside Halm and leaned against him with her whole weight. Perhaps it was exhaustion. For the first time in days she patted Otto again. Halm said: "We'll be leaving soon." She nodded. That gave him more courage and he said: "For California." She nodded again. He said: "How do you know?" She merely made a face, which meant: What do you take me for? I've been married to you for a quarter of a century, your chances of hiding anything from me are close to nil. He didn't dare ask whether the liver extracts were helping. He was afraid that, if Sabina had nothing good to report, her face would cloud over again, with that film of estrangement, that layer of aloofness, that pathos of *nolo me tangere*, which she had acquired since returning from her talk with the specialist. It must have something to do with death.

He put a cushion under Sabina's head and went into the house to get a bottle of white wine. When he came back with the bottle and two glasses, she shook her head ever so slightly. There is no more minimal and absolute and considerate way of expressing negation and rejection. Coffee? Coffee, yes. When he came out with the coffee she was still lying on the bench in exactly the same position as before. One hand on Otto's head. For the first time since hearing the verdict, she spoke without being prompted. Once again she began with the specialist. In the midst of breaking the news he had received a phone call and had gestured an apology for the interruption to his explanations. He had already told her that her mother's cancer was the worst kind, an intestinal polyp. . . . "Excuse me a moment." So now a woman he knew was calling to find out how things had been this year in the monastery on Corsica, whether this year the baron—Sabina didn't catch the French name—had been inclined toward exhibitionism or voyeurism. The specialist, who had been vainly trying to interrupt that shrill voice, finally got in a word to say that this year he hadn't been able to rent the monastery at all, the Agnelli family had grabbed it because the increasing security risk promised to be slightly less there. As if to get rid of the shrill voice, the specialist said they would be meeting anyway the following evening at the Kiderlens.

"Aha!" said Halm. "Yes, it's a small world," Sabina said. Still, California is a long way off, thought Halm.

Her mother was in pain again, Sabina said, but she attributed it all to the scar formation. Everything unpleasant is now due to the scar formation. Yet she knows. She doesn't want to put it into words. She is pinning her hopes on the liver-extract treatment. But she knows there's no chance of recovery. But she keeps on hoping, of course. But she doesn't believe it. But she does hope. Without believing. Her father doesn't say anything anymore. Not a word. He sits beside the bed, holding Mother's hand, neither one saying anything. If there's no hope, said Sabina, it had been a mistake to transfer her to the Allgäu hospital. All that wretched business with the intestinal tube, day after day, and the enemas. Before being transferred to Oberstaufen, her mother had been able to have her hairdresser come to Saint Mary's Hospital. Sabina was probably implying that it was not only she but her mother as well who had been in favor of this liver-extract experiment.

The phone rang. Sabina sat up with a start. Oberstaufen? It was Oberstaufen. Her mother wanted to go back to Stuttgart, right now. "Yes," said Sabina. "Maybe it can be fixed up today." Sabina rang the hospital. An hour later the ambulance stopped in front of their house on Buowaldstrasse, Halm was standing with Sabina and Otto outside the garden gate, Sabina got in, Halm walked back with Otto down the flagged path to the house. He said: "Oh, Otto." Poor Sabina: twice in one day to Oberstaufen. But at least this time she doesn't have to drive herself. He said: "Otto, now I'm going into the house to get my Nietzsche. Let's see whether he has anything on sympathy without pity." Soon another horror was to follow on the heels of this one.

He picked up the four volumes and laid them down outside on the table beside the Heine ones. In his second phone call, Mersjohann had asked whether he could give a talk on Heine, which would mean an extra five hundred dollars. A woman refugee from Germany had established an endowment, and every year at the end of October a whole day was devoted to lectures. Since the salary wasn't all that great, he would like to send a few extra lectures Halm's way. So Halm was reading Heine. But now first to Nietzsche. Then it turned out that right now he didn't feel like him either. He wanted to sit with his legs up, contemplate the greenery, and to be conscious of his calmness. Regardless of what was in store for him, he thought, he was calm.

The phone rang again. He let it ring. But the caller was persistent. Halm had to give in. "Lena, it's you! If only I'd known! We thought you two were in Greece." "Sure, Traugott's there," said his daughter. Could she come by, not for just an hour, for a few days, just for a few days, she would explain everything. "But of course, come at once!" said Halm. He could tell from her voice that she was at the end of her tether. She arrived with luggage. Halm paid off the taxi and carried her two suitcases from the garden gate down to the house and inside the house up to the top floor. There were still two rooms known as Lena's and Juliane's, two attic rooms papered by Sabina herself with a floral wallpaper. They were more like jewel boxes than rooms, jewel nests. The growing up of their daughters had inspired Sabina to ever-new decorative visions.

Lena immediately came downstairs with him again. Halm sat down across from her. But Lena, accompanied by Otto, who insisted on resting his nose on her shoes, came around the table to sit down on the bench beside her father, not wanting, evidently, for him to have to look straight at her. He had deliberately sat down exactly opposite her, wanting her to feel that the scars on her face didn't bother him. She must have read his mind.

So: Traugott has been gone for a week. Instead of returning to Stuttgart he had no doubt driven straight on to Greece with the girl he'd just taken the supplementary course with in Munich, and they were now probably on the island of Sakontos where he had been last year with Lena, in the cottage they had reserved again for this year. "What kind of a course was that in Munich?" Halm asked. "Speech therapy," answered Lena. "Perhaps on his way back from Greece, fatigue will again cause him to drive over the embankment near Salzburg, as he did on your way back last year," said Halm. "I don't think so," said Lena. "Traugott never makes the same mistake twice." "Oh, Lena," said Halm, putting his arm around her. "I so much wanted to object," he went on, "but because I didn't trust my motives I didn't dare. I really didn't like him. All that meditation business, that religion out of books, but I didn't trust myself to show my dislike."

"Don't worry," said Lena, "he noticed right away that you don't like him." Helmut said it wasn't until she had her breasts reduced to please Traugott that he knew he had failed as a father. He should have warned Lena of this self-idolater. Then the accident. "So now he's gone. Be glad, Lena. Your lovely breasts. How could he? Then causes you to crash through a windshield! Are you still going to that scar-remover?" No, she wasn't, he was terrible.

"You're coming with us to California," said Halm. "They have the best surgeons in the world there, they'll fix you up so there'll be nothing left to see. As it is, there's hardly anything to be seen." Lena went indoors. A few minutes later she could be heard playing the piano.

That evening Sabina phoned. Her mother was home again. She would spend the night with her. Sabina's voice said more than her words. Next morning around nine she came back. Either Sabina's face had grown smaller or her eyes larger. The face had stopped like a clock. It bore no resemblance to the kind of face normally brought to a family breakfast table. Lena's presence had no visible effect on that face. Should he cry: "Sabina"? She was carrying a pair of dainty slippers in her hand, more fanciful than any Sabina would ever buy. Carefully, as if this were her sole purpose in entering the room, she placed them on the table. They must have belonged to her mother. Sabina said: "So now she's dead."

Halm drew a deep, audible breath through his nose. But, she went on, her father didn't know yet. That was asking too much of her: he wouldn't be able to bear it, he wouldn't be able to face a funeral. They would have to let him go on believing that Mother was still in Oberstaufen. No, that wouldn't do either. There was only one solution. Sabina went to the telephone and called up Dr. Weichbrod. Would he, as a doctor and a friend, undertake to tell her father that his wife was dead?

Then she began to talk: the people at Saint Mary's Hospital had immediately drawn five liters of water off her mother. They could only shake their heads when they saw her. Even on the way there she had been vomiting all the time. It was like diarrhea. And smelled like it too. She was hot, inside and out. They had wrapped her in cold sheets. It didn't help. At eight o'clock the priest looked in. Would she permit him to anoint her? "Are things that bad, then?" she had asked. No, it wasn't an extreme unction, it was to aid the healing process. Halm gave another loud sniff. Ten minutes later she was asleep. From four o'clock her breathing becomes more labored. Her mouth drops open, her head jerks forward. "Like a bird when it's dying," said Sabina. Her hair and head vibrated. She pressed her feet against the foot of the bed. Everything vibrated. Feet and legs cold, up to the knees. She managed to ask Sabina to open the window. She knew exactly how those hospital windows were opened and could tell Sabina where to find the handle and how to use it. Then she said nothing. At seven the priest arrived; he walked over to the bed carrying the host, then said: "Oh, your mother's dead."

The staging of the funeral at Prag Cemetery went off surprisingly smoothly. And a production it was, with the black-clad procession walking toward the bombastic architecture of a Babylonian fin-de-siècle monument. Up the operatic stairs. Inside, organ music. The coffin was slid into a quaint kind of housing. With that huge mountain of flowers it was hardly noticeable that, at the end of the ceremony, the coffin was missing. And the roaring, rushing sound could just as well have emanated from the organ as from the furnace. Halm was thinking: perhaps the thoughts I am having are exactly right for this kind of funeral. He found any kind of funeral appropriate. In the face of death, anything is appropriate.

They spent that afternoon with her father, her brothers Franz and Elmar, and Elmar's wife Gitte. Her father refused to enter the house. They had foreseen that. Many years ago he had told Halm he hadn't been well treated in this house by his wife's mother. Mr. Gottschalk came from Heslach, a penniless schoolteacher who had married the Heimbucher girl. Although the Heimbuchers owned no big business, no factory, not even a butcher shop, they did have this house on Buowaldstrasse. It was their pride and joy. The "country house." That's what the builder, Kugel the baker, had called it, the originator of "Sillenbuch Farmers' Bread," which had enabled him to build a house in the country near the woods. But it wasn't the Heimbuchers who had been smart and efficient either, it was the Gutöhrleins. Heimbucher the postal clerk was lucky to have married a Gutöhrlein; that was how he came by way of the house. Gottschalk the schoolteacher was lucky to have married a Heimbucher who was descended from the Gutöhrleins. How else could a hard-up schoolteacher have acquired a house, and a country house at that?

Sabina's father had moved out of the country house as soon as he could. Needless to say, it wasn't he who had earned the money to buy the apartment on Hegelplatz into which he and his wife had moved: it was his wife, a direct descendant of the efficient Gutöhrleins, who had taken a night-school course as a tax consultant and subsequently opened her own office.

So now she was dead. During that afternoon old Mr. Gottschalk spoke only one sentence, directed at Sabina, as soon as he had found a seat after being helped down the steep path by Franz: "Why didn't you tell me yourself?" Halm was about to spring to Sabina's defense, but her glance prevented him. He knew from her expression that she agreed with her father. She went over to him at once and laid her face against his shoulder, and they remained like that for a while. Elmar started on his subject. If he'd had any say in the matter, his parents' house should have been sold long ago. A ramshackle old house, but 2,700 square meters, in the Stuttgart suburb of Sillenbuch, situated on a slope, at the moment worth two million marks at the very least, which would mean 700,000 for each of them. His words were obviously meant for his younger brother Franz, who had long been expected to set himself up in some solid business. Once again Elmar's remarks, for Halm, led to the embarrassing conclusion that even if the rent Halm was paying to the brothers were raised each year, he would never be able to pay as much as a sale would yield. No one could pay such a sum. "A twelve-apartment building might go up here!" exclaimed Elmar. Sabina: "There's one going up right next door!" Elmar leaped up. "Aha!" he cried. "There you are! What do you know?" he exclaimed. "So that g-g-g-gay nephew has sold! And what about us?" To Halm it seemed as if they were all looking at him. Another of those sons-in-law like the Heimbucher postal clerk and Gottschalk the schoolteacher.

At family reunions the story was always told of how the country house had been built by the baker and sold to a Baroness von Meldegg, how she lost all her money after 1918 and had to take in the Heimbuchers as tenants, and how Aunt Luise (a Gutöhrlein, of course), who had emigrated to America, provided the dollars with which her niece—the Heimbucher grandmother (a Gutöhrlein, of course)—bought the house from Baroness von Meldegg. After the documents were signed, Grandmother Heimbucher is said to have stayed six feet off the ground for weeks in celebration of her triumph.

At this point in the Gutöhrlein saga, Halm always had to think of the husband of that levitated grandmother, and of Heimbucher the postal clerk, who not long afterward hanged himself from one of the graceful gables. Franz, who happened to be the one telling the history of the house, hadn't been endowed with as much Gutöhrlein efficiency as his brother Elmar, but he too was telling the story to the sole glory of the Gutöhrleins. The part that was always told with the greatest relish was how the legendary aunt, Luise Gutöhrlein, had fled from the Welzheim Forest to the city of Stuttgart, had played the violin in a silent-movie theater on Charlottenplatz, and from there had fled to Paris, London, and Southampton where, dressed as a man, she had joined a ship's band and thus reached America. And what was told in the greatest detail was where the American Luise, whenever she visited her niece in Sillenbuch in the twenties, had hidden the dollar bills she left behind. In the sewing basket, in laundry piles, thermometer cases, tea infusers, between Bible pages, in pipe bowls: those were the kinds of places where Grandmother Heimbucher used to find the green money. She would smooth out the Easter Bunny bounty and stockpile it until by 1929 there was enough for the great coup.

For the first time Halm was listening to this dollar story with interest. Soon he would be earning dollars himself, although they wouldn't amount to enough to impress Elmar. Luckily Franz was also against selling their "home." Without Franz they would have long since had to surrender to Elmar's financial arguments. On the other hand Franz was an unreliable ally. Sometimes he turned up in a Mercedes 450 and sometimes by streetcar. And he wasn't married either, whereas every sentence uttered by Elmar the bank manager was reinforced by his wife Gitte with her rough voice and short sentences. Gitte was an attorney. Sabina suspected that Elmar was pressing for the sale merely to please his wife. Halm liked

Elmar just as much as he liked Franz. The very fact that Elmar stammered whenever he wasn't quite sure of his ground endeared him to Halm.

As long as old Mr. Gottschalk was sitting with them at the table, he nodded at whomever was speaking. Then at some point he was no longer there. He could be seen wandering about in the garden. He was visiting the flowers and shrubs he had planted himself in the days when he was still living here. He had never felt comfortable in this Gutöhrlein house, but in the garden he always had. Once he had admitted as much to his son-in-law Halm, but only because he had been a witness to Sabina shouting at her husband, who was supposed to remove an inferior shrub and instead had removed a lilac bush. "Sons-in-law have a hard time of it," he had said, glancing up at the gable from which Heimbucher the postal clerk had swung.

On returning now from the garden he had a blade of grass between his teeth that reinforced the slow head shake with which he responded to Sabina's wish that he move back into the house. "But I promised Mother I'd see that you came back to live in the house!" said Sabina. Her father shook his head more slowly still. So that evening Sabina drove him back to Hegelplatz. With the blade of grass between his teeth, she said, he had whistled softly to himself as she walked with him from the car to the elevator.

After everyone had left, Halm said: "As far as I'm concerned, you can go ahead and sell. Isn't that right, Otto? We two will always find a place to stay." Otto looked up as if he agreed. Sabina pointed to the ceiling. Now to deal with the girls. Not that the gesture implied annoyance or even weariness. As long as anything was left undone that she considered necessary, Sabina couldn't be tired. She shouted up the stairs: "Lena, Juliane—come down please!" First of all it was made clear to the girls that they had withdrawn too early from the family circle. Juliane said cheerfully that she'd heard everything being said there three times already, it simply wasn't worth listening to a fourth time. Sabina said: "Family conversations don't have to be intellectual. If you girls behave like that, some day you'll have no relatives left." That sounded like a threat, but Juliane made a so-what face, and Lena didn't react at all.

Halm admired Sabina once again for being so impervious to facts. It was out of the question, Sabina said, for Lena simply to give up Traugott and come crawling home. Lena said she would never go back to Traugott, no matter what. Juliane asked whether Lena was expected to kick out the other woman? "Who are you to talk?" asked Sabina. "Now I'm going to catch it too," Juliane said cheerfully. "You'll go and look for a job right here—I'm not having you go off to Berlin again," said Sabina. Juliane registered astonishment. "All I'm saying is: Christoph," Sabina continued. Juliane blushed furiously. "So you've been spying!" she cried. "Spying!" exclaimed Sabina. "If I have to pick up your filthy laundry because you girls are too lazy to load it into the washing machine, I consider myself entitled to read any letters that fall out of your pockets. A man twenty years older than you, with two kids almost your age and a wife!"

Juliane said she didn't care where she sprayed *mousse à toilette* onto fossilized asses to clean them up, whether here or in Berlin, but she did object to having to listen to someone who'd got hold of a piece of paper that was none of their business. She refused to have any further discussion on the subject. But if that was a condition for remaining in this house, she'd leave this very evening. And what's more, for Berlin. And stood up and went upstairs. She closed the door with exquisite gentleness.

Sabina looked at Halm and Lena. Now, she could have used some support. Lena's expression was deliberately deadpan. Halm nodded. Sabina always wanted to put things right. She believed it was possible to take a hand. He, too, was against their cheerful twenty-two-year-old Juliane becoming the prey or victim or lover of a forty-four-year-old *pater familias*. But how to prevent it? The idiotic thought occurred to him: Why does she have to read the bits of paper she happens to come across among her daughters' belongings? But he would never have put that into words. Sabina was right. And the fact that she wanted to put things right on the day of her mother's funeral merely emphasized how important it was to her. Get a move on! Help her! Bring Juliane back! Right this minute! Before the quarrel becomes entrenched! At the moment everything tends to become incurable. For God's sake, get up! Before Sabina gets up and has to scream! Think of California—get up!

But he couldn't, he could only say: "Lena, would you mind bringing her downstairs?" Lena rose and left the room as if she were dragging each foot through sticky mud. As soon as Lena had gone, Sabina said: "Forty-four, two kids, teaches at a special school." She made it sound as if his occupation told the whole story.

Lena came back alone and sat down on the piano stool. Juliane would only come down if the stolen letter was returned to her immediately with the promise that nothing more would be said about the whole matter. Halm saw Sabina looking at him. He was needed. He felt the movie of his consciousness wanting to come to a halt. No new facts, demands, obligations. Preferably an empty screen. Preferably nothing. Nothing but off to California. Lena had swung round on her piano stool and was dashing off some rebellious fast runs (*presto agitato*, thought Halm) until Sabina leaped up and declared that she'd go mad in this house: playing the piano on the day of a funeral! Lena dropped her hands at once, Halm was already through the door and running upstairs. Now he had the strength he had been lacking. He roared: "Juliane, come down at once. Please! Please!"

2

WITH PASTY FACES THEY got off the train in Cologne at 6:23 A.M. and lugged their seven pieces of baggage to the rear of the station onto Breslauer Platz. The bus for Brussels was supposed to leave here at 8:30, "across from the Rheinufer Station," according to the information sheet of the charter flight company. Halm, Lena, and Sabina were the first in line. Later arrivals lined up behind them. Then someone arrived who knew where the bus would be stopping. Halm lugged across the two heavy suitcases; Lena and Sabina carried the five smaller pieces. Then the bus stopped at an altogether different place. Halm cheerfully picked up the heavy suitcases once more. No one would succeed in spoiling his happy mood.

As they crossed the German border he pressed Sabina's hand and felt disinclined to relinquish this intimate pressure for the next few months. He looked at her, she at him. If it hadn't been for Lena sitting there so rigidly upright, Halm would have whispered to Sabina that, to judge by his own mood, they must be on their honeymoon. Lena refused to be drawn into any conversation; she looked straight ahead as if she were driving the bus, pressing her lips together with relentless force.

In Brussels, Halm's mood underwent a severe test. It was always the wrong hall, and in every new hall the wrong line that they joined; not a soul here admitted to knowing anything about this FFT charter flight company, let alone to representing it. Halm's palms were burning, his joints were aching, there wasn't a dry stitch left on his body. He told Lena and Sabina he was sure the legendary Luise Gutöhrlein hadn't exactly traveled in luxury either, when, dressed as a man, she fiddled her way across the Atlantic in a ship's band. Eventually a company by the name of Belgravia took pity on the FFT travelers.

When they buckled themselves into the sagging seats of the plane Halm could have sung for joy. He couldn't remember ever having had such a devil-may-care mood. He had taken the seat between Lena and Sabina. He punched Lena's arm, kissed her forehead, pinched her, laughed at her. When the aircraft took off, he managed through his happiness to win what was almost a smile from her. He immediately wanted to make the most of this. She must admit it was glorious, starting up and away like that! As curtly as possible she said: "There's nothing to keep me here." "Nor me," he said and kissed Lena's temple. But weren't those terrible words? There's nothing to keep me here. In his case it was rejoicing. In hers? Both of them wanted to get away from this disillusioning German environment! Wasn't it enough that both of them wanted to get away? Can you feel how we're climbing! Lena, that's what it's all about, climbing like this! There seems to be no end to it! And then up there at 33,000 feet how quietly they flowed along! A hot dinner will be served. Lena, did you hear that? "Sabina," he said, "listen—I was just saying to Lena that it can't be any more wonderful, we're at the top now, at the very top. We're flying to San Francisco. The three of us. How lucky can one get! A hot dinner will be served! Lena, Sabina, we've escaped! Don't look back. Our ears are now attuned to other names. Northern Hebridean Islands, how does that sound? Iceland, Greenland. Look over there—the mountains are buried up to their necks in snow. The sun has stayed way behind us. We're taking a short cut. Time flies,

Lena! How about a smile?" Can a self-idolator wound a person so deeply that she can no longer turn her head, even when what she would see might be Hudson Bay?

And in San Francisco the weather is fine, says the captain. Seventy degrees. Ideal, Lena, seventy degrees! Halm was apparently attracting so much attention that a poorly dressed Oriental woman sitting behind him asked him to fill out the landing cards for herself and her mother. Born in Aleppo, in 1922, that's all she knows. Since money need only be reported if a passenger is carrying more than five thousand dollars, Halm puts a dash after this question. She corrects him. The poorly dressed Angel Khato and her pathologically obese mother have more than five thousand dollars on them! Halm felt his impecunious state like an astringent. Penniless is what the German teacher had been called by the Gutöhrleins. Halm had all of thirteen hundred dollars on him.

Sabina wanted to set foot in the New World with hair neatly combed. The comb broke. Holding the two pieces out to Halm she asked: "What does this mean?" Halm replied instantly and passionately: "That your hair doesn't need combing, Sabina! What an idea, combing your hair—absurd! Your crown of untamed locks proclaims your eternal beauty!" When he was in the mood, Halm liked to use inflated language. Now comes my lesson on Rainer Mersjohann, so that you'll recognize him at once. The blond mop of hair that he used to slick down into a wave with brilliantine may have subsided. In those days the mop glittered like gold. But his eyes will shine no less blue from behind the golden lashes, or will they? And he moves like a candle that refuses to go out! And the hands, beautiful, splayed piously in constant fanlike motion attached to swinging arms. A tall man in velvet. Of velvet. And not inclined to tubbiness, like Halm, but slender, tall, as I said. In short: Ariel! Don't grin when he aspirates every *t*! He was born in Münster, where even people who don't write perfect sonnets speak that way. He went on sending poems from America, those first few years. English and German. And remember, he's invited us, let him feel that we regard him as our savior. He really is. To have Messrs. Kiderlen and Rimmele off my back for four months—paradise! To know that the continent of self-idolators is beyond the horizon for four months—paradise! To have escaped from the steep north slope in Sillenbuch for four months—Sabina, do admit that the Gutöhrlein monument has its shady aspect, whereas California is lying there—just look around you!—in full sunshine. The Golden State. What an airport—just look! Let's not hurry. Let's savor the moment, Sabina, and ease ourselves into the Promised Land bit by bit. Oh Sabina—the amount of trouble you took to look after all those tiresome details that need looking after before one can get away: I'll always be grateful for that, he whispered to her before the passport inspection. To have Mrs. Niedlich come to the house every day to look after Otto—brilliant, Sabina!

But then there was no Rainer Mersjohann at the airport. There weren't that many people waiting that he wouldn't have noticed him immediately. "You two wait here, in the baggage area, don't let anyone go off with you, I'll phone Washington University." Halm looks for a telephone, has no coins, finds a bank, obtains some coins, telephones, is told that Mr. Mersjohann is never on time, must be on his way, he certainly wasn't in the department, might be at home, here was his home number. What a marvelous dialect: home number! Then slowly and undismayed back to the family. "Just sit down. And don't despair, please." Met or not met, they were in California! His own despair threatened to strangle him. Surely after a quarter of a century and all those thousands of kilometers, Mr. Mersjohann, that velvet scion, that sweet-talker, might have shown up on time, for God's sake. Surely things weren't going to turn out here to be just like everywhere else! He insisted that California be different from everywhere else.

Finally a man approached wearing blue-and-white check trousers, a green-and-white check jacket, and on his head a low-crowned straw hat with a wide black band. "You're the Halms!" said the man. "You're Helmut," he went on. "You're Lena." But Halm couldn't say: "You're Rainer." It wasn't Rainer. No one could have a clearer mental image of Rainer than he did. He could have drawn or painted Rainer and reproduced him in any medium on earth; but this, as he instantly saw, wasn't Rainer Mersjohann. Halm had no choice but to pretend to regard the other man as Rainer Mersjohann. After all, that was how that person wanted to be regarded. Halm had to keep stealing glances in an effort to obtain a vestige of Rainer Mersjohann. When he ran into someone from the past he usually didn't recognize that person at once: but he always succeeded in gradually accommodating the earlier image to the present one, in accepting the present one as the continuation of the earlier one. Rainer Mersjohann then and now—they were two, for the time being. He had to bring the two together. For the time being it was painful not to have met his former friend.

The man who had come to meet them led them to a dark-green station wagon. All university cars, he explained, were this dignified green. The man who now sat at the other end of the front seat was a stranger. Corpulent, with sagging, bluish cheeks, and hanging from those cheeks a colorless curly beard that met under the double chin. When he took off his hat, a shining bald head was revealed. Where hair might still have grown, it had obviously been shaved off. What had happened to the soft, poetic gleam in Mersjohann's eyes? What had happened to the golden eyelashes?

Without looking at him, the stranger said: "Don't stare at me like that! We're driving through San Francisco!" And started a running commentary. "Downtown, Treasure Island, the Bay Bridge, over there you can already make out Oakland, Berkeley, Albany, San Pablo, El Cerrito, Richmond, and so on, all grown together. Behind, to our left, the island of Alcatraz—beyond that, if you turn right around, the Golden Gate Bridge." He spoke softly, calmly, without looking here or there when he mentioned here or there. Halm was suffering. He listened to him avidly. By this time his eyes were fixed on him again. For weeks now, Halm had been longing for Rainer Mersjohann. Perhaps their friendship would revive. At home he had no friend. He had lost them all, one after the other. Always for the same reason: his friends had always let him feel that they were prepared to forgive him this or that. He could have remained their friend although. . . . No, thank you. Rather nothing than that. If reservations were necessary he would rather have no friends.

They turned onto Contra Costa Avenue. They were in Berkeley. Twenty minutes by car from the house to the campus of Washington University in Oakland. The house belonged to a Professor Rinehart, who was at present in Spain. The alleged Rainer unlocked the front door and hurried inside: the burglar alarm had to be switched off within thirty seconds or it would report a break-in at the security system headquarters. The fridge was full, according to one of the professor's instruction sheets, which contained, section by section, detailed directions as well as an inventory of the house. To be on the safe side, Rainer had brought along some beer. And proceeded to carry four six-packs past the speechless Halms. Halm had to stop thinking of the past. Here sat an amiable giant drinking that beer as if *he* had just come off the eleven-hour flight. The giant needed five cans right away.

They sat in a semicircle in the kitchen nook, looking out onto the front garden and up to the street, then again through the open kitchen door and the dining-room window right out over the waves of treetops and roofs as far as the glittering Bay and beyond to the outlines of San Francisco. Sabina said this view was glorious. The giant looked at the Halms with his jaw thrust forward, his lower lip drooping. The old Rainer's mouth had been more closed than open even when speaking. This new Rainer's slack, protruding, crooked lower lip seemed as if it could never again meet his upper lip. And those eyes! Behind red-rimmed lids rather a veiled look.

Halm had to make an immediate adjustment or go back home again. Forget Ariel, meet Falstaff! "Well, we haven't got any younger, have we!" said the giant. Halm was taken aback. Sabina remarked that the little front garden toward the street looked almost Japanese, didn't it? The giant slowly swiveled the head on his round shoulders toward Sabina. Like a howitzer, thought Halm. "Right on, Sabina!" said Rainer. Japanese garden is what this part is called in

Professor Rinehart's description. The watering instructions for this area read like an introduction to Shintoism, he said. Obviously Professor Rinehart or his wife or both were crazy about Japan, one had only to see all that stuff standing around in the glass cabinets and hanging on the walls. But now for the mechanics of the place. First the most important, the alarm system. You touch 3388 and have thirty seconds to get out, and thirty seconds to come back in again. The giant explained it all as if the Halms must be able not only to use this equipment but, if necessary, repair it. Halm didn't understand a word but pretended to pay close attention. The giant seemed to be aware of this. In the midst of explaining the six-foot-high baking, broiling, and roasting oven, he simply stopped and said quietly, with something like a sigh: "Maybe we should forget about it," and that it was time for him to leave. And left. But then the screen door outside the front door turned out to be stuck. The giant growled. One of the three hinges had come loose. Halm said never mind. The giant looked at him over his glasses, which had slipped down on his nose. "So that's how you want to treat a house that doesn't belong to you," he said, with three ponderous nods of his great head.

This Mr. Mersjohann now took off his hat again, which made the curly beard fringing the double chin look even more preposterous. He knew where to find tools in the basement, and he set to work. Halm acted the handyman. Those hands . . . it could be Rainer. The pious spatulas, the mannered way of moving his hands even when reaching for tools—that was Rainer, that was Mersjohann. Those long hands, neither plump nor blue nor red, those Saint John's hands that always stuck out of sleeves that were too short. "Oh, Rainer," said Halm, "I'm sorry!" "What about?" "That we have to put you to all this trouble," said Halm. "But I can't rent you a house that isn't in good shape, can I?" Rainer went on to say that he hadn't checked everything out, when the professor's son handed over the house to him, so now it was up to him to fix it up. But Helmut was welcome to bring him a beer if he liked. Halm realized he was beginning to admire this new Rainer. So down to earth! And so calm. So relaxed. So helpful. In the days when Rainer had left Europe, the word "hectic" had not yet been in fashion. And obviously it wasn't here either. After fiddling around with the door as if time didn't exist, he finally had everything in working order: the screen door swung freely and closed perfectly. His old Rainer would never have managed it. But the present one had. With Rainer's hands!

Rainer left. A pity, but Halm didn't want to keep him. "There's something very sweet about him," Sabina said later. And the way he'd explained the washing machine, the drier, the stove, the enormous oven—Sabina was amazed. And it's not even his own house. But he had obviously studied the professor's instructions in detail. "What a lot of trouble he went to," said Sabina, "and how good he is with his hands." "Yes," said Halm, shaking his head. And he had always tried to explain everything to both of them. Sabina: "Did you notice how surprised he was when you showed no interest? That wasn't very polite of you." "I did my best but I simply don't understand these things," said Halm. "Because you don't *want* to understand," Sabina said. She thought Rainer was fantastic. "Perhaps that's what America's all about."

Lena had disappeared into her room. Sabina and Halm cleaned up everything to do with kitchen and food until all was as spick-and-span as they were used to at home. Had they ever cleaned up together at home? Then they walked the few blocks down the street to the shopping area. The supermarkets were open even on Sunday evening. Those grapes, Sabina, look! And have you seen these fish, Helmut—look! And corn and kefir and avocados and artichokes, and how cheap! Sabina saw at once that they would manage on the salary. They'd only have to use some of their savings toward the $800 rent. The great advantage was that they wouldn't be down in the flats but a bit up the slope with a view of Bay Bridge, the Bay, and San Francisco. Helmut immediately felt at home among the neighboring houses, which derived either from Granada or Stratford-on-Avon. Side by side, but so deeply ensconced among trees and shrubs that the varying traditions seemed merely hinted at among the massed greenery.

Halm brought Lena from her room, where she was sitting as

if she had been abducted, and swept her and Sabina off for a walk up the hill. A narrow, almost perpendicular path led between fences. Yosemite Steps. Yet another derivation. They walked uphill until they had the full view. A dark plain, pricked by intensely glittering lights. Chains of lights on the bridge across the Bay. San Francisco: rising terraces of gold-green splashes of light against a silhouette of purple hills. Beyond and above all that, spanning the horizon, a dazzling fiery sky. And under this sky was, one knew, the Pacific. Ah Lena, ah Sabina, he probably has spent too much of his life in Sillenbuch. The sight seemed almost to burst the bounds of his emotional grasp.

3

ON FINDING THAT HE STILL noticed that odor next morning, he asked Sabina whether there was anything they could do about it. That was the smell of another elderly couple, said Sabina. With every couple, a special odor gradually develops in their rooms that they themselves no longer notice. Most strongly in the bedroom. "You speak as if you were the Minister of Elderly Married Couples," said Halm as he got out of bed.

Sabina hadn't slept well either. The mere thought of that air, she said, made her stop breathing. "This air has a color," he said. "That's enough," she said. "I'm breathing very shallowly," he said. "As soon as I breathe more deeply the air has a smell, or rather, it has a color." Sabina jumped out of bed and cried: "Professor Rinehart is an anthropologist!"

They drove according to the map that Rainer had drawn for them. Along Shattuck through Berkeley as far as Ashby, then left up toward Oakland Hills as far as the Claremont Hotel, a white monstrosity which, according to Rainer, had some claim to being enchanted; driving around it, if they made it, they would see the Crocker Gate of Washington University of Oakland, and they would know they had arrived.

They found their way there and gazed silently at the students crowding through the two square, reddish stone columns of Crocker Gate onto the campus. Halm wondered aloud whether he shouldn't take up driving again: people drive more slowly here. And Rainer's wife runs a driving school. He could take a few lessons from her. "You want to dump me," Sabina said. "That's right," he said and went on waving until she was out of sight. He stood like an obstacle in the flood of students surging toward the gate, then let himself be carried along into the paradise of trees and hills.

Rainer's sketch No. 2: the campus. In this sketch, too, Rainer showed himself to be a whimsical guide. Once through Crocker Gate, the facilities supplying students' needs on the Student Union Plaza would be almost behind him; take a bearing on Coit Hall up the hill on the right and note it well, it contains the lecture rooms. Keep heading for that object up there looking like some stranded classical structure. Down to the left, Lincoln Library, recently completed, will loom out of a huge grassy bowl; made of green glass, protected by curved marble shields of leaflike design, reflected in the water surrounding it. Up on your right now, Pierce Hall, an arbitrarily Assyrian object on its own hill, housing natural sciences. So far there has always been something up on the right or down on the left, but now the gently rising lawns lay ahead, the trees increased, becoming almost a forest, but the campus designers hadn't planned a forest. The sequoias and redwoods are mere clusters of trees, groves, as Rainer says they are entitled to be called, and between them the path swings up and down and crosses the dry bed of Okra Creek over a little humpback bridge. Almost straight now, but not treelined like a European avenue, the path points toward his goal: the granite and slate of the Wyoming-Gothic of Fillmore Hall. Third floor, Room 306, the office, the domain of the quick-witted Mrs. Carol Elrod.

The door being open, Halm couldn't knock. Rainer might well have added to his directions: white skin, black eyes, a round forehead encircled by little flames of black curls. She said neither too much nor too little. Her manner was neither too cool nor too familiar. Halm immediately sensed that all further arrangements could be left to her. She was wearing a denim skirt and a sleeveless blouse. The rounded shoulders seemed meant to complement the round forehead. Her office was small and cramped. In front of her desk was a chair, set at right angles, there was no other way, so that when she offered this chair you sat with your profile to her or had to turn your head ninety degrees toward her.

She showed him the office on the fourth floor, Room 407-F, which he was to regard as his own. Then she told him how to get back to Coit Hall. He didn't say that, coming from Crocker Gate, he had already seen Coit Hall above him on the right. He had a poor sense of direction; for him the way back was always a new route in which he never recognized the way there. "Just stop by after class," she told him. That must mean she expected to see him after his class. Sometimes she spoke German, sometimes English. Her German was slangy, with a touch of Berlin about it. "Check your box once a day," she said. Anything that concerned him would land in his box. Washington University was famous for its "events"—once again she couldn't find the right German word: a first-generation kid sometimes had trouble finding a German word, sometimes an English one. Between her two front teeth there was an attractive little gap. With her unevenly cut wavy hair she looked more like an English or German Romantic poet. But also like a sheep. A heavy lower lip. Like Rainer. But, instead of drooping, clearly supporting the upper lip. And from the always slightly averted face that sidelong look. Byron as a sheep, thought Halm, that will never do. He must stop staring at her. He thanked her so effusively that she could not regard it as mere routine.

On the way back to Coit Hall he felt annoyed at his shabby, limp old briefcase, probably because the campus paths winding across the lush, undulating lawns echoed with the sounds of youth. He felt as if he were being whirled around, submerged, swept away. He had to stop and look up into the trees. Anyone wanting to experience trees should come here, he said, so softly that only he could hear it. That trees inspire reverence is something I noticed before I knew it, he said, just as softly. He was startled by the screams of two coeds dashing toward each other, not to fight but to embrace. This was the first day of school.

Coit Hall could be approached on all four sides by steps. German conversation in Room 101, German language in 102. Through the little oblong window in the door, Halm saw a girl sitting in 101. He went in, said hello, and sat down as far as possible from her. It was ten to nine. The student asked whether Halm was here for the conversation class too. Halm said yes. She must be surprised that a man of his age should attend a conversation class. Even for an instructor he was too old. The girl stretched her arms and yawned. Halm read the two lines on her T-shirt: SMALL THINGS AMUSE GREAT MINDS. Between the line ending with THINGS and the one starting with AMUSE were the small things that weren't small. By five to nine, three students had turned up. By five past nine there were seven. Then someone looked in and asked whether they could spare a chair. Halm said yes. That left all the chairs occupied. Then a girl arrived dragging herself along on crutches. A student had to go out to get a chair back again.

Halm noticed that he was sweating. He introduced himself, said he wasn't much of a hand at conversation, that he tended to avoid opportunities for conversation, but that he was looking forward to this class because it wasn't going to be a conversation as such but a conversation game. So let's get started, for instance, with the various possible opinions on conversation—in other words, whether, in order to impress people, it was better to tell the truth or whether lying had a better chance of success, or whether the most satisfactory conversation was not in a foreign language because then you lie in all innocence since you never quite know what you're saying and consequently can be more daring than in your native tongue because you aren't responsible. . . . All he was saying had been thought out in advance.

After class, on the way back from Coit Hall to Fillmore Hall, he felt defeated. He was exhausted, drained. For fear the students wouldn't speak, he had spoken too much. As a result, he had kept some from speaking who might have spoken. Just as he was crossing the humpback bridge again, he heard his name. A student had caught up with him, a tall blond girl. She held out her hand, said her name was Fran, that she was looking forward to taking the course with him, she loved German literature, especially Rilke and Stefan George. She wasn't the one with the two-liner T-shirt. She was also heading for Fillmore Hall. She asked whether this was his first time here. "Oh yes," he replied. She said she had the feeling his conversation class would be very lively. In class she had been among those who had said nothing. "Now you're making conversation!" he said. She laughed out loud. Then she said she was very shy, she probably wouldn't say a word in class for four months.

They fell silent as they walked along side by side. Then she said: "Are you also an admirer of Rilke and George?" "Oh yes," he said, "of course!" He was wondering what, of all the things going through his mind, he should say. She said she had spent a year in Vienna, that was where she had learned to love Rilke and George. "A year in Vienna, how wonderful!" he exclaimed. If only he hadn't said right away that he also was heading for Fillmore Hall, he could now have turned off onto one of the many paths and disappeared from sight among the grassy hillocks. Outside the elevators in Fillmore Hall he remarked: "As I said, I'm not very good at conversation." She replied that, on the contrary, he was very good at conversation because he stimulated people to speak to him. He rejected the notion with a brisk wave of the hand and looked up with what he hoped was a pained expression at the floor numbers as they lit up. They entered the elevator. "Going up?" she asked a student who was already inside. "Trying to," he said, and Halm, although he also taught English at home, once again established to his chagrin that he would never master this language. Somehow it seemed embarrassing to be returning from his very first lesson in the company of this girl. Carol Elrod apparently thought so too. Halm felt he must be blushing, so he said he had to hurry off to his office. As he left he heard the girl asking for Professor Ackermann.

With a sense of satisfaction he unlocked the door of 407-F,

which for almost four months would now be his own door. PROF. HALM, the sign on the door said. Professor Taenzer, whose office it was, was on a sabbatical. Halm dropped into the desk chair. From above he was showered with icy air. He pushed himself away from the desk and rolled back until he was safe from the direct jet of cold air. The office had no windows. He had first assumed the square fluorescent light panel in the ceiling to be a skylight. Next to the neon, a grille, the source of the cold air. He would have to keep a sweater and a scarf on hand here. The green walls were papered with children's drawings and paintings. How embarrassing to have to look at pictures done by children for whose existence one is not responsible. The pictures could not be removed. Professor Taenzer, who of course couldn't get enough of them, had glued them on, forever. Halm must get hold of some posters, even if they were of Neuschwanstein Castle.

Rainer had apologized for this office, saying that Fillmore was the oldest of all the buildings. The fact that the German department was housed in it indicated the status of German here. The Latin Americans, until recently also in Fillmore, had moved in January to the new Menlo Hall. Suddenly with a hideous grinding sound a key is thrust into the lock. A janitor says "Hi!", goes to the empty wastebasket, and leaves again. Halm is not aware of any lapse of time passing between the sound of the key and the door opening. Suppose he had been doing something here that one was not supposed to be seen doing? The janitor had been a black with Chinese features. With a name tag on his jacket: Elisha. As soon as the man was outside again, Halm could say "Hi!"

After the language class he went back to the department. He wanted to show Mrs. Elrod that being accompanied by a coed had been an exception. How had the first morning gone, she wanted to know. The language class had been no problem, he told her, but as for the conversation class—he'd only been able to get three students to speak. "Why not ask them why they're there at all?" asked Mrs. Elrod. Rainer had laughed in his face when he had asked how to conduct such a class. And this wonderfully astute woman, Mrs. Elrod, had had the foresight to set up a meeting for two o'clock that afternoon with two teaching assistants, both of whom had been giving conversation classes for two semesters. And tomorrow afternoon at three in the Foundation Building. Matters of insurance. The day after that, his library card and a photo for his social security card.

He was just about to invite Mrs. Elrod for lunch when he discovered that he had lost his wallet. A galvanizing shock. He simply could not afford to lose his wallet. It seemed best to behave as if he unfortunately already had a lunch engagement. "Aha," said Mrs. Elrod. He pretended to have no idea of what she meant and said casually that his wife and a friend were coming to lunch. Good God, where were these lies leading him? And why, he asked himself? See you this afternoon, then. With the air of a busy man he went to his office and phoned Sabina. She had already found the wallet. Thank God. That trickling away of thwarted shock. She wants to drive over right away. Halm had some difficulty persuading her not to. Who, if not he, would not benefit from fasting! Five past four at Crocker Gate!

He then proceeded to look for a way out that would not lead him past the department, and instead of going to Coit Hall he went farther onto the campus. Everywhere there were students lying like monuments on the grass. When after grazing for hours, cows settle down to ruminate, similar godlike groupings result. Noonday peace on campus, enhanced by the bells of the campanile. Suddenly he saw gravestones. On the bare lawn. A few students were lying around among the graves and on them. Reading, dozing, ruminating. Some of them who had drawn up their knees and placed a writing pad on them were using the gravestones as backrests. In front of one gravestone, one leg drawn up, the other stretched out, the girl who had spoken to him after class was lying on her back. She had placed one arm over her face, but he recognized her from the bright blue shorts with the broad white stripe and from the white terry T-shirt with the low round neck. She was lying directly in front of the gravestone. Her brown legs shone in the sun. Her blond hair looked more brassy than blond on the grass. She was wearing old, faded sneakers. He had seen this now. He could leave. He did not leave. Admit that this is a fantastic day! I admit it, said the I that had been addressed to the I that had addressed it. Only then did he leave. Fortunately he was used to young people. Although they didn't lie around on graves at home, or turn up looking like that in class, there were some pretty weird-looking types. That no longer bothered him. The more conspicuous they were, the less it bothered him. He was beyond all that. Thanks to . . . oh no, why bring up that name again! There could never have been a more obvious mistake than his Nicole fiasco.

He went back to his office. How agreeable that it was so hard to find this office. It didn't face on the corridor. Facing the corridor was merely the door marked 407 behind which a few steps led up to a door with no number; behind that a landing with four doors leading off to offices 407-C to 407-F. Painted on the floor of the landing was a red arrow pointing to a little door so low that it might have been designed for dwarfs. It was open, revealing a round hole leading into a metal tube. A sign on the wall said FIRE ESCAPE. Beside the hole, a pile of old books. He couldn't resist reaching in and picking up as many as he could with one hand. In his office he examined his loot: an old volume of German dialect stories published in Leipzig (no year). And: *Dictionary of Anecdote, selected and arranged for the Pulpit and the Platform by the Rev. Walter Baxendale*, New York 1889. He opened the book of anecdotes right away, and his eye was caught by the reference:

> DEATH. Bound to. In Virgil there is an account of an ancient king who was so unnaturally cruel in his punishments that he used to chain *a dead man to a living one*. It was impossible for the poor wretch to separate himself from his disgusting burden. The carcass was bound fast to his body, its hands to his hands, its face to his face, its lips to his lips; it lay down and rose up whenever he did; it moved about with him whithersoever he went, till the welcome moment when death came to his relief.

Naturally this reminded him of the girl lying on the grave, one leg slightly drawn up, one arm across her face. How firmly, how decisively she had shaken his hand when she had caught up with him on the humpback bridge! That was a moment when he had been more alive than before or after. Life needs expression too, he thought. Death has more than enough.

At a quarter to, he was at Mrs. Elrod's. So her office door was always open, whereas the door from her office to Mersjohann's was apparently always closed. But he was there: he came out, without a jacket, in a white shirt and mauve tie, his hands clasped behind his back. Did he stoop as he walked? Halm would have liked to see the hands, because it was from them that he had recognized his Rainer. Mersjohann looked at Halm with a curiosity intended to look affected. "Since our beginnings tend to stay with us, let's hear how yours were," said Mersjohann. "I already know that you're being seen with our dumb beauty, so what else have you been up to?" Carol said it was her fault: she should have warned Halm of the typical California college girl—blond, Porsche, father a doctor in Pacific Heights, San Francisco, and sharper than a shark's tooth. "Back to work now, Mr. Chairman—at four-thirty the messenger from the printer's will be here, every year the German department is the last, I could die of shame. . . ." Rainer pretended to dash into his office. "See you tonight at my place!" he called out.

At the moment, things were worse than ever, she said with a pained look at Rainer's door. The Schubert paper! She'd bet anything that Rainer wouldn't finish it until he was sitting in the plane. When the captain said, "In a few minutes we'll be landing in Houston," Professor Mersjohann will assume his homespun Westphalian smile and nod and say: "On time, just the way we like it—a double bourbon, please, steward." "He'll want to use you," she said in a low voice, "as an excuse for drinking—don't offer him even the slightest opportunity."

From his office Rainer called out in a jocular tone: "When I hear whispering I get persecution mania!" Carol immediately raised her voice as she went on: "Of course you didn't have lunch with your wife, that was obvious. But not with that little blond either. With the tiny bit of strength left to me by this lunatic department, I'll work away at solving that riddle. But here at last I see our twins coming—I call Barbie and Susie twins although they look no more alike than a fried egg and a scrambled egg. They are one by nature, twins of destiny; otherwise—one from Kempten, one from Cologne—they wouldn't both have landed as TA's in Oakland. Two years ago we had a German writer as a guest professor here, Tassilo Herbert Messmer: after three months of California he still believed that TA didn't mean teaching assistant but transactional analysis. Now meet Barbie and Susie—this is Professor Halm."

The two young women first needed to complain loudly outside their chairman's door that five hundred dollars a month wasn't enough. The one from Cologne spoke, the one from Kempten nodded. Mrs. Elrod put it to the complainer from Cologne that she had never been as happy anywhere as in California. The complainer from Cologne: "But of course!" The one from Kempten nodded. But then: During vacation they had been in the East where they had encountered the Rassias method—this method must be brought here! Enough of those conversation courses that send everyone into a trance! With drill instruction, the student responds sixty-five times during each lesson; with our system three to four times! So far there's only been drill instruction here in Spanish, French, and Italian; German seems to consider itself above all that. With that new method the instructor really has to come down hard on the students with both hands and feet. Clear the decks and fire away. After one hour of drill instruction everyone's sweating like after a boxing lesson, instructor and students. Halm said: "How interesting"—unfortunately he had to leave now, his wife was expecting to meet him at four at Crocker Gate.

When Sabina wasn't at the gate he became obsessed with the idea that Mrs. Elrod was watching him from one of the highest points on campus and discovering that he had lied. How in all this chaos was he to find Sabina? Students surging out of the campus and swarming obliviously across the street. Impatient cars, buses struggling to reach their stops. Coming up from the Bay a violent wind, a fierce light. Coeds who after hours of suppressed vitality are now chewing away and letting bubble gum burst in front of their grinding jaws. And those breasts bouncing against the blouses. Buses with opaque black windows swallowing up girls whom Halm believes, at this moment, he will never be able to forget. For a spastic youth lolling in his wheelchair, a platform is lowered from the bus door onto the sidewalk, the wheels of the wheelchair spin, the electric motor can't cope with the slight elevation that the platform presents to the wheels; everyone stands and stares, a black finally pushes the wheelchair onto the platform, the platform rises, pulls the wheelchair into the bus, the bus drives off. Scraps of paper and plastic cups swirl after it in the hot wind.

Sabina nudged him in the ribs. "Oh Sabina, thank God you're here!" She'd been waiting here all the time. Oh of course, he'd been watching out for the green Mercedes whereas he was supposed to be looking for a light yellow Volvo. As soon as they were on Shattuck Avenue, which cuts clear across the cities, Sabina was able to speak. Lena hadn't yet come down from her room. "It's jet lag," Halm said. "Let's hope so," said Sabina. He asked Sabina to drive slowly. He didn't want to pass anything without having seen it. Sabina had already discovered the best florist. She came out with a typical Sabina bouquet. Everywhere she goes, she manages to make flowers look as if they came not from a florist's but from a meadow, or at least from Cézanne. The Chinese florist accompanied her to the car door.

Lena said through her locked bedroom door that she wouldn't be going with them to the Mersjohanns'. She was asked why not. "Must one explain everything?" she said. Halm and Sabina said she could at least join them for a cup of tea and watch the sun go down behind San Francisco. No answer. Halm gestured to Sabina to abandon the attempt.

Downstairs in their bedroom changing for the evening, Halm remarked that the air still smelled exactly as it had when they first came in. And when they entered the Mersjohann house—half

Stratford-on-Avon, half Rothenburg ob der Tauber, he had remarked to Sabina outside—he immediately exclaimed that Sabina's theory that every married couple produced a special odor was not correct. Here at the Mersjohanns' there was nothing of the sort. "Or we're not a couple!" said Rainer. Halm said quite seriously: "Rainer, I envy you." Now Elissa wanted to know from Halm whether his remark about the wonderful air in this house had been made at Rainer's instigation. Had Halm wanted to support Rainer's claim that his smoking had no effect on the air in the house? She refused to believe that Halm hadn't been told by Rainer of this eternal bone of contention. Elissa hated smoky rooms. Since Rainer smoked practically nonstop she had fixed up a second living room for him, next to his study, in the basement, and there he could smoke as much as he liked. But she was afraid the smell was gradually drifting up onto her floor. They weren't even sleeping on the same floor.

"You would have made a good gold digger," said Rainer in German, a language that Elissa didn't understand. And quickly told Elissa, who had pouted at the words in the foreign language, that he had just confirmed Helmut's gifts for gold digging because he had shown such a nose for covert tensions. And turning back to Halm: Elissa was descended from the very earliest gold diggers. Halm said that every marriage was based on whatever the spouses could under no circumstances agree upon. Differences are what keep a marriage together, not harmony. Halm tossed all this off lightly because he had sensed a certain amount of suspicion in Elissa. And he wanted to win this woman over. This descendant of gold diggers. Her short hair reminded him of J. F. Kennedy, her chin of Venetian gondolas, with its lovely curve. Watched over by a finely chiseled nose. And bold eyes. Or cool? Or mocking? Or ready to mock? He was glad that Rainer had a wife who attracted him. He would find it easier to feel close to this woman than to his former friend. If she was not too suspicious. He would have liked to say: Living in such a house, one can't help being gracious. That brushed stucco, that vaulted ceiling with its dark beams. This isn't a living room, it's a chapel, a hall. Built onto the three-storied main building on its slope. At the level of its second floor, the house is permitted to share in this solemn hall. You looked out over the Bay, could see San Francisco; but from up here you could see not only the beginning of a bridge but three bridges in their entirety, even the justly famed Golden Gate Bridge in its entirety; and through it and over it you could see the Pacific that was at that moment preparing a bed for the sun.

Now into the three-story part of the house. It was full of nooks and crannies like an old ship. A spiral staircase led downward. So that was where Rainer slept, lived, worked. His doors led out into nature: onto a little rocky landscape bordered by bushes and trees and overgrown by giant ivy leaves. Elissa had not come down with them. As far back as fifty thousand years before Christ, so Rainer told him, this had already been an Indian dwelling. He pointed out the caves, the grinding and cooking hollows in the rock. Before going up the spiral staircase again into Elissa's world, he put out his cigarette, as if he didn't mind. He had emphysema anyway, he said; Goethe had also suffered from that. The young Goethe had written: "Widen my breast"; the old one: "Oh make my breast wider!"

Upstairs Halm once again looked admiringly about him in Elissa's chapel. Elissa said that in the course of the evening Rainer would keep finding new things to show them downstairs, as a pretext for further cigarettes. He was in the process of killing himself. Now her smile was purely decorative. Rainer stood slightly stooped, his legendary hands clasped behind him; his drooping lower lip was moist inside. Elissa was wearing a sleeveless dress of soft dark-green silk. As Halm served himself from the salad bowl she was holding out to him, he looked down into her heavy breasts. A second later he dropped the salad spoon onto the floor. Rainer brought another spoon. Halm immediately started praising the house. The cream-colored plaster and the ceiling beams, and the—"the paneling," Rainer prompted almost before Halm needed the word. What appealed to him was not good taste or affluence. Good taste didn't impress him in the least. In this house there was a great feeling of dignity. Wherever one looked, one could see something not designed for use. And anyone who creates such arrangements wants them to be seen, thought Halm, so I look at everything and pretend that it's all utterly fascinating. Which it is. The heavy mesh firescreen had been drawn back far enough from the hearth to reveal a naked female figure lying on top of the prepared kindling—flesh-colored, absolutely lifelike, in a pose suggesting that this woman was yearning to be incinerated. The set of fire irons stood in a crocodile's skull provided with appropriate holes, and the handles of these implements were apparently made of bones. In the middle of the room, washed by the waves of the floral, peppermint-green, wall-to-wall carpet, a wide, knee-high glass cabinet with mirrors for walls. In it, on black velvet, landscapes made of crystal. The only living thing in this grotesquerie, a tarantula. Every Friday, they were told, it was fed a live cicada. Orange and black stripes cover the hairy tarantula. A skull crowning the mantelshelf—it still has all its teeth and is that of a woman, says Elissa—is in turn crowned by a tarantula or rather the skin and hair cast off by the tarantula. Elissa points out the flap on the back through which the tarantula crept out of its first outer casing. She wished she could do that, she said, walk away from an outer casing that doesn't fit anymore. "You can," said Rainer.

Along the walls, resembling side altars, four glass cabinets with rocks. She had inherited these rocks, said Elissa, from her mother. A Miss McCleave, Rainer whispered in such a way that Halm immediately envisioned a Miss Gutöhrlein to the tenth degree. Her mother had traveled to shows throughout the world with her rocks, bringing back prizes for pyrites, fluorites, quartzes. Halm wanted to know everything. He was pleased that she was pleased by his curiosity. Elissa thanked Halm for his interest. But it was for him to thank *her*! No, no, she was the one, said Elissa. Most visitors behaved as if they were beyond being impressed by anything. Halm was thinking: This utterly comfortable body in dark-green silk. . . . "Our oldest boy is writing a thesis on theories of mineral deposits," Rainer interjected. "That's why he's now with Bethlehem Steel in Spain." "In Galicia," said Elissa. Halm had to think of cantatas in which a soprano is accompanied by a viola. "Galicia," echoed the viola, where the Romans had already been digging for gold, using water for drilling, constructing canals forty kilometers in length for washing out the gold, lining the canals with sheepskins to catch the gold dust in the wool. "Hence the Golden Fleece," said the soprano. "Three hundred thousand slaves guarded by two hundred thousand soldiers," said the darker tone. At intervals the slaves left some rocks untouched so that the governor, who was always expected but turned up only once every few decades, might see how much they had removed. "The stone columns are still standing, according to Milton," said Elissa. "Milton is doing research," said Rainer. "So's Jamey," said Elissa. "Concealed deposits," said Rainer.

The first time she said "Jamey," they moved on, as in a real church, to the next altar. At the point occupied in a church by the high altar stood a low, squat column supporting a domed cage containing a parrot. A huge creature. "That's P," said Elissa. Rainer took over smoothly: "Jamey brought it home." Jamey went to college in Orinda. He drove there every day. From Rainer's scooping gesture Halm immediately gathered that, in order to get to Orinda, Jamey had to drive every day through the hill on which they were now standing. It was in Orinda, too, that Elissa had her driving school. They always drove there together.

Halm felt uneasy. This story sounded as if it was bound to end badly. And he didn't like listening to such stories. One day, when Jamey is eating his sandwich lunch on the college green, he sees a bird in a tree. He gets hold of some seed, climbs up the tree, is not yet quite within reach, and the bird flies away. Jamey comes down, goes to his girlfriend in the dorm for a pillow slip, takes along some more seed, climbs up the tree again, near the top the trunk gets very thin, the treetop sways, Jamey doesn't move, for a long time, doesn't budge, then moves one millimeter at a time, then he's there, has caught it, the bird, brings it home in the pillow slip, says that this is P. They go to a pet store. It turns out to be a yellow-headed Amazon parrot worth seven hundred to a thousand dollars. They immediately clip its wing tips so it can't fly away, then buy it this cage cathedral for which Elissa later finds the marble column and this spot in the room. P had only spoken with Jamey, he said. In other words, since Jamey left P had been mute. Ever since Jamey had brought down this bird from the treetop, Rainer had known that the boy would not stay in college. Jamey had said after his very first year that he would not pay good money to learn something he had no wish to learn. They hadn't taken him seriously. But then one evening he hadn't been at the college green where Elissa always picked him up. The police arrived. Jamey's friends phoned with threats. Months later he phoned. From Orlando, Florida. A few days later from Burlington, Vermont. A day later from Columbus, Ohio. A week later from San Diego.

Thus they sang the legend of their Jamey. He was a real charmer, they said. A genius in the art of living. At home in any element. For a time he had worked as a professional scuba diver in Southern California, scrubbing hulls of rich people's yachts. Then he was no longer allowed to set foot in the state of California. Something to do with drugs. When they were still getting phone calls, they once asked him whether he was studying. Only crackpots study, he said with a laugh and hung up. Whenever he phoned he paid for the call himself. Now he no longer phones. But maybe some day he'll phone again. Postcards are still arriving. By now he must have crossed the continent thirty times. Unbelievable, the speed at which he travels. And all by hitchhiking. There must be something irresistible about his hitchhiker's signal. Perhaps he's traveling from festival to festival. Religious music was his special interest the last time they'd heard from him. The days when he would phone today from Phoenix, Arizona, and fifty-four hours later from Orono, Maine, are over. Maybe he's wanted by the police in many of the states. The way he's wanted is the way only the very best are wanted. They all looked at the large framed photograph on the wall. There were two photos there, but it was clear that now they were looking not at Milton but at Jamey. Both the boys looked like young Rainers. "Maybe he'll even call today," said Rainer.

According to Halm's estimate, Rainer drank four of the six bottles of wine. He'd already been drinking the sherry as if it were soda water. And from time to time he had disappeared for a smoke. Halm asked if he could take a few driving lessons with Elissa. Elissa said she only taught motorcycling. "Motorcycling!" Sabina said, almost rudely. "Oh well, then you'll just have to learn to ride a motorbike!" Halm sensed that Elissa would like to show them her motorcycle. Halm's interest in motorcycles instantly became passionate. Rainer, who was allowed to smoke there, was happy to come along. Sabina followed. Elissa patted the Kawasaki, or whatever it was called, the way one pats an old horse. A BMW was, of course, infinitely better, she said. And only twice as expensive, said Rainer. "She rides this thing to Orinda every day," he said, repeating the scooping motion to depict the tunnel. Why not think about it, said Elissa, she'd give him a discount. Although after Thanksgiving her school would be closed. "That's when she takes off," said Rainer, to look for Jamey. Till April. Halm nodded. Sabina also nodded.

The Halms drove down the Euclid switchbacks, then turned onto Marin Avenue which led straight down the hill like ten ski-jump approaches built one above the other, the cross streets always forming the level platforms. Then straight down again. Halm had to slow Sabina down: she was showing signs of an intoxication not due solely to the California cabernet sauvignon.

As they walked from the garage into the house, dogs that didn't sound like very big ones were barking next door. The cicadas immediately took over again. Halm grasped Sabina's hand and pressed it and drew her close. But that was the last thing Sabina wanted. Lena still had her light on. Halm was thinking that Lena should rescue Jamey. They knocked on Lena's door, called her name: in vain. Suddenly Halm roared: "Lena!" Whereupon Lena, softly: "Yes." "Come out, at least for a few minutes!" Lena, with no special emphasis: "I'd like to go on reading for a bit." They went down the steep narrow staircase. The bedroom still smelled of the anthropologist couple. Halm felt discouraged and flopped onto the huge double bed. A thunderous noise answered him. The head of the metal bed was surmounted by a huge but apparently very wobbly brass victory arch. Halm and Sabina looked at one another and nodded. Then, when they were lying side by side in the dark, Sabina said: "What a couple." Halm said: "And what a house." "That, too," said Sabina. Halm was thinking: So that was the first day. Sabina seemed to be asleep already. He surrendered entirely to the sound of the cicadas. It was as if the world consisted solely of this sound. Elissa's tarantula was fed with these singers. The girl in the bright blue shorts lay on the green grave. Suddenly it seemed important to him that these blue shorts with their white stripes did not have a straight edge but were cut in a curve front and back and that these two curves ended in slits on either side. He couldn't get over that.

4 ON HIS SECOND DAY HALM

picked up a copy of the *Campus Gazette* from the covered bin at Crocker Gate. The headline of the day: SEX BLIND ADMISSION. So far only 33 percent of the students were allowed to be female. From now on, the admissions office would turn a blind eye on sex. English is a language for headlines; he could not reconstruct this line in German.

When he arrived with his *Gazette* at the steps of Coit Hall, he saw the girl from the grave and the student with the Small Things two-liner sitting on the steps. Today the girl was wearing dark-blue jogging pants as well as a T-shirt with an inscription. The one with the two-liner said: "You can't be a professor." Halm pretended to be caught out. She went on: "You're never late." The other girl said: "I don't feel so hot today." Halm looked at her. There was gray, blue, perhaps green in those eyes. At the moment he saw in them a cloudy day in southern Sweden. He said: "I have to invade the hall." He couldn't have said anything more foolish. Room 101 was anything but a hall. He had meant to say that, because yesterday there hadn't been enough chairs, today he wanted to make sure no chairs were taken away. But that was all too complicated, so, to make it simple, that fatuous sentence. He really could have asked why the girl wasn't feeling well. Actually he had wanted to ask them both how best to translate SEX BLIND ADMISSION.

The fact that three chairs remained empty today gave him a feeling of defeat. He passed around a sheet on which he had drawn the shape of the table. Each of them was to enter their name where they happened to be sitting. SEX BLIND ADMISSION—now that was a topic of conversation! And tomorrow Mrs. Elrod's suggestion: The Motive. He was always concerned with supply. He could never use anything for which there wasn't already a replacement. With his last piece of bread in his hand he would starve to death. That was his notion of freedom. SEX BLIND ADMISSION did no more to thrill the students than had yesterday's topic. Directly across from Halm sat a student who so far hadn't said a word. From the seating plan Halm saw that his name was Jeff. Brassy blond like the girl from the grave. Stiff hair sticking out like a visor. Jeff yawned frequently. Usually his hand made no movement to hide the yawning mouth. Halm suffered from this yawning. How could he get even with him? SEX BLIND ADMISSION didn't seem to interest him in the least. In Stuttgart a student would at least try to hide his yawns. He must be in some kind of a trance. Halm shouldn't have gone off so haughtily when the TA from Cologne had been explaining drill instruction. He was sweating with frustration. What saved him from total disgrace was a bearded student explaining that Washington University had always kept the foreign service supplied and that fewer women were needed in the foreign service, hence that proportion. Howard was the bearded one's name. He was over thirty, and there was something in his face that can't be learned at universities. Howard always stepped into the breach when Halm faltered. Halm clearly sensed a desire to help. That felt good. But surely it isn't necessary! He'd manage all right. Help can be embarrassing, too. Don't bother, Howard. Please.

This time the girl caught up with him well before the humpback bridge. Might she see him in his office today, she asked? He was available in his office at noon, that's right, after German II, of course she could come, 407-F, Fillmore Hall. She said she was sorry she hadn't spoken up in class today either. On the bridge Rainer Mersjohann was approaching them. Should they stop? But Rainer was already walking past, slightly stooped, with a humorous word of greeting. Just like in Shakespeare, thought Halm. Maybe the humpback bridge has inspired him. Halm was glad when the girl turned off to the left immediately after the bridge. Probably she spent her free time on the grave. An idea that pleased him.

"Hello, Mrs. Elrod!" "Hello, Mr. Halm!" They were the only ones in the department who didn't call each other by first names. He would have liked to have said Carol to her. "Mr. Ha-alm! Remember the first thing you're supposed to do when you come in? Look over to your left to the boxes, yours is stuffed with invitations, bulletins, and suggestions." When he looked up from the papers, he met her gaze. He had to look down at the papers again. He should have settled back into that gaze; he would have been in good hands. He looked at the papers and said: "It's quite a pile, Carol, isn't it?" The most important thing, she said, was the party at Rainer's, it was an official one, to welcome him, the dean would be there, perhaps even the provost and, purely theoretically, even the president. She would make no comment on the sexist skat evening on Saturday at Roy's since she assumed that would be Mr. Halm's favorite engagement.

A stocky little man of about Halm's age appeared in the doorway. A face full of beard. Fritz O. Dempewolf. He just wanted to tell Mr. Halm that he had also put a little note in his box. And he was gone. Carol said: "Our mini-Solzhenitsyn." And just then Roy Kinsman could be heard coming along the corridor. "Hey! I almost tripped over our rotten potato!" he called out in a voice normally used for swearing. "Why shouldn't a hollow nut trip over a rotten potato?" Dempewolf shouted back with a cockiness somewhat lacking in credibility. In the room Roy then said: "Asshole! Whenever I see that guy I get constipated for two days. But don't tell him so, he'll only take advantage of it." He'd be seeing Halm Saturday night for skat, he'd give the party on Friday a miss, otherwise his house wouldn't be ready Saturday for the skat evening, and skat was more important than the party.

When Halm emerged onto the steps after German II, the girl was sitting there again. She hadn't been able to find 407-F, she said. As they were about to enter the elevator together, it was of course Carol Elrod who came out. "Look who's here!" she said, with a jerk at her handbag as her heels tapped out an angry tattoo on the floor of Fillmore Hall. Or was he just imagining it because he had a guilty conscience? "*Bon appétit!*" he called after her as she stalked away. What a talent she had for expressing what she felt! The girl said Carol was her favorite person on the whole campus. No one did as much for anybody as Carol did. He pulled out his bunch of campus keys: "Here's proof!" It was Carol who had assembled them and given him a list with all the numbers of the keys and the numbers of the matching doors. But then, what with their teeth on all four sides, he couldn't manage to get one of these things into the keyhole. And the numbers on the keys were so small that he couldn't read them on this dim landing. The stupid thing about these keys was that each of them had to be tried out in four different positions before one could say it wasn't the right one. If he had been half his age, they could both have laughed at his clumsiness. At his age, however, he could have resorted in such a situation to the linguistic supermarket of psychology; no doubt, as with lapses of the tongue or of memory, there was also a ready-made interpretation. He sweated. He gave up. Perhaps he'd left his office key at home today, he said. There could not have been a less credible explanation.

Since he couldn't look continuously into her eyes during his explanation, he lowered his gaze and read the words on the outer ring printed on her shirt. FEDERATED FIREFIGHTER. On the inner ring there were only the letters AFL-CIO repeated over and over. In the middle was a red circle with a big yellow F on it. Of course, her name was Fran. Short for Frances, probably. Francesca seemed like a suitable name for her. He suggested going to one of the Student Union coffee shops. He hoped she didn't think he didn't trust himself alone with her in this remote office and so had engineered the key fiasco.

There, in the midday sun, they also sat alone. Everyone else preferred to sit in the shade inside. So now to her problem, an essay for her essay course with Professor Littlewood, to be handed in by next Tuesday, on a poem of her choice. She would like to write on a German poem. She could, of course, ask Professor Ackerman or Professor Mersjohann, but she'd rather ask him. If she could, she'd like to write about Rilke's poem, "The Panther," make a new translation and then write about it; she had brought along Robert Bly's translation. She hands it to him. He reads it half to himself, then the original. They are sitting at a little round table. On the marble top, a cup of coffee, a glass of milk. Rilke in English and German. They sit in the sun and the wind. Yes, Mr. Kiderlen, you may well look down from your lofty viewpoint! Once again, half to himself, he read out the Bly translation:

> From seeing and seeing the seeing has become so
> exhausted
> it no longer sees anything anymore.
> The world is made of bars, a hundred thousand
> bars, and behind the bars, nothing.

Fortunately, this was not intimidating. Until the very last line: not intimidating . . . *reaches the heart, and dies* for *hört im Herzen auf zu sein. Im* Herzen, Mr. Translator, *in* the heart! Maybe that can't be done. But maybe it can. If it can, then here, in this sunshine, at this little table. This poem can only be translated by two people sitting, at the end of August between twelve and one, all alone at a little table outdoors, who have nothing in common in the whole wide world except for these three verses of a Rilke poem. Admit that this is a fantastic day, he said to himself. I admit it, said the I to the I who had addressed it. To the girl he said in a level voice: "What a nice thing to be doing—sitting here with you in the sunshine translating this poem." Before he could finish the sentence, she called out to someone passing behind him. The person stopped and asked whether she would be going along to the Coliseum to hear David Bowie. She raised her chin slightly, gave a little shake of her head, and said she was going to the opera. That sounded pretty supercilious. David Bowie! She's going to the opera!

Now they were tossing words at each other. Nothing can be bandied back and forth like words! He kept firing off Rilke's words; she would fling back English words to match them. Then he would fire off some English words. Sometimes they even chose his. This back and forth was almost like the weaving of a fabric. At least that was how it seemed to him. Finally, the version on paper was:

From bars which pass, his eyes are so exhausted
no things can they now hold
His eyes behold all bars, as if behind all bars
there were no world.

His lithe and swinging stride is strong,
and circles down into an end.
It is a dance of power around a point
in which anesthetized a great will tends.

Rarely enough the drape of his lids lifts up
totally silent—and then a picture passes in
to penetrate his body's silent tension
and in his heart ceases to be.

Not that he considered his English good enough to translate this poem. But this very presumptuousness was what inspired him. He wanted to do something that was beyond him, to transcend himself. He was the moving spirit in this word game. Then he gets up. If she wants to show him what she intends to write about her experience with this poem—he'll be glad to discuss it with her. And lowers his head like a flag, raises it, says good-bye, and leaves.

She remained seated. He strode off as if to catch a train, while she was still putting away her papers in her shoulder bag, which looked a bit too elegant for a student.

He hurried back to Fillmore Hall, went in by the side entrance, stood outside his door, took out his wallet, extracted the office key, opened the door, sat down, then fled from the icy shower by thrusting himself backward on his swivel chair right up to the almost empty bookshelves. He looked at the children's drawings without seeing them. He found it interesting that this time he had been able to take the right key out of his wallet without the slightest hesitation. Now he remembered that he had taken this key off the bunch because it was the one he used every day: he didn't want to be forever trying out four different keys. But earlier, when he had been standing outside the door with the girl, he had forgotten this. Who found it interesting? Who's asking whom? *He* is asking *you*. *He* is frustrated, disappointed, furious. Halm was aware that he was furious, disappointed, frustrated, but at the same time calm and contented. The one who was frustrated, disappointed, furious wanted to separate himself from the one who was calm and contented. *He*-Halm couldn't understand anyone running away from a table where one was sitting with a girl like that. *He*-Halm said: Admit that it is wretched, is asinine, is pitiful, is disgraceful—admit this at once and unreservedly! Halm felt he was being shouted at and said: All right, I admit it, though not unreservedly, but I won't specify my reservations, otherwise this distasteful dialogue will go on forever. *He*-Halm: Coward. *I*-Halm: I'd be the first to admit that. *He*-Halm: You'll never be able to atone for that. *I*-Halm: I sincerely hope not. *He*-Halm: Go on, go to the department, get hold of a list of undergraduates, look up her address and see whether she has a phone! *I*-Halm: What an . . . an . . . unspeakable simpleton you are! What she wants is a good mark with the least possible effort, she just wants plenty of time for swimming and jogging. Perhaps also for her boyfriend. She's already indicated that she needs lots of time every day for swimming and jogging. I'm supposed to help her gain time for swimming and jogging.

And for the boyfriend, perhaps! She's spoiled. To quote Carol: Porsche, Dad's medical practice, Pacific Heights. She's a girl for whom too much is always being done. At first by her parents, then by her girlfriends, then by her boyfriends: now it's my turn, it's as simple as that. Everything else is a result of your fantasizing, based on God knows what blindness, what lack of observation and sophistication. There's nothing as alien and incomprehensible to this girl as what we are now bandying back and forth about her. *He*-Halm: Defeatist! *I*-Halm: Get lost. It'll pass. Tonight we'll try some of that California red wine, I understand it's not bad. *He*-Halm: You old soak. *I*-Halm: Better than being all wet. *He*-Halm: Now he's making puns! And this is the man who intends writing about Nietzsche!

Halm dialed the number on Contra Costa Avenue. Sabina: at three he has to be at the Foundation Building to see Dolores Chen and decide on the right kind of medical insurance for their time here, from there he'll go straight home, by bus, and what's she doing? There's a cat prowling about in the garden, she's watching it. And Lena? Doesn't want to be spoken to. Halm hurried out.

He was the last to join the insurance session. Dolores Chen spoke very fast and knew it and explained it by her being from New York, but she'd be glad to answer questions. Most of the questions came from a man from East Germany who was also here for one semester. Halm had instinctively sat down beside him. The East German was only about five years younger than he; all the others were fifteen to twenty-five years younger. At one point Miss Chen asked Halm whether he had any more questions, and in order to single him out from the sparsely occupied chairs she called him "the older gentleman." He had no further questions. If he did, he would ask his compatriot Zipser from Leipzig, who already knew as much as the lady from New York yet persisted in asking for further details. He asked one question that even the well-informed Miss Chen couldn't answer. She'd find out for him; he was to call her. To Halm it seemed that Zipser was asking on behalf of the entire German Democratic Republic. After the session they exchanged phone numbers. Zipser was staying at the Faculty Club, the log building, situated at the highest point, that looked like an oversize hunting lodge.

Halm went home by bus. Toward the end the only other passenger was a blind black man. They both got off at the terminus. As they were standing on the sidewalk, the blind man asked which way he was facing. Halm stammered, the driver called out of the bus: "Down Solano." Halm walked rapidly away, up to Contra Costa. On this street he felt safe. He could only look at these houses with a kind of craving. He felt like stopping in front of each one of them. Closely parked cars on both sides of the street left only a narrow lane for driving. When two cars met, one had to back up and find a spot to allow room for the other. But there were very few cars moving anyway. This street on the hump of the hill lay dreaming. That's right, Mr. Kiderlen, have a good look at Mr. Halm walking along a warm, peaceful street in the mild evening light. A huge tree finally brought him to a halt: it was not tall, but its massive branches, covered with what looked like elephant hide, spread in every direction. A house built of dark wood formed a magical symbiosis with this tree, which showed itself off like a body builder. Two plaster dwarfs, almost life size, in other words two giant plaster dwarfs, stood under the tree but looking down the slope, toward the house. From the open windows came the sound of someone practicing *Albumblatt für Elise.* Yes, Mr. Kiderlen, I can recommend this scene to your arbitrary smirk. Oh, if only I could send it to you the way it is! Together with the cicadas creating their own element.

For some thirty yards along the street, *Elise* has the upper hand over the cicadas. Then both are audible. Then only the cicadas. On Fridays Elissa feeds them to her striped tarantula. Back home he would sometimes pick up the weekly that Kiderlen brought along to the staff room as if it were some smart accessory, but reading the trendy articles, such as those glorifying cold weather, simply made him feel that these aesthetic products of a fashionable disgust with material comforts were of no concern to him. Here he felt genuinely attracted by people. It was an effort to walk past them. He kept his eyes as long as possible on each person coming toward him.

As soon as he saw the Japanese front garden he noticed that Sabina had followed the watering instructions left behind by the Rineharts. The leaves, gleaming like plump green pennies, were still wet. Inside the house Mrs. Rinehart has seen to it that it was almost impossible to move without seeing yourself in some mirror. Usually you can see in the farther mirror the mirror in which you see yourself. So Halm notices immediately that his jacket collar is sticking up on one side. Did this mean he hadn't put on his jacket this morning until after leaving the house? Had he looked that ludicrous all day? Well, why not! It was just fine if he had looked that ludicrous today, just fine!

He walked through the living and dining room into the anthropologist's study and looked straight down onto the terrace with its reddish-brown flagstones and the steps leading down to the lawn. He saw Sabina crouching. She had put out some food for the cat, which had come up the few steps from the lawn. The path to the food now led past Sabina. Sabina did not move. Nor did the cat. Then came a moment when the little cat started to move. Toward the dish. At the point closest to Sabina the cat stops, looks at Sabina, her front paws seemingly stuck in another world. Her back legs must be stretched, then actually drawn forward. After another endless interval, after fighting every kind of innate and acquired resistance, she has dragged herself all the way to Sabina. When almost there, the cat arches her back, twists her body, and stretches her neck until her head nestles in Sabina's cupped palm. Now Sabina's hand starts its gentle stroking, pressing, fondling. The cat surrenders to this miraculously cooperative hand, nestles into it and twists her body as if the hand were a warm shower of inexhaustible delight. She wants the shower to reach every spot. At some point the cat actually has had enough; now she can walk over to the dish and eat. After all, her hunger is still there. Sabina can straighten up and leave.

Halm hurried over to the steep, narrow stairs, opened the door at the top, and congratulated her on her conquest as she came up the stairs. "Ah, Sabina, you know how to do it!" Sabina said: "Did you hear? She hisses when she wants to miaow—that's how tense she is. She really wants to miaow and purr, but what first comes out is a hiss. So young and so mixed up."

Halm called out: "Lena!" A distinctly long-suffering "Yes" came from her room. Halm shouted that he'd like all three of them to sit down together for supper and look out on San Francisco and the reddening sky. And he wasn't going to take no for an answer. "Your parents have bent over backward to please you. And if you don't appreciate it we'll wring your neck." He couldn't be more facetious than that. The door slowly opened, and Lena emerged in her inimitable slow motion. She halted in front of her parents, one hand clasped in the other. She happened to stand so that the evening light coming through the picture windows shone full on her. The accident scars around her mouth and nose glowed red.

5

THE MORNING SUN HIGH-lights the tips of San Francisco's buildings as they emerge from the mist. It proceeds like a watercolor artist, starting with the pillars of the Bay Bridge. As long as he was in the house, Halm preferred to look out the windows. Sure, he had to check on his jacket collar, but after that he wished to avoid any mirror, difficult though it was in this house.

Immediately after passing through the massive square pillars of Crocker Gate, he behaved as if liberated, plunging, as it were, into the youthful flood as it surged over the undulating campus. The students here were more conspicuously young than their contemporaries at home. Although it was only nine o'clock, some were already lying or sitting on the grass, which here and there was still wet from the artificial rain spraying at automatic intervals from invisible nozzles. Dogs were already waiting on the grass for their masters and mistresses to return from the stone fortresses. Today, again, coeds were dashing toward one another with shrill cries, then embracing as if this were a wildly improbable encounter in the Gobi Desert. Sometimes Halm's eyes latched onto an approaching coed so firmly that he was afraid his head would be dragged around as she walked past him.

By the time he reached the classroom he felt as if he worked his way through a fantastic thicket. He began by apologizing to the students for yesterday's topic: SEX BLIND ADMISSION. He promised he would never again force themes upon them for which no one could summon any interest at nine in the morning. Good-bye, topicality! After all, we're only interested in the substance we ourselves are made of. So: let's continue our conversation about conversation. He hoped they still remembered their first session. And quickly went on speaking to prevent anyone from saying no to this risky question. Conversation per se, he said, scared him, but conversation about conversation appealed to him. He suggested that each of them now tell the class whether they always said what they thought and, if not, what they said instead, and whether what they did say had any connection with what they thought but didn't say, and how? In other words, do we try with what we say to indicate what we think, and yet conceal it . . . ?

Most of the time he directed his words at the girl. Also Jeff. In addressing Jeff he emphasized his voice and expression. He wanted to help Jeff not to yawn. Fortunately, the seemingly ever-concerned Howard displayed some interest in this subject. He disputed the enormous distinction Halm had made in the first session between a foreign language and a mother tongue. According to Howard, the relationship between suppressing and expressing remained constant whatever the circumstances. Freud had had a formula for how what is suppressed takes its revenge by a slip of the tongue. Halm felt like saying that yesterday while sitting at a cafeteria table he hadn't had a single slip of the tongue although all that time he had been suppressing what he really wanted to say. Didn't Freud have a somewhat punitive notion of self-suppression? Isn't every language a foreign language, Halm would have liked to say—to exclaim even? Foreign to what we are. What we are must not be revealed. In any language. So, today's contention: every language is designed to conceal more than it reveals. . . .

Too bad that the girl didn't participate. It was impossible to tell whether she was listening. Her chair was pushed way back from the table they were all sitting at; here, too, she had drawn up one leg at a wide angle; her right foot rested just above her left knee. On the grave she had also drawn up her right leg. It looked as though she wanted this bare brown leg to be her main contribution. One hand was clasped around her raised ankle. She sat lightly on her chair, looking now at one speaker, then turning her head toward the next, but slowly, as if unaware of doing so.

After class she caught up with Halm again. She wasn't satisfied, she said, with whatever ideas she'd had so far about the poem. Halm stopped, as if only in standing still could he give due thought to some advice for her. He didn't want to meet Rainer. And if he had to, at least not as melodramatically as last time, on the hump-back bridge. Hadn't she first encountered the poem in Vienna? In that case the best thing would be for her to put down everything that had influenced her at the time; this made it possible to discover the impact of a poem on one's life; that was the most one could ever learn about a poem. And suddenly it dawned on him that he had to keep silent about the impact of the Rilke poem on himself at that moment. To stand with this girl on a bend in the path on these undulating lawns is a mistake. Start walking again.

Two dogs were trotting along in front of them, a fat elderly male, maybe a mixture of husky and chow dog, and a slender young boxer bitch. The old shaggy one trots along very close to the almost naked-looking young bitch and about half a head behind her. She will have nothing to do with the old dog and turns aside onto the grass, he takes advantage of her veering off, and mounts her from behind, whereupon she immediately plants her threatened rear firmly in the grass. But he performs his intercourse movements against her flank. Not liking that either, she scampers off, the old dog following very close to her side. A second, much younger male dog, who would suit her much better, appears on the scene. The old dog growls, bares his teeth, the younger one is chased off. The old dog resumes his trotting as if glued to the side of the bitch. Wherever the pair passes, the students stop and laugh.

Halm started off with a huge stride and, as justification for that exaggerated stride, glanced at his watch. So: just put down what happened in Vienna, then within the web of that time the pattern will emerge of which the poem is a part. He said. At the highest point of the bridge, Rainer passed them with his Shakespearean flourish. On noticing that Halm would be a few minutes later today, Rainer must have delayed his approach to the bridge long enough for the encounter to take place once again at the most embarrassing point. And, needless to say, Carol stepped out of the elevator with an even more pronounced pout and an even more critical expression. "There you are," she said, walking away more slowly this time to show that she could look even more reproachful when walking slowly than when walking quickly. "What a beautiful woman!" the girl said. Halm nodded as vigorously as he could.

The girl got out on the third floor, so he went on to the fourth, although he had meant to pick up some works by Heine from the library of the German department. Now he was sitting under the cold shower, realizing that he had forgotten to bring either scarf or sweater. He sat there letting the cold air flow over him. He hoped Elisha wouldn't choose this moment to come and grind his key in the lock. Elisha didn't, but instead Professor Torres with his even more raucous South American laugh burst onto the landing. Halm found himself powerless to prevent that split consciousness from taking over again. *He*-Halm was furious. *He*-Halm had to speak. Speak out. One can pretend not to understand a word. Let it peter out. Every high tide must at some point recede. By tuning out, you can turn any sound into mere noise. Everything he felt compelled to say could be classified in advance as *noise*. Noise from the coast. Noise of the surf. Noise of life. It will pass. Soon enough.

But next morning when Halm entered the classroom, he had to swallow twice: the girl wasn't there. He had already sat down when the door opened once more, but it was Gail swinging herself in on her two crutches. And laughing. If it was laughing. It could also be effort that was making her mouth gape like that. And behind all that metal her teeth were invisible. This plus the crutches produced an unfortunately ferocious effect. Yesterday he had prepared it all so nicely: what do we suppress when we say something? What do we say in order to suppress something? How much can we infer from what is being said about what is being suppressed? Today he asked each and every student to express an opinion. As a teacher it was his job to persuade every member of the class to contribute. With drill instruction, each one of you would have to respond sixty-five times an hour! So *once* per head per week—he must insist on that! Today it would have been her turn. Suddenly he had lost all desire to enthuse about suppressing. Let's talk about something else.

After class, walking down the steps of Coit Hall in the bright sunshine, Halm felt happy. He was himself again. Composed. Calm. Serene. He could look at things objectively. To have let himself be upset by that girl—he smiled at the thought! If for once she wasn't there, it was as if she had never been there. So there you are! He had no objection to life going on. How wonderful to see laughing people everywhere! But he didn't have to be one of them. Nothing could be pleasanter than the fatigue that was now filling his veins. He heard his name. It was Jeff. Pushing his racing bicycle, he walked beside Halm as the girl had done yesterday. The same blond hair. The same eyes. He just wanted to tell Halm that he was enjoying the conversation class very much. He said that in English. "Everyone likes you," he said in German. "Especially Fran!" he called out as he rode off downhill to the left where the marble slabs surround the dark-green library walls like shields. Halm didn't call out after him. We know, don't we, that life is confusion. Sounding like noise.

On the bridge Rainer approached, stopped, expressed pleasure. "You look great, all alone!" he said. Once his paper on Schubert's text interpretation had reached the point where it would grow on its own, he would be knocking on Halm's door. He wasn't going to allow this fall to go by empty of Helmut and himself. Helmut shouldn't be too quick to go looking for other company. So long! And waved. But this time his arm didn't make a great Shakespearean flourish as if doffing an ironical hat: he merely raised his hand until it slowly came to a stop at chest level. The Saint John's hand of the sonnet writer. Halm followed him with his eyes, wanting to tell him how much he enjoyed meeting him every day on this bridge, but he couldn't find the words. That Jeff! Halm shook his head.

Anyway, it was now time to prepare himself for Carol. He must go to the department. He had to walk through the ever-open door of 306, utter a cheery greeting, then glance to the left, to his box—yes, once again bulging with papers. Carol expressed surprise that he had found his way to the department, and alone too! Halm felt as if he had been coming to this office for nineteen years. A pleasant feeling. He countered with forced geniality: nowhere rather than in this room would he have people pretend, out of sheer courtesy and hospitality, that they were glad to see him, etcetera. Carol's lips slid back from her magnificent protruding teeth, and the gap between the two front ones seemed to widen. It's important to give people the impression that one likes them, she said, as if summing up their conversation. Halm acted hurt. One must genuinely like people, not just pretend to! "Come off it!" she said, she could tell from that remark that he came from Germany. Why, he hadn't even thought it worthwhile to try out her tip that the students discuss their motives! And she could understand that. He simply has a different method: he takes on each student individually, explores their motives in a tender clinch at the cafeteria table, and follows them to the grave! She only hoped that with so much individual attention he would manage to complete his program by the end of the semester. A little at a time and that thoroughly, a tried-and-true pedagogic principle. He stammered. She laughed. He swore black and blue that she was quite wrong about him. "I wish I were," she said. Then they both laughed, and it was time, luckily, for him to go to German II.

Next morning the girl in the blue shorts with the white stripes again sat as far away from the table as possible, contributed her drawn-up brown leg, and asked afterward if she might come to his office at noon. Wearing a black blouse, beige slacks, and low-heeled, almost brandy-colored shoes, she stood outside the door of 407-F, carrying her running shoes in one hand. He took the key out of his wallet saying that it had been in there the other day too, and managed to tell her about his embarrassment over the key without mentioning his age, yet in a kind of coquettish version: how he had fallen victim to his own fussy ways.

From her round shoulder bag she took two texts, Shakespeare and Stefan George: which of the two would he prefer for her next essay theme? On Monday, if she might, she would bring the "Panther" essay to his office. She was afraid, though, that she was pestering him. He couldn't help watching her lips meeting and parting as she spoke. Her mouth doesn't open and close. Her speech is a constant parting and meeting of her lips. Continuous. At the corners of her mouth she has tiny little craters. Scars. These minute lunar landscapes provide an austere framework for these lips as they gently flow apart and together. One of Carol's critical comments on the typical California coed was: And that year-round tan! How little did that tell about the many vibrant colors of this face.

Yes, he'll be glad to read it all, and they can meet here again on Monday. She stood up, paused for a second, then left. After opening the door, she turned around and wished him a pleasant weekend. The recipient of this wish remained seated, staring fixedly. There is no reason ever to move again. Except that Sabina is picking you up shortly after one at Crocker Gate. His first question: "Lena?" "She doesn't want anyone to speak to her," Sabina replied. "Slow down, Sabina," Halm said, "we're in California." "You have to talk to Lena," Sabina said. "She can't possibly spend three and a half months sitting in her room holding a cup of tea, staring at the wall, and settling accounts with that Traugott. And then she's furious when one goes into her room. She doesn't want to be caught sitting there and staring." Halm said: "Sitting and staring." Sabina said: "She simply has to come with us to this party tonight. If she won't go, I won't either. The best thing for her would be to take some courses every day in college. Spanish, for instance." "Slow down, Sabina, slow down! Look, here each house is different from the next! And the people in this sunshine. They really have a good life here, don't you agree?" Sabina told him he simply has to go with her tomorrow to the Monterey farmers' market. All those colorful, fresh-smelling fruits and vegetables under one roof! Later they were all on the table, those colorful vegetables, brought to their full flavor by Sabina.

Halm said: "Lena, you must admit that we're lucky to be sitting here—first a big dish of artichokes, then three kinds of squash, green asparagus, rice, cheese, and all this as we look across to San Francisco buried in the softest haze. And the tips of the skyscrapers cheekily poking their noses out, like young birds in a nest. Come on now, Lena!" "Yes," said Lena, "very lucky." "And just wait till we get to the Mersjohanns', their beautiful house, the people you'll meet there!" He wanted to get her all fired up, but he saw that she couldn't be fired up. She didn't want to go with them to the Mersjohanns'. "But you *must* come with us," he said. He would have to force her. For her own good. Next week she'd have to come along with him to the university. Spanish, philosophy, music, whatever she liked. She could meet the professors at the Mersjohanns'. She shook her head. He mustn't give in, he shouted. For her sake! Abruptly she got up, went to her room, and locked the door.

After a while he went to her door and resumed negotiations. He apologized for having tried to force her for her own good. Later she could reproach him as much as she liked, but first she should go along with them, or rather, first of all she should open the door. It was already past four o'clock when she agreed. Sabina offered suggestions as to what she should wear. Lena accepted them impassively. She let herself be dressed like a child. Sabina had gone to the Chinese florist's and created a bouquet that might have fallen from some Elysian fields.

They drove to the traffic circle from which Marin Avenue leads off straight as a die and up almost vertically over the ski-jump platforms to Euclid. No one said a word. The daughter had been pressured, forced: for her own good. It would be up to the parents to prove it had been the right thing to do. Lena hadn't bothered to powder over the scars around her mouth, chin, and nose. That was her answer to the pressuring. The scars looked as if polished. But he didn't dare say anything, not even against that Traugott!

Lena maintained that the psychoanalysis was solely to blame, for it was during Traugott's analysis that the marriage had gone to pieces. In liberating himself from his mother, Traugott had also liberated himself from his wife. It had all happened without any emotional upheaval. Quite matter-of-fact. Cutting the umbilical cord with his mother had been long overdue. No one could have known, of course, that his wife was also attached to it.

Under the high-vaulted ceiling of the chapel wing, the guests stood elbow to elbow. They were also standing out on the terrace and so preoccupied with one another that they seemed oblivious to the Bay, the city, and the bridges. But perhaps the lofty site did have an effect on the prevailing mood. Everyone was beaming. Whoever one looked at—everyone was beaming. Listening or talking, they were beaming. Halm had never seen so many beaming faces in his life. He also felt the urge to beam. First he had to assess the level of dress formality. Higher than expected. He pressed Sabina's hand: she had insisted on his wearing a tie. Sabina nodded, she knew what he was thanking her for.

Rainer led the Halms from group to group, invariably finding a common subject for conversation; he allotted the time according to some mental ranking of the groups, from the president's wife down to Fritz D. Dempewolf, the mini-Solzhenitsyn. Neither the president nor the vice president had been able to come, both having had to go to Washington D.C. on behalf of the university. The president's wife informed Halm of this overriding reason with an expression in her wonderfully feminine face that positively beseeched his understanding. Halm heard himself say: No matter where the president and the provost might be, he felt highly honored that their absence should be explained to him with the most cogent reason imaginable, and explained by whom, indeed! If the president had come and *she* had been absent, that would have been a deficiency for which he could have found no mitigating formula. "But then you wouldn't even have known who was missing!" she said with a laugh. "Oh, don't say that!" said Halm. "Before I met you there was something missing, although I didn't know what, you're right. Now I know."

Halm felt as if his class in 101 were listening to him. His aim was to demonstrate how easily one can chatter away in a foreign language. He felt he wasn't responsible for what he was saying. He became intoxicated. Was it only the cocktail? He had quickly to interject that everything he was saying was attributable to the English language or to this cocktail or to both. With a bittersweet smile the president's wife regretted that he was now looking for extenuating circumstances. Rainer supplied a whispered German translation of this idiom so discreetly that Halm could go on holding forth without any inhibitions. But then Rainer snatched him out of the conversation as he would a soufflé out of the oven. Halm hissed at him: "You must be crazy!" As he was being led away, Halm called out apologies to the president's wife as she laughed. He would have preferred to call out something grandiloquent to her. But that wasn't possible. Nothing was possible. One was simply dragged away. Meet Mr. and Mrs. Holmquist, the dean and his wife. Lena had drifted off and was looking out the window. And where was Sabina? Sabina was near him. The dean, an expert on Scandinavian literature, happened to be talking about his project: the campus has to be provided immediately with seven hundred computers. He has already entirely computerized his *Edda* research. His wife said she would guarantee that the scenery for *Walküre* on which she was now working would remain computer-free. She was, she said, transferring Wagner to the Pacific Coast. The Valkyrie would emerge as surf-minotaurs from the waves and carry the heroes off to a Pacific Valhalla.

Halm didn't know how to convey his rapture. What a couple they were, these Holmquists! His Scandinavian expertise was being fleshed out by her operatic stage designing, and her stage world was being invested with a kind of scenic dignity by his Scandinavian research. The experience of Rainer always prematurely separating the Halms from the people he had just been introduced to was repeated with each group. What great people! All of them! Or was it the light shining up from the glittering Bay or even across from the Pacific? Sabina had claimed: "Light from the sea makes everyone look distinguished."

Halm could not recall ever having been so delighted by a social gathering of such well-dressed people. So lively! So effortless! So free of suffering! There seemed to be no problems! Just listen to the combined sound of all the voices in the room: you can hear and feel that overall it is composed of sheer affability. And the visible corresponds completely to the audible: a room vibrating with silk, linen, and coiffed hair, with skin and jewelry and magnificent teeth. Wherever you looked, someone was saying to someone else precisely what that person wanted to hear, and *that* person in turn responded with exactly what the *other* person wanted to hear! And each seemed to be so adept at this that all of them together created an atmosphere of perfect well-being.

Ah, Roy Kinsman! So he's come after all! Halm was pleased. The chairman's responsible, said Roy, so tomorrow they'd have to sit on chairs that weren't yet ready. And goes on to tell the group about the joys of pig breeding on his hobby farm in Upper Happy Valley: the piglet is placed on its back in the food trough, he holds the piglet, Sally presses its testicles into the scrotum, and snip-snap, that's the end of the equipment. As soon as the little ones start to squeal, the mother sow begins to hurl herself madly against the door. If she were to get in she would attack without mercy.

Sally confirmed all this with gleaming lips and shining eyes and in a voice that was remarkably deep, especially compared with her husband's rather high voice. It was a tenor-contralto marriage. Sally came from Texas. And was a sculptor. That seemed appropriate too, Halm found. In fact, here everything seemed appropriate to everything else. For what could this gleaming Sally-mouth be more suitable than for producing Texan sounds! This mouth positively labored to bring forth that vowel-addicted Texan drawl whose every vowel echoed with all the other vowels. Halm would have liked to go on watching, but Rainer was already dragging him away to meet Kirk Elrod, Carol's husband and the university's poet laureate. After they had joined Mr. Elrod, Rainer explained this lifetime literary function to the Halms. The poet laureate is paid for being a writer-in-residence on campus. There are no rules as to how he is to do this. Rainer apologized for not having explained this to the Halms in advance. The poet said: "We make Schubert's text interpretation responsible for everything!" The fact was, he hadn't yet written a single sentence of this all-paralyzing paper, said Rainer. "There are babies that kill their mothers during pregnancy," said Kirk Elrod. That was what he liked about the professors among whom he is now spending his twilight years: the fact that they torment each other with the same demands with which they make life miserable for their students. This senseless pressure to produce paper after paper must have a religious origin. Turning to Halm: "Publish or perish! Not a writer's motto, a sheer campus product. Here's to the campus!" They drank.

The poet and Rainer immediately had their glasses refilled with straight bourbon. "Here's to our guest from Germany!" The poet said: "Where in the world could such maniacs as Rainer and I live? Only on campus!" "Only on the campus of Washington University in Oakland, California," said Rainer. "Here's to Washington University in Oakland, California!" said the poet. They drank. "You should know," said the poet, "that the president of this university has a soft spot for alcoholics." Rainer protested: "Kirk, I beg you!" Kirk ignored him. Did Halm happen to have read his novel, *Inspiration Inn*? Halm hesitated. Rainer came to his aid: "Well, *I*'ve read it three times, Kirk!" In that case Rainer could tell his friend Helmut how the novel begins—one stormy night when the Pacific breakers prevent a visitor from leaving a female alcoholic—or was it a male alcoholic?—actually for the alcoholic alcohol is more important than sex, and during that night the novel unwinds as an alcoholic whim in search of redemption.

He didn't know his own book, said Rainer. Alcohol is hardly mentioned that night; the raging Pacific breakers in the resounding bay are the element that carries the story. "Can you understand why *Inspiration Inn* has been such a success?" asked Kirk Elrod and added too quickly for Rainer to be able to reply: "Four million copies." He still had one or two, if Halm were interested. Halm said he would like to read everything Kirk Elrod had written. The poet said he would let him have all the copies he wanted: after all, they lived on the same hill. "Cheers!" They drank. "Did I tell you what Kennedy wrote to me when *Inspiration Inn* came out?"

Before Halm could answer, Carol had detached herself from the next group and was saying: "Kirk! This time you're off course with your senile blandishments! You've only known Mr. Halm for three minutes, and normally even you wait five minutes before dishing up the same old story again." "You know," said the poet, "Carol's responsible for my senility not being too conspicuous. At this very moment you're witnessing how well she does it! Drink up! Every time we leave our house on Grizzly Peak Boulevard, she says: 'Today you really must take care not to repeat everything three times!' And I say: 'Dear heart, what d'you mean, *I* have to? I'm senile after all! It's up to you to take care that I don't repeat everything three times!' "

Everyone laughed, the poet loudest of all. He choked and went into a coughing fit. Now Halm realized what a giant he was. The coughing stretched him, doubled him up, stretched him. When he saw the chair that Carol quickly carried over, the fit subsided immediately, and he said quite calmly: "You'd like that, wouldn't you? Then preach a sermon at home on how impossibly I had behaved again. She just doesn't like it when I start talking about my age. For Carol the subject of age is taboo. Right, Honeybunch?" "Yes, darling," said Carol. "So now I never mention my age," he said. "This virtually means a ban on speech for me, since the only thing still of interest to someone of my age is his age. Right, Honeybunch?" "Yes, darling," said Carol. He: "When I was young . . ." "Darling," said Carol. "Yes, Honeybunch," he said.

"Cheers," said Carol. "Oh," he said, "cheers! This is a rare occasion, this is unique, Carol encouraging me to have a drink!" "Because as long as you're drinking you can't talk about your age," said Carol. He: "But I wanted to talk about my youth!" She: "Anyone who talks about his youth is talking about his age." "Fortunately," he said, "there is something that interests me even more than my age." "Alcohol," said Carol, her protruding teeth disappearing behind her heavy lower lip. Elrod turned to face Halm: "I must have told you what my second wife's mother said when *Inspiration Inn* was published." Kirk Elrod could end a sentence in such a way that it could sound as much like a question as a statement.

Suddenly he became very quiet. "Honeybunch," he said, "I'll have that chair—my cramps." His face twitched, relaxed, twitched again. Now he was sitting on the chair. Carol was holding one of his hands and rubbing it. Was it all right for them to leave, he asked in an undertone. Petite Carol led her wizened giant through the crowd like Moses leading his people through the Red Sea. She was wearing a white dress with straps made of gold rings over her rounded bare shoulders.

Halm noticed Dempewolf standing beside Lena at the window. Rainer said the job wasn't over yet and beckoned the Halms. "Have you met Leslie Ackerman and his wife Joyce?" The hand that Leslie Ackerman offered the Halms was also holding a glass, his left hand being needed to cover his left eye; perhaps something had flown into it. Leslie was the man for contemporary literature, said Rainer. His specialty: Thomas Mann. Joyce is writing a doctoral thesis on hermaphroditism in myth and literature. Joyce, a beautiful death's-head with yellow glasses and flaxen braids, smiled effortlessly at the Halms. Halm glanced involuntarily at the mantelshelf, at the death's-head crowned with tarantula skin and complete with teeth. Yes, Joyce had the same rectangular smile. Rainer said that Leslie, by the way, had represented the United States in the high jump at Sapporo. "Now I get beaten by East German girls," Leslie said almost apologetically. "You're sure they're girls?"

his wife said. This question was passed on as a joke to Zipser from Leipzig, who said that, as a specialist in construction statics, he was in no position to give information on the sexual genuineness of his country's female athletes. Halm felt that Zipser had taken the question more seriously than it was meant. Rainer said this was a task for interdisciplinary efforts. And pushed on. To a man who looked as if he were made of moldy newsprint. Professor Debeaugrande. Above his right ear a bald patch the size of a fifty-cent piece. The only color about him was his lemon-yellow set of teeth. The professor asked Halm in French whether he spoke French. "Not really," said Halm, and waited in vain for Sabina to say that in their family French was her responsibility. But Sabina was no longer around. Where was she? Professor Debeaugrande said that his mother tongue was only French. He didn't explain what he meant but instead introduced Halm to his more or less centenarian mother who was standing, dressed in pink chiffon and white angora stole, beside her yellowed sixty-five-year-old son.

The professor explained why he was teaching only French here and not Latin, which had originally been his field. Halm learned that there had been constant complaints here because he had insisted so pedantically on strokes over long syllables. He had found himself forced to do this because American vowels were so bad that they couldn't be formed into long *e*'s, *o*'s, and *u*'s. Americans tended to slip into the diphthong, or—especially southerners—the triphthong. After seventeen years he had admitted defeat, the professor said. Halm felt like saying that not fifteen feet away stood a female Texan vowelist: Go over there, Professor, then you'll no longer demand that American vowels be suitable for speaking Latin!

Halm saw that he was within three feet of P, and behind P's cage stood Elissa. With a black man. Today was Friday. He might ask her whether the tarantula had already been fed. He simply abandoned mother and son and moved for the first time without Rainer's guiding hand from one group to another. The black and Elissa fell silent as he came around the cage. They looked at him as if to say that, since he was interrupting them, he must now tell them why he was doing so. The black was wearing rose-pink bib pants; Elissa had on a close-fitting purple two-piece consisting of a pleated skirt and three-quarter-length tunic. Something sleeveless, emphasizing everything. Since Halm said nothing, Elissa introduced them: Othello Jesús de García, head of the drama department. Halm looked at what Othello Jesús de García was wearing on a jade chain around his powerful neck: a kind of Aztec Medusa. Neither of them showed any intention of sparing Halm the feeling of having interrupted them. They simply said nothing more. All he could do was nod and leave. Their approval of this was obvious.

He barely managed to avoid Debeaugrande and mother. Over to Sally and Roy. Sally was just saying how their neighbor in Upper Valley, from whom she had learned how to castrate piglets, always bit off the testicles with his teeth. For religious reasons, said Sally, with a smile that made her gleaming lips look for a moment like a quivering rectangle.

Rainer would not tolerate Halm joining a group he had already been with. Although, except for Carol and her husband, Halm hadn't noticed anyone leaving, there were now far fewer people. The crowd looked positively thinned out. Something seemed to keep drawing the guests off so slowly that one didn't notice them leave. Then, all of a sudden, they were gone. The president's wife! Unthinkable that she should have left without saying good-bye! How could she! He felt hurt. That is the appropriate punishment for conversation.

When almost everybody had left, he approached Fritz O. Dempewolf, who was still standing with Lena at the window. Dempewolf apologized to Halm for having offered Halm's daughter a taste of truth. He couldn't help it. He had lost the gift for small talk somewhere along the way from Silesia via Siberia to California. Halm took this as a dig at him personally. Besides he couldn't believe, said Dempewolf, that the father of this daughter was under the illusion that he had come to an elite establishment here. He, Dempewolf, was the lowest-paid member of the department, although he had been here for seventeen years. That seemed to indicate that he must be the worst teacher, but that wasn't so, in this respect he had no complexes: it was simply that this was a country where every *single* thing—not, as in the rest of the world, merely everything—was a matter of money. So he was fighting for better pay merely for the sake of the money, not because he felt discriminated against by the inferior pay, for, as he'd already said, as far as his teaching abilities were concerned he felt quite competent. It was simply that here one needed money, nothing but money. In Russia, for instance, you need contacts, friends, relatives, in Russia you need people—here, money, nothing but money. Needless to say, after thirteen years of Siberia and with the sole desire to get as far away as possible from the Soviets, he shouldn't have gone to America but to Australia—too late now. But what the hell! The Silesian is disappointed by the world.

"Oh, excuse me, I haven't fled halfway around the world to look at the mendacious made-for-export grin of an East German comrade. Maybe we'll meet again. My invitation stands." And he turned on his heel and left. Zipser from Leipzig looked after him with a smile and said: "He always runs away. Has he something against me? You never know how much you have to answer for." He was happy to meet someone from Stuttgart. His great role model was from Stuttgart, Professor Leonhard. Leonhard was ten times farther ahead than he, Zipser. A genius. When Halm told him he lived less than ten minutes away from the TV tower designed by Leonhard, Zipser was even more delighted. He would rather spend a semester in Stuttgart than here. But the International Research and Exchanges Board existed only in America. And the effect of earthquakes on buildings, his special field, could be observed better here than on the Swabian plateau. IREX pays four hundred dollars a month, with free board and lodging at the Faculty Club. Zipser spends half his salary on photocopies he intends to take home.

"How very commendable!" said a man with a magnificent head of frothing gray hair. Professor Felix Theodor Auster, philosophy. He has just heard from Halm's wife that Halm is writing a book on Nietzsche. So is he. Here is his address. Within walking distance of the campus, by the way. At the moment he is busy correcting the galleys of his essay "First Nietzsche, Then Kafka," for *Studi Tedeschi;* he'll have an extra copy made for Halm. In this essay he had described himself in a wily understatement as a non-Nietzsche expert. Unfortunately he could hardly offer Nietzsche here, since the department was still on the sociology trip. Semantics instead of language. In Europe Nietzsche is now being quoted too much because over the last twenty years he had been quoted too little. That's all there is to the academic life: quoting and being quoted either too much or too little. Not long ago a colleague in Berlin had dropped dead while quoting Nietzsche. Fortunately academic life wasn't without its dangers. In any case it should be barred to married men. A married philosopher: that's something like that creature. He pointed to P sitting mute in his cage. He was especially looking forward to Halm's lecture on Heine. With his Nietzsche essay he'd also tuck in a copy of his booklet *On Heine's Conservative Irritation* into Halm's box. Had Rainer, he asked, made use of his points?

Rainer's lower lip drooped farther than ever, revealing the accumulated moisture as in a half-filled roof gutter. He obviously didn't know what he was being asked about. Auster shook his head but said in the kindliest manner that he had sent him his Schubert essay: "The Philosophical Song, or: What Did Schubert Know Before Schopenhauer?" Rainer said: "You write too damn much." "Publish or perish," said Auster, and to Halm: "You know, my ambition is to be quoted by literary scholars. I couldn't care less about philosophers. I shouldn't care about anything, I know. Especially about being quoted. But I care even less whether I care or not. Oh, Leslie! . . . Excuse me, I see Leslie Ackerman, I must give him the pleasure of telling him I quoted his paper on decadence in the *Quarterly*, I must tell him that; meanwhile you may solve the sixty-four-dollar question: What makes a person more popular—quoting or being quoted? See you later." Halm called after him: "Don't forget the Nietzsche essay and the booklet, will you!" Auster stopped in his tracks, turned around, the very picture of composure, and said: "I won't!", then he hurried off. But it was obvious that he was acting both: composure and haste. Acting clearly gave him pleasure.

Finally the only ones left on the peppermint-green pile were the Halms and Elissa and Rainer. Halm now realized that it was time to leave. "Well, my friend," said Rainer, "now you've been introduced and you're free to do your own thing, that's how things are here. And the wives," he said to Sabina, "they can do as they please anyway, anything goes." Sabina said: "You say that so sadly." "Do I?" he said, tilting his head so far back that one could no longer see inside his slack half-filled lower lip. Well, if that sounded sad to her, she must have absolute pitch.

They were standing outside the house; Elissa hadn't come out with them. Rainer stood on tiptoe and tilted his head even farther back as if trying to look over a wall that was too high. "A Hansel and Gretel house is what the Americans call it," he said, pointing to the house. "Nasty story," he added, "Hansel and Gretel, I mean." He threw away his cigarette, clasped his hands behind him, and seemed to freeze in that posture. "You're scarcely fifty," said Halm as lightly as possible. "Don't ask me to turn a somersault," said Rainer. "And where's Lena?" asked Sabina. "People do get lost," said Rainer. Then to Halm: "Take care." And went back into the house.

"Now what?" said Sabina. Halm told Sabina she could bring the car around, he would wait for Lena, she must be with Elissa. Then they sat in the car. Instead of Lena, Elissa came out to say she would drive Lena down later. The Halms nodded, smiled, were baffled, drove off. Sabina enjoyed swinging down Euclid and then turning onto uncompromising, vertical, steep Marin; with parted lips she coasted down the avenue with its dense framework of trees and houses. Halm remarked that, although one could no longer say that they had ridden during "a dull, dark, and soundless day in the autumn of the year, when the clouds hung oppressively low in the heavens . . . , through a singularly dreary tract of country," to arrive "as the shades of the evening drew on, within view of the melancholy House of Usher," still . . . At first everything had seemed to him so radiant. Now he'd forgotten to ask Elissa about the tarantula feeding.

Sabina turned off earlier from Marin; today for a change she wanted to enter Contra Costa from above. This took them through even more enchanted streets. Tree tunnels, not streets. Houses not meant to be taken entirely seriously. Sabina drove at walking pace, stopping and stopping again; they exclaimed about what they were seeing. "Still," said Halm, "all this doesn't seem to be quite enough. To those who have it. Oh look, Sabina, look!" In a "tunnel of green gloom" a family was sitting by open windows under a yellow light.

From their own living room the Halms saw the light of the sunset behind San Francisco. "Fantastic," said Halm, "how quickly a cocktail party is over." He went on: "There couldn't be a more beautiful day." And, he thought, one hardly dares say it, a more difficult one. The only sound was that of the cicadas.

6

SINCE LENA, AFTER BEING brought home late that evening by Elissa, hadn't been in the mood for conversation, Halm and Sabina had hoped to find out more from her on Saturday morning, at breakfast. But at breakfast she sat turned away. She has pulled a sweater over her nightgown; apparently that's all she intends to wear today. Halm wanted to go off to his study as soon as possible, to the texts handed him by the girl.

"One doesn't spend one's first Saturday in California sitting around the house," Sabina said in the tone of voice with which one proclaims a law. She has been looking at maps. They'll go for a swim, eighty miles to the south. In Santa Cruz. Lena said she had work to do. Halm said he had to drive inland that evening, to Upper Happy Valley, to a skat party at Roy Kinsman's. That was no reason to spend the entire day in the house, said Sabina. She was beginning to sound martyrish. "Come on now, get dressed, both of you!" "Without Lena," said Halm, shrugging his shoulders. If she weren't here, her parents would be going without her anyway, said Lena. "But you *are* here!" said Sabina. The conversation threatened to turn into one of those vicious circles that go on until someone jumps up and storms out.

Halm stood up saying he was ready to leave any time; they were to let him know when they had come to an agreement. Sabina: He was to stay right here until they were agreed. Halm: Couldn't the outing be postponed till tomorrow? Perhaps Lena would agree to come tomorrow. Tomorrow they could spend more time at the beach than today. But Sabina wanted to go to the beach today. At once. Right now. "This sunshine, this sky, I ask you! Their first Saturday in California, and skat! And you never play cards, not even at home!" Because there was no longer anyone he wanted to play with, said Halm.

The phone rang. It was Rainer. Roy had just phoned, he couldn't get the chairs ready in time, they would have to postpone their skat for a week. "Sabina will be happy," said Halm. Rainer said: "What are *we* going to do?" And he stressed the "we." Halm told him Sabina wanted to drive to Santa Cruz, to the beach. "That's fine," said Rainer. Later in the evening, after a day devoted to Schubert's text interpretation, he'd like to impose on the Halms. Halm urged him to come over.

Sabina, when she wanted something, was like one of nature's irresistible forces. But Lena was nowhere near ready. She said she had a headache. Sabina wouldn't accept that. Sabina always knew exactly what was best for each member of the family at any given moment, which was why she could enforce it even on those who weren't yet aware of it themselves.

Halm sneaked out of the room. The door to the study was open to give the impression that he was still taking part in the discussion. Sabina's voice became shrill. That good-for-nothing! That Traugott! Was Lena proposing to spend her time from now on cowering behind locked doors just because of him? Lena: It had nothing to do with Traugott! Traugott was not a good-for-nothing. Traugott was a victim of his mother. Incapable of anything he hadn't had instilled in him by his mother. Sabina might like to think for a moment whether she didn't find something familiar about this. Sabina's voice became very loud. All this psychology rubbish! Nothing but stupefying, stultifying jargon! Lena went to her room. "Oh, poor Sabina," Sabina said.

He had to make the most of his time until they reached an agreement. He already had the copies in his hand: Shakespeare's 129th sonnet and a few lines of Stefan George's. Shakespeare first:

> Th' expense of spirit in a waste of shame
> Is lust in action; and till action, lust
> Is perjur'd, murderous, bloody, full of blame,
> Savage, extreme, rude, cruel, not to trust. . . .

Undoubtedly this only sounded beautiful in English, but his curiosity as to what it might mean in German compelled him to put down a choice of German words in the margin.

He stood up, noticing as he did so that Professor Rinehart's chair and desk top were sticky, and walked over to Sabina, who was sitting at the table staring down at it. He thrust his fingers under her hair and gently massaged her neck. "Come, Sabina, we'll drive to the beach." He would refute the 129th sonnet. Sabina said: "Leave me alone!" She jumped up and disappeared into the stairwell leading down into the basement.

There was a ring at the front door. A black couple. Both well filled out. Both wearing short-sleeved sports shirts. The man at once began to preach. "Enjoy life on earth! Awake! Work can be a pleasure! Is yours? Are you grateful for what God has done?" At the end of each sentence his tenor voice rose like that of a Mozart character singing a question. And the woman raised her face. It was useless for Halm to tell them he was a Catholic. His wife had been a Catholic too, said the man. She nodded gravely. The man offered a special treatment for Catholics. Halm had to hold the screen door open as long as the black man kept talking. He must on no account let them in, otherwise by this evening he'd be a Jehovah's Witness. He gave them a dollar for two pamphlets. One should take nothing for granted, neither awakening nor sunshine. Halm stared at the tattoo on the man's forearm: an enormous figure 13, and on the figure a cat arching its back. Of course it made him think of the humpback bridge over Okra Creek. Of all that this week in California had brought, that had become the predominating moment: he and the girl on the arched bridge. Probably Rainer's sudden appearance had been a contributing factor, his ambiguous Shakespearean gesture. *Th' expense of spirit in a waste of shame/Is lust in action. . . .*

Meanwhile the preacher had moved on to the persuasive factor of success. In 1945 they had numbered 65,000, now they were more than two million. "We are flourishing!" Halm fished out another dollar. "Oh no, we are not supposed to take extra money." But how else was he ever going to get rid of them? If he let go of the screen door it would bang the preacher's head. Halm said: "You must excuse me." The couple looked at him in a kind of orchestrated astonishment. Blacks can convey everything by their expression, whereas he could resort only to the well-sprung screen door that Rainer had repaired. He let it fall shut: *lento maestoso ostinato*. All their contrived astonishment was of no help to that splendid couple.

Although Halm was embarrassed when he finally closed the front and living-room doors, he had succeeded in closing them. How badly he handled the simplest situations. It is not for school that we learn but for life. He was getting poor grades. He looked up into the sky above San Francisco. It almost hurts, that blue. Incredible how alive one could feel there. "Sabina, come, let's go to the beach!" he called down the steep stairs. Sabina appeared at the bottom and said: "Not without her!" That meant it was up to him to resume negotiations. He knocked at Lena's door and spoke in a calm, businesslike voice to the closed door. If Lena believed it had been a mistake yesterday to allow herself to be persuaded by her parents to go to the party, she could stay home today without further explanation. However, if she had reason not to regret having given in yesterday, it was only fair to let herself be persuaded to come with them again today. The decision was entirely up to her. For one moment the house was filled with a reverberating silence. Then came Lena's wonderfully quiet voice: "I'll come."

"She's coming!" he shouted, dashed down the steep stairs, turned right at the bottom into the bedroom, and put his arm around Sabina. Sabina detached herself from his embrace, bent down, and put the little slippers, a relic of her mother's, under the bed. In every family there must be one person who goes on talking. Today it was Halm's turn. Until Lena and Sabina could speak to each other again. The speaking-straight-ahead in the car facilitates the resumption of contact. People can speak with one another without having to speak *to* one another. Sabina extolled the ten-year-old Volvo. Halm praised the piercing blue above the scorched hills of California. Sabina couldn't get over the fact that in this huge, arid basin the freeway ran for miles between walls of blossoming oleander! In the midst of an army of cars they flowed calmly southward. "Just look at these cars," cried Halm. "No two alike!" "And how little impatience they show!" said Sabina. Driving was still a pleasure here.

Then they had to drive over the ridge that San Francisco also has to climb if it wants to see the Pacific. Everything shimmered with heat. The two solid lines of cars crawled so slowly up the hill that they were almost at a standstill. Sabina, the mechanic, repeated the gist of Professor Rinehart's pedantic instructions for the proper use of the elderly Volvo: never let it get too hot! Lena and Halm anxiously observed Sabina's attempts to drive the Volvo through the blazing midday heat in the crawling uphill traffic without letting it overheat. Halm was enjoying it all, even the tension as to whether the Volvo would make it or not. He enjoyed passing a place called Saratoga. The Volvo made it. They were up and over, the road led downhill and out toward the sea.

The bay that begins there is so vast that it can only be perceived as a bay on the map. Santa Cruz: the first place as one approaches from the north. The promenade: one continuous fairground. The Halms made their way through the hurly-burly to the beach, where the sand was so hot that whimpering with pain they promptly put on their shoes again. Wading through water and scrambling under overhanging rocks, they came to a quieter beach. So now, Pacific, here we are. Greetings from Messrs. Kiderlen and Rimmele—it's quite true, they made me promise, back there in Swabia. Halm said it out loud. The roar of the surf permitted that. Even radios right next to you operated soundlessly. That's the Pacific for you. You can say what you like. He listened to whether the breakers were asking him to convey their greetings to Messrs. Kiderlen and Rimmele. He decided they were not. He would inform Messrs. Kiderlen and Rimmele: The Pacific accepted your greetings but did not return them.

Halm now felt an urge to use inflated language again. But if your name isn't Hölderlin, you have no business opening your mouth. That's what the Kiderlens teach you. They of all people! When Kiderlen, fresh from university, attended his first staff meeting, he said that the sign in the school yard: NO RIDING AROUND ON BICYCLES, should, even in a Stuttgart school, be stylistically correct, so he would like to suggest: BICYCLE RIDING NOT PERMITTED. And because Halm then murmured audibly that this took care of their major problem for the whole school year, Kiderlen from then on seized every opportunity to embarrass Halm in front of his colleagues. It so happened that Halm liked to use inflated language. But before Mr. Kiderlen—with that Hamburg weekly tucked under his arm every Thursday—had used that term, Halm himself had not. He knew he couldn't speak calmly. He had to get worked up, otherwise he remained silent. Whenever he began to speak he felt like a man from the Stone Age striking a rock to produce a spark. Ever since Kiderlen had parodied him a few times, he had become more silent. Maybe Kiderlen was right. Maybe he tended to be a pompous schoolmaster. All right, if that wasn't to be, then he'd just shut up. It was only for a few more years anyway. Was Kiderlen Hölderlin? Kiderlen was cleverer, more subtle, more intelligent, composed, controlled. Halm could arrive at this conclusion with greater calm than ever before.

There, Pacific, now you know everything. You must know everything about every person who ends up at your coast. And I know of nothing and no one to whom I would rather confess than to your breakers. O breakers, what an all-enveloping cloak you are! Halm said: Hölderlin, here we go! Normally he said that before using inflated language. The Pacific had left him no time for that. As they lay on the sand Halm said: "Sabina, I could live here." Sabina said they should write the Zürns a card. Halm said: "We seem to be talking at cross purposes." As if it might help, he pointed to some boys who were tossing an American football back and forth over tremendous distances. In throwing the ball they gave it a spin so that, like a shell from a rifled barrel, it rotated during flight, thus staying on a straight course right into the hands of the receiver.

After they had looked long enough at the waves of the Pacific, they decided it was time to go in. First one had to get used to these surging glass walls which, as they gathered momentum and tumbled forward, shattered into a wall of foam—no, exploded into a vortex of foam, burst into fountains of foam, burst into white spume, spume that broke up on the beach into myriad bubbles and foaming water that quickly retreated beneath the next wave and out to sea again. How those glass walls came surging in one behind the other at intervals of twenty or thirty yards—as if they were pursuing each other! They chased each other toward the beach, where they exploded, burst, dissolved. A sequence that pleased Halm. He thought that here the waves were higher than at the beach they had found too crowded. Over there people had stood in rows, either letting the waves roll over them or trying to mount a wave on a board and ride it toward the shore until the wave broke. Here there was nobody with a board like that.

"All right," said Halm, "let's try." Lena and Sabina went in as far as where the waves had already broken up into whirlpools, where they wallowed in the foam. Halm wanted to go farther out. He had to. Beyond the breakers it was possible to swim. But how to get through the surging glass wall? Go far enough out until you reach the wave just before it breaks, then dive right through it, then you'll be in the calm, calm Pacific where the waves have no sharp foam crests but great round backs. He felt a bit apprehensive while having these thoughts. But he had traveled so many thousands of miles to reach this ocean that he wasn't going to let anything scare him off now. The surf is the feast. This surging forward, then foam and thunder. It's all too much. The sun, the salt, foam, thunder, scorching heat and salt. Got it now? Are you ready? You're ready. Pick the wave you're going to take. You'll take the next one.

The next one came and, the closer it came, the bigger, the higher it grew. He looked up. Ten feet at least, he thought. Then it was upon him. He didn't get through. Perhaps he lacked determination. As the wave broke over him, it simply bowled him over. His back and his head hit the sand, which was far from soft, he tumbled over backward, was whirled, twisted, tossed under water. The breath was knocked out of him. He was in a rampaging, collapsing crystal palace in which he was suffocating. Now. What now? Then he got a grip, his hands clawed into the sand, trying to prevent the receding water from dragging him back again.

He was lying on the sand, unable to move. Lena and Sabina were bending over him. No fuss, please. He was quite comfortable lying here. Grin, to wipe that look of terror off their faces. No matter what, he wasn't going to let them lead him away. He'll lie here till he can make it on his own. It feels wonderful, lying here, with a bit of foam and spume wafting around him, as it were. He told Lena and Sabina they should also sit down in this harmlessly advancing and retreating water.

As he sat up, various parts of his body hurt. Sabina said: "Well, I must say, this is all we needed." Sabina tended toward understatement. She had brought along mangoes and melons, and seedless black grapes that tasted as if, should all other fruits become extinct, it was up to these grapes to combine the subtleties of all the fruits of the earth in one flavor. Sabina and Lena made several more trips into the water. Not Halm. The Pacific had twisted a few of his bones.

On the way home, all three were somewhat boisterous. Over and over again Lena and Sabina described how the giant wave had broken over Halm, how he had disappeared and simply failed to reappear. Then all of a sudden there he'd been, much farther along, lying on the sand, not at all where they had expected. Halm listened. He wasn't quite ready to relive those moments in the green-and-white vortex of the collapsing crystal palace. He was glad to be able to identify with external viewpoints. Changing the subject, he wanted to know from Lena how she'd enjoyed last night. Sabina had informed them she wasn't going to drive home on Highway 17 again but would stay on the Pacific side of the mountains. Although Highway 1 North wasn't a freeway, it must, judging by all indications, be very scenic. They would be driving right beside the ocean and not cross the mountains until San Francisco, and from there they would cross the Bay Bridge to the mainland. She liked to adorn such decisions with the question: "O.K., everyone?" A true Gutöhrlein. For a few years Sabina had been a lay assessor and had made life difficult even for judges.

So they drove beside the sparkling Pacific, uphill and downhill, and listened to Lena, who was now obviously happy to talk. Having mentioned last night at Rainer's and Elissa's that she played the piano, she had had to play something for them. Halm said it was a near miracle that Lena should have responded so simply and directly to a wish. Where did they have a piano in that house? Downstairs in Rainer's room. Rainer had almost no books but lots of records. The biggest collection of Schubert records on the West Coast, he claimed. Elissa talked about Rainer, even in front of him, as if he were ranked one level lower than herself. Rainer listened to everything. He seemed to find it enough that Elissa should talk about him at all. What she actually said wasn't that important. Elissa had done almost all the talking. They had sat down there outside Rainer's rooms on the warm rocks of the Indian camp. Elissa had said that until the stink of cigarette smoke from the party had disappeared she couldn't stay upstairs. Downstairs

Rainer had had to sit six feet away with his cigarettes. And during the time they sat there he had drunk a whole bottle of whisky. She kept wanting to cry "Stop!" but hadn't dared. "That's enough to kill anyone," said Sabina. Lena told them that Rainer was waiting nervously and impotently for Elissa to declare war. That he would be the loser was obvious. He already was. What wasn't yet certain was whether only Rainer would be destroyed by it, or both—Rainer and Elissa. Lena's parents, although they were now driving from one melodramatic scene to another, couldn't swallow that.

Sometimes, when the road had swung up to a particularly high point, Sabina would stop at the side and look both ways down the steep cliffs to where the inaudible breakers whipped up their foam as if their purpose were to decorate the dark shoreline rocks with white. At many points, cars had turned off onto the sandy tracks and driven right out to the edge of the cliff. There was no going any farther west. This was it. The cliffs were defined not by fences and signs but by the noses of cars. The occupants sat behind their windshields looking out onto this ocean and drinking from the cans they were holding. And since they all remained inside their cars to admire the Pacific, it looked as if the cars, too, were admiring the ocean. Halm felt that the people admiring the ocean contributed as much to his emotion as did the ocean itself.

Sabina did not turn off, did not stop the Volvo a mere few feet from the precipice. They got out, walked over, gazed at the ocean and at the onlookers. The people in the cars saw only the ocean. Those are the truly devout, thought Halm. Sabina said: "Half Moon Bay! Now just look at that—I wouldn't have believed it!" They hadn't heard that tone of voice from Sabina since her visits to Oberstaufen. Halm thought: Thank you, Pacific.

But war, Lena—why war? That's no more than normal marital role development. Marriages in which these roles are developed are virtually indestructible. Elissa, to put it bluntly, has the permanent adversary role, Rainer the inexhaustible tolerance role; he enjoys being tormented, maybe even tortured, and, what's more, by no one but Elissa. If anyone else were to treat him like that, he would kill them. Because it comes from her he enjoys it. Of course he suffers. Of course it's also terrible for him. But for him the suffering is no more terrible than it is for her to inflict it. He knows that. That's not merely a consolation: it's the very thing that makes the pleasure possible, the game, the space, the marriage. If such roles don't evolve, the marriage is quickly over. Two years, maybe five, finished. He had been about to say two years, maybe three, but then they would have been talking no longer about Elissa and Rainer but about Lena and Traugott. Now that Lena had come to life, he wanted to avoid that. Once the roles are in place, each quarrel serves to cement them! He warmed to his subject: Every threat to a marriage strengthens it. As soon as one party to a marriage notices that he is in danger of drifting away, this produces in him an adhesive force. The greater the strain, the greater the adhesive force. The one is a function of the other.

Halm thought: That's right, Mr. Kiderlen, I'm saying this during a blissful evening drive beside the sparkling Pacific. We all know that the two roles that go to make up a marriage tend to produce an agonizing comedy. The agonizing part is identical with the comic part: that you can't get away from each other! Otherwise marriage would be simply unbearable, he said, and hoped Sabina would be able to handle all these tricky curves along this steep cliff road.

Her father and mother didn't know the Mersjohanns, Lena said. She was concerned for both. How could they be more or less painlessly separated before it was too late—that was the main question. Separated before the war broke out that would destroy one or the other or both. They must get away from each other. While there was still time. But how! Lena's voice became almost shrill. Their quiet Lena. Their self-contained Lena. Halm had often felt that Lena was determined never to let anything upset her. When had she ever shouted, cried, complained! She had always understood, accepted. And now she had just shouted. Why? Surely she didn't have her eye on Rainer? Under the pretext of having to save him, trying to break up the marriage? That was soap opera, not Lena.

He was ashamed. Had he, despite all precautions, absorbed too many movies? Ever since that day when he had regarded his Nietzsche project as shattered, since the day, after seven months of persistent silence on the part of a publisher who could be considered competent, when he had received his manuscript back with a routine rejection letter which seemed to imply that hundreds of similarly unusable manuscripts on Nietzsche were received every day (there could be no other explanation for such a routine letter)—ever since that day he may have been a bit lax, may have sometimes stayed on at a movie that would formerly have driven him away immediately. He had become susceptible to that solution-happy, mass-oriented kitsch. He wished he could take back his mental accusation of Lena. He knew that Lena and Sabina were aware, in a nonverbal but essentially valid way, of what he was thinking. That's how it was in this family. So would they kindly take note that he was ashamed of his movie-esque imputations. Please, Lena, please.

"Oh, just a moment!" he cried. "Just a moment! I've just remembered—my God, how long it takes to recall something that happened a long time ago, and there's no way to recapture it—I've suddenly remembered how Rainer Mersjohann disappeared from Tübingen. He became engaged, very young. She, eight years older, also from Münster, wants to visit him. A former boyfriend of hers, on his way to Switzerland, gives her a ride. She gets out in Tübingen, on Weizsäckerstrasse. The friend drives on. She rings the doorbell, is shown to Rainer's room; he is surprised but pleased, is about to kiss her, hesitates, asks how she got there, oh with so-and-so, he knows the name, wasn't that a former rival of his, and *his* fiancée lets him drive her from Münster to Tübingen, allows that fellow to drive her, to *him*? And slaps her face. Annegret was her name. He must have given her a pretty good slap. The fiancée ran screaming onto the street. The next day he left Tübingen.

Gradually the whole affair came to light. His landlady, married to a watchmaker who used to beat her up, had heard the whole thing and tried to stop Annegret from running away, but there was no stopping her. Yes," said Halm, "her name was Annegret. The landlady said that the stupidest thing a woman who got beaten up could do was to run away. Then she was left with nothing but the beatings. But if she stayed she could keep the wrong done to her as capital, and that was good for something, she could live off it, and not badly either. . . . Thus spoke the wife of the watchmaker who, because his work was so stressful, would frequently beat her up."

Highway 1 North led steeply up over a mountain to San Francisco and, turning into a freeway, swung past the herd of skyscrapers standing peacefully in the evening light. Then across Treasure Island and the Bay, then slipping into the tree tunnels of Contra Costa, and they were home. The cicadas had already established their exact tone over the area. The two dogs in the next house were yapping. Two pugs, said Sabina, one of them blind. Sabina has already met their neighbor Bob and his wife. He's a schoolteacher. On the side, with a second vehicle, a pick-up truck, they operate a gardening business. Outside the door was a package of books from the poet. The alarm system gave the returning family a mere thirty seconds to identify themselves before it summoned aid.

Sabina made some buckwheat pancakes filled with sour cream. For dessert there were the grapes again. When Rainer arrived, Lena had already retired to her room, and although he stayed until two in the morning she didn't emerge. Rainer had brought them a Schubert record: *Death and the Maiden*. He was in a good mood. He was so happy, he said, that the Halms were finally here. Sabina made some buckwheat pancakes for him too. He claimed he had never tasted anything so delicious. They discussed the cocktail party. In their opinions of the individual guests, Rainer and the Halms were in total agreement; together they reviewed everybody and everything as if they were showing slides from a joint vacation.

Halm mentioned that a package of books had already turned up outside their front door. Rainer said: "Yes, go ahead and read them," they contained something about California. In prose. The poems, of course, were not poems. Last week a Bengali poet had visited the campus. He had come to San Francisco because he was translating Jack London and wanted to see London's Beauty Ranch and the ruins of the legendary Wolf House, but someone had also included Kirk on his program so the two met at the Faculty Club. The little Bengali was constantly bowing to the towering Kirk, of whom, needless to say, he didn't know a line. Despite that letter from Kennedy, Kirk had, after all, remained a local celebrity. That morning the Bengali had been given two of Kirk's poems to read. At lunch the Bengali said he had especially liked one of them. Whereupon Kirk: Yes, but the other was very good too: it would survive anyone who happened at this moment to be present in this building. Now the Bengali was nodding as often as he had previously been bowing. Respect for a Kirk Elrod was not to be acquired by a bit of reading, said Rainer. But quite apart from that, *Inspiration Inn* was more than a story of alcoholics.

If you go on drinking like that, the whisky'll run out, Halm felt like saying. Why don't you slow down a bit. But Rainer, as if he had heard all this, drank faster and faster. Now he was telling them about how he had happened to come here himself. Tübingen wasn't mentioned. He started right away with an uncle in Emden, with whom he had always spent his vacations. Since the uncle knew him well, there was no problem about Rainer asking him for money—after all, his uncle knew that Rainer would never borrow money he couldn't repay. At first Rainer had worked in Detroit as a dishwasher; then in Philadelphia he had advertised: Young German seeks family. Twelve families had responded. He had lived with them one after the other. He had worked at a mortuary, as an embalmer; then in an ambulance, with no driver's license and hence inside, at the rear—on one trip he had helped a woman give birth to twins; then as an orderly on night shift, going to university in the daytime; then in Charlottesville, Virginia, as a gardener with his own equipment, independent, sleeping in his van, where he also wrote most of his doctoral thesis, on truth and lies in Kleist; first teaching post in Morgantown, West Virginia, then Middlebury, Vermont, then Davis, California, then Irvine, now here in Oakland. He had reimbursed all the families for their expenses. He doesn't owe anything to anyone. Except Elissa. And Milton. And Jamey. Assuming Milton and Jamey are his offspring. That's what he assumes. He still does. Although it would be more logical and more salutary to assume that they were the sons of another man. He knew this man. This man was now living in Washington. A sadistic Pentagon intellectual given to wearing fur coats. But then there were people who believed in God. In the same way he believed himself to be the father of those sons. Pure, beautiful fiction.

Perhaps all this could be attributed to the English language, he said. To its California version. This was the land of words. A world of words. People here were crazy about words. Words took care of things here. So then there were no things left. Elissa had grown up in this tradition, in which words were less dependent on things than where he had grown up. The Halms had met Elissa's latest friend: Othello Jesús de García! Rainer was longing for a decision. But how could he not also fear it? Jamey would come home when his parents had put an end to the present state of blurred commitments. Jamey couldn't stand lies. Not a single one. Not even the tiniest. The future would show to whom Jamey would choose to go; of course each of them hoped to be Jamey's choice. Elissa's sticking around because she knows that Jamey can only return to Rainer. She drove Jamey away. She blames herself for this. She is sticking with Rainer out of a desire to punish herself. He was profiting by this touching remnant of conscientiousness in Elissa's easygoing nature. In November she was going to close her driving school and from then until April would be on the road in the southern states; it was highly probable that Jamey, given his life-style, would spend the winter in the South. So in a way this would halve the area where one was likely to run into him. A crazy calculation. But Elissa liked crazy calculations.

Although Rainer must have drunk more than a bottle of whisky, he could still hold forth. Halm must defend Elissa. Rainer might take it amiss if Halm agreed to these accusations by saying nothing. Perhaps Rainer was expecting Elissa to be defended against him. Apart from Rainer, no one was entitled to pass such judgments on Elissa. So Halm said that Rainer's entire peroration was imagination. That made Rainer give him such a frightening look that he immediately added: Might be imagination, as long as there was no evidence. The photographs of Milton and Jamey were, after all, two versions of Rainer. The two boys had one face, and that face was his. To be precise, it was the one he—Halm—remembered vividly from Tübingen. Had he met Milton or Jamey anywhere, he would have recognized them more quickly than he had recognized Rainer at the airport. So there you are. Rainer said: "You're talking garbage, my boy. Milton and Jamey no more resemble me than I resemble myself. You should have kept out of this."

Rainer had to stand up. He could no longer cope with what was going on inside him. "Anyone who defends the person who breaks a contract, breaks that contract himself," he said. "I'm sorry, Sabina," he went on, "that you're married to this unscrupulous man. He can't be much good. Even if he doesn't step on people's toes, he does step across bridges. I'm warning you. I'm really sorry about this. For your sake." And left, obviously being swept out of the house by his emotions. He slammed the door.

Halm had to hold Sabina back by force. She didn't think they should let Rainer drive in that condition. Halm said there was no way of stopping him, he was a Westphalian. Sabina had picked up Rainer's record. *Death and the Maiden*. Did the title have a different ring to it now compared to earlier in the evening? Halm thought about the cemetery, about the Virgil story. Sabina asked him whether they should listen to the record. Halm thought not. Sabina simply wanted to maintain a link with Rainer. Sabina said:

"What a sense of justice. What an acute sense of justice." Halm recalled how Sabina as a lay assessor had made life difficult for the judges with her acute sensitivity.

When they went down into the bedroom, he remarked: "Upstairs I don't notice the smell anymore, but down here I do." "Horrible," said Sabina. Halm pretended to believe that Sabina meant the smell of the other couple. But it was obvious that Sabina meant much more. Maybe she even meant him.

7

HALM FOUND SOMETHING TO cover the desk top and the chair. How had Professor Rinehart managed to produce this stickiness? Perhaps it had something to do with anthropology. Halm read the two photocopies: Shakespeare's 129th sonnet and Stefan George's "Ein Letzter Brief."

Did she really only mean him to decide which text would yield the better essay theme? Or did she mean him? Was she trying to tell him something? He could hardly take his eyes off the first lines: *Th' expense of spirit in a waste of shame/Is lust in action.* With the George he concentrated on the middle: *you saw that I was waiting day and night for it, i could not say it. i could sense it only in dreams. nor was i free to say it since you were the one who should have found it.*

Halm couldn't go on sitting in his chair. That huge wrestler, the Pacific, had twisted every bone in his body. Was there a spot left that didn't hurt? What embarrassed him most was not being able to put on his own shoes and socks. His wrenched back made it impossible for him to close the gap between hands and feet. He gingerly pushed himself up without putting any weight on his spine and, equally gingerly, let himself glide down into the armchair.

Come on now, don't keep staring at the texts, do your homework. Shakespeare, or the impotence of knowledge. George, or the muteness of the stricken. Which subject could you tell her more about? You don't have the time, your real homework is: Heine. Collecting Heine phrases. Week after week, simply collecting phrases that have impressed you. Then reading the collected phrases over and over again until you have some idea of why these particular ones impressed you. He could only hope that the title he had already been obliged to give Rainer over the phone would still apply. "Emigration as Emancipation."

Once settled in the armchair, Halm reached, not for Heine but for the two copies. *Th' expense of spirit in a waste of shame/Is lust in action; and till action, lust/Is perjur'd, murderous, bloody, full of blame.* Through the open door he could hear Sabina's ballpoint firmly hurrying across the paper. It seemed she could hardly keep up with her writing, she had so much to tell them at home. Who could he write to? Describe how from among them all one girl suddenly stands out. Brown legs. And the shorts that instead of a straight hem have a rounded one. Rounded toward the back and toward the front. Leading to slits at the sides. She was the only person who had shaken hands with him. How firmly she had held out her hand. She had looked at him with gray or blue or graybluegreenish eyes. Everyone else who had passed by and at whom he had looked had almost pointedly ignored him. Everyone else had behaved as if under an obligation to avoid meeting his eyes. But she had walked with him over that bridge. It swayed slightly as one walked across it, that humpback bridge over dry Okra Creek. Thank you, Rainer, for that name.

How seriously did he have to take Rainer's wild outburst? Rainer was his boss here. How unfair of a boss to take advantage of his position in such a way. Perhaps by this time he had forgotten what he had said while he was drunk. Even if Rainer had forgotten, the cause of his outburst remained. The best thing would be for him to ask Rainer, when he was sober, whether he still meant it. But when was Rainer sober? And what if Rainer were to repeat it?

You're no good. Halm wouldn't want to hear that again. In front of his own wife! Sabina must be waiting for him to deny it, refute it, to attribute it to alcohol or some other extenuating circumstances. He couldn't. He felt that Rainer was right. He was no good. The way he was sitting there and, instead of working, thinking about a girl and wallowing in his inadequacy. The most ridiculous figure in the world: a teacher who falls in love with a student. Falling in love! This expression has always provoked feelings of disgust in him. One should be able to turn to someone. But the affliction is universally condemned. For being ridiculous. Despicable. Repulsive. Unmentionable. Rainer and Carol are probably collecting everything that is to be learned about Halm's behavior on campus. The focal point of the highest concentration of information is Carol. How does she know that Halm was at the cemetery? Who told her that Halm had been sitting with the girl at a cafeteria table? Rainer and Carol are two of a kind. Both with that dominant lower lip. Since meeting Kirk Elrod, he no longer knows what to think of Carol. He must be all of seventy-five; she barely forty. Thirty years . . . just like between himself and the girl. She's probably twenty-two. How Elrod had coughed, how his cramps had contorted him, how Carol had led him out. Thirty years. Carol and Kirk, they're his kind of people. He will join their ranks. As long as he's here he will try to make life as easy as possible for them. He will try to help them bear the terrible burden of that difference in age.

This compulsion to speak of age! Even before joining Elrod's group, he had already heard him answer the How-are-you? question with: "What can one expect, at my age?" Then someone had asked Elrod for his opinion on a play. "Only the young can afford to make such unrealistic, uncompromising assertions," he had replied; he was no longer interested in such things. To Halm it seemed that every text in the world could be translated into a text spoken by someone over fifty. It is a different language. The thing is to prevent it from becoming a person's only language. There is a fear of becoming ridiculous, unbearable. The ultimate complication is that there are people past fifty who behave as if the fact were of no particular interest to them.

Until this moment he had never thought that clearly about death. For an instant the ability had been granted him to intensify the clarity of his perception of dying. The sense of being dragged under had been quite palpable. Clearer than ever before. Until the perception contains even the faintest presentiment of what will really happen, it must increase a billionfold in clarity, force, brutality. An adequate perception is impossible. That is the protection, the beautiful protection. The terror engendered by this perception—the clearest so far—of being totally, unmitigatedly, dragged under—was nevertheless a sweet terror. With the real force there can be no more dialogue. He hoped he wouldn't scream. He wanted his death to be quiet, clean, swift. He had to turn his thoughts away. That endless moment when the surf had rolled him over must be avoided. He felt drained now, but also cured. He had got through. Thirty years. He only had to visualize that for a single moment and everything was over. He was saved.

Now he could open Elrod's *Inspiration Inn* and start reading. He had the strength to take an interest. He wanted to become an admirer of Kirk Elrod. He wanted to give Elrod pleasure. And nothing would please Elrod as much as an extensive, detailed, credible enthusiasm. And since he was afraid of Rainer—although there was no longer any reason to be—he wanted to draw Carol away from Rainer and toward himself. Carol was a force. Perhaps he should also try to get Elissa over onto his side. Rainer, since he was in such a bad way, could become dangerous.

Fortunately that Monday was a holiday. Labor Day. Sabina knew this from TV. She also knew for sure that the university would be closed that day. It was America's May First. Probably everyone had thought Halm knew this. And the girl who had planned to come to his office on Monday? She had simply forgotten about Labor Day. He could consider himself lucky that he would see her only a day later. Or rather: Why should he care that he wasn't going to see her until Tuesday?

After a late breakfast he asked for Lena's and Sabina's attention. He wanted to tell them about what he had been reading in order to get a better handle on it. Make yourselves comfortable! Don't keep your eyes only on San Francisco—look farther to the right, to the north, toward Golden Gate Bridge, which we can't see from here—that's where the novel takes place. Look across to where you will see nothing but what I'm going to tell you about Kirk Elrod's *Inspiration Inn.*

One hot autumn day in the early thirties, two men, one Ed Crowley, chief engineer of a leading San Francisco construction company, and John Frey, his survey assistant and driver, set out in an almost brand-new Model A Ford sedan to drive in a single day along Highway 101 from Eureka to San Francisco. They got only as far as Petaluma. In Geyserville, Frey had already discovered that the radiator was leaking. They had to drive slowly and keep on adding water, so in Petaluma, some forty miles north of San Francisco, they gave up. Golden Gate Bridge hadn't yet been built, you see. And they were too late for the last ferry. John Frey translated a Swiss proverb into English for Mr. Crowley's benefit: If you can't fly there you can't limp there. He regretted, said John Frey, that they would have to spend the night in a town for which he was not prepared.

They had come to a more or less friendly agreement: Ed looked after everything that had to do with bridge and road construction on their trips, the object of these trips being to bring back contracts for bridge or road construction. John's job was to look after everything else: from fish chowder to historical landmarks. But only factual things, please, Mr. Crowley had said at the time. He wasn't interested in anything contrived, anything laid on for tourists. His words: "I'm not buying fantasies." It was a straightforward division of labor. But he did love music, especially singing. John Frey always had to take along his *Book of Swiss Songs*, and on their long drives it was up to him to sing for as long as he could. Between Eureka and Geyserville, John had sung *My loved one is an Alpine maid/Born here in the Tirol. She always wears, so it is said,/A fine black camisole.* After Geyserville he had to concentrate on the engine.

So he had no advice for his boss about Petaluma. But Crowley himself had once had a boss who always raved about the swordfish steaks at Washoe House in Petaluma, served with a Sonoma chardonnay under a huge buffalo head while one looked out onto eucalyptus groves. So John could see that Ed was trying not to let his dependence upon John run away with him. The garage mechanic examining the radiator said: Twenty-four hours at least. In that case Crowley would take the first boat tomorrow morning on the Petaluma River to San Francisco, to make sure that the projects, some of which were ready for signing, were in the office by tomorrow. Construction would have to start in the spring.

John Frey would wait for the repairs. He had already spent almost ten years in this country and still suffered from bouts of homesickness. He came originally from the Rhine valley, the canton of St. Gallen, and had just recently heard, at a gathering of the Grütli Club in San Francisco, that on the coast north of San Francisco there was a bay, Muir Cove, and in it, accessible by a cliff path, an inn operated by a very old woman known locally as the "Swiss lady." Every Swiss in California was sure to have been there once. At the Wilhelm Tell Hotel in Tomales they told you how to get there. Tomales was only a few miles west of Petaluma, almost at the coast. Mr. Crowley had no objection to John Frey driving to Tomales in a car borrowed from the mechanic.

At the Wilhelm Tell in Tomales they laughed when he asked about the "Swiss lady," but they told him how to get to the cove and to Inspiration Inn, the Swiss lady's place. It was a miserable drive. Up and down and round about. And dark, too. A farmer let him spend the night in his barn. Next morning he was at Muir Cove. Jutting out into the water was a rocky spur that one could only get around at low tide. At high tide one had to climb over it: scale of difficulty—two to three. He parked the borrowed car at the Pelican Inn by the edge of the redwood forests, at the south end of the cove. So clambering over the rock he reaches the northern part, and is fascinated by the inaccessibility of this Inspiration Inn, if there really is any such place. After the rock, the cliff path became very narrow, rising until it reached a platform in the cliff wall just about the width of a house. From this semicircular area, passages led off into the interior of the cliff. If it hadn't been for a sign over the middle passage saying INSPIRATION INN, the whole thing could have been taken for ancient Indian dwellings.

The owner was sitting alone at a stone table in the middle of this semicircle. Frey introduced himself and was happy to learn from her that her ancestors had come from the canton of Appenzell, from Trogen to be exact. That made all that twisting and turning and clambering worthwhile. Her name was Gret. She was happy too that, although the season was over, another Swiss should have once again found his way up here. She hadn't really expected anyone before April. At her age one didn't mind being alone. She was gaunt, and around her long neck hung a gold franc piece on a velvet ribbon. Heavy clouds started charging in from the Pacific, and it began to rain and blow so violently that John Frey couldn't return that day. The doors withstood the storm. There were no windowpanes or roof tiles to be smashed. It was possible to walk around the niche inside the cliff to a sheltered exit. From there they could look out through a small, shuttered opening.

The whole cove beneath them was a cauldron of foaming, raging spume. Wasn't she afraid that one day a tidal wave might rise all the way up to her place? Not even the one of 1906, shortly after the earthquake, had risen that high. Her father, she told him, had bought these caves a year after the earthquake from the Coast Miwok Indians, who had moved north into the Hoopa Valley reserve. For four hundred and sixty-seven years the Indians had marked each year on the wall of a special calendar-cave, with details of the water levels in the cove and in the fresh-water cistern that formed part of the cave system. In four hundred and sixty-seven years the fresh water had never given out, nor had the salt water ever penetrated the caves. Her father had been an engineer. And a doctor. And a few other things that no longer existed today.

This was how John Frey learned the history of the Stäbler-Sulzer family, who arrived in Philadelphia on September 9, 1765, on the good ship *Chance*. The narrator said she told what she had to tell to anyone who wished to hear it. She told it to all those, she chanted, "who have not through false training grown indifferent to their early origins." Her narrative was one long paean of praise of her father; almost every time she mentioned her father she would add: "They don't come like that anymore." Her father had taken the gold franc she wore around her neck from his younger brother. Their ancestors had brought the gold piece with them in 1765 on the *Chance*. Of the five children of the Stäbler-Sulzer family, only one survived the forty-two day passage—the youngest, a son. The mother had hung the gold piece around the child's neck on a leather thong. This gold piece had long been used in the family for divining purposes. Since 1765 the gold piece had always gone to the youngest son. The gift of divining, by means of a pendant gold piece or a hazel wand—a gift that had always been in the family—was now to reside permanently in the youngest son. But there had always been one condition attached to the gift: the practitioner must never have consumed a single drop of alcohol.

So things remained like that until one day Gret's father followed his youngest brother from the farm into Philadelphia and discovered him sitting in a tavern on a dreary suburban street with a girl, in the act of hanging the gold franc around her neck. Gret's father snatched the franc from the girl's neck and, instead of returning to the farm in Lancaster County, joined a group planning to travel west beyond the Ohio. In Martinsville on the Ohio he left the group, took a boat to the Mississippi and down the Mississippi to St. Louis, worked for a year on a water supply for a brewery being built by a Swiss, then joined a wagon train that called itself the Oregon Liberty Trail.

But Frederick Stabler left the wagon train earlier: his goal was not Oregon but California. There he found work as a doctor and a water diviner. In an area where it never rains between April and November, there was room for a man who knew not only where water was to be found but how much could be expected. After the 1906 earthquake a kind of respect for the earth's internal forces began to spread. People were afraid that water might disappear entirely, and the desert would advance to the ocean.

Frederick Stabler was soon a made man. At thirty-three he marries, and on his wedding day he drinks wine. After that he no longer believes in his gift, so no one else does either. He trains as an engineer. His wife plunges into needlework. Her handiwork is displayed under plate glass. Her backgammon tables gain fame throughout the West. He constructs the first Stabler pump. A surprisingly simple pump. So now he could have rested on his laurels. But he wants more than that. He travels to Europe, including Switzerland, visits and inspects machine factories, and has a trunkful of sketchbooks by the time he boards the *Titanic* in Southampton.

During that terrible night he does not join in the dancing but remains in his cabin studying his sketches. The noise that sounds as if the ship is scraping against a dockside tells him enough. Even before reaching the deck he hears the engines stop, and as soon as he is on deck he sees the white mass of the iceberg disappearing behind the ship in the dark. He is one of the first to put on a lifebelt, but on seeing the crush around the lifeboats he dashes below decks again. In an abandoned first-class cabin he changes his clothes. Dressed as a woman, wearing a fur coat and a bonnet, he goes up on deck again. There all is panic. He has had the right idea: only women are allowed in the lifeboats. In front of him a woman says that, if her husband isn't allowed in the boat, she won't go either. "I'm Guggenheim the banker," says the husband. But without truculence. The officer, who is holding a revolver, shakes his head. Mrs. Guggenheim says she will stay with her husband. Then a man thrusts himself forward, saying he is Mr. Bruce-Ismay, managing director of the White Star Line. The officer forces him back with his pistol.

Frederick Stabler gets into a lifeboat as a woman, is rescued, reaches California for the second time, immediately deserts his wife: he wants to work at all hours, all he wants to do is work. His pumps become even better. Stabler City grows up around the factories. Frederick Stabler has an idea: he wants his pumps to be built solely by alcoholics. He develops a work system to which any alcoholic should be able to adjust: there are only work groups, no foreman; the work group produces the entire pump, the work group establishes working hours; the work group obtains from the warehouse whatever it needs and delivers its products for final inspection. The group is responsible for what each member does. There is only piecework. By a majority vote, the group can decide that it no longer wishes to work with a certain individual. A man who is expelled from one group may apply for admission to another. If he is not accepted by any other group within two weeks he must regard himself as dismissed.

Stabler City alternates between chaos and discipline. Every Saturday Frederick Stabler puts on a party. These parties become famous. Stabler pays for a full-time orchestra, which he dresses up in naval uniform. All his employees with their families are invited to each of his parties. Every party is a fancy dress party. Admission is granted to anyone who turns up in a costume representing something that he is not. Stabler himself invariably appears at his parties dressed as a woman. Each time as a different woman. For years he has been regarded as a transvestite. Some people say he is mad. Later his enemies will say that he made his money as a rumrunner during prohibition, that he operated a whole flotilla sailing back and forth between Muir Cove and Canada. That's the kind of dirt scraped up by envy.

It is true that Stabler City is a wild town. In Stabler City more people are shot to death than in Chicago. But there are no suicides. Nowhere else has the ideal that working and living should be equally enjoyable been more nearly achieved. The bankers simply shower Stabler with money. Everyone wants to invest with Stabler. And he loses his sense of proportion. Nineteen twenty-nine brings the end. Stabler wants to kill himself. He wants to be the first suicide in his city. But he is prevented from committing suicide by Eileen. With Eileen he flees to this little bay, his Muir Cove. No one knows where his is. He has always kept Muir Cove a secret, but there are rumors that he has something going on the Pacific coast. Hence also the bootlegger legend.

He first noticed Eileen at one of his fancy dress parties. She always came dressed as a naval officer. He made a contract with the woman, who was thirty-three years younger than himself: for every day she spent with him, the sum of $999 would be remitted to her family. Even after the crash the payments were continued by a bank in San Francisco. Eileen, a girl of Irish background, leaves Muir Cove one day to go to Mill Valley to pick up a supply of ice cream. In his caves Stabler has stores of every kind, but no ice cream. Without ice cream, Eileen says, she can't live. In Marin Valley she is seen by a brother of her husband's and recognized in spite of her male attire. Her brother-in-law follows her to the cove and tells his brother Pat what he has seen. Pat organizes a siege. If Stabler will hand over Eileen he can go wherever he likes. Stabler leaves it up to Eileen. She decides to go back to her husband. At that point Stabler draws his pistol; Pat, believing that Stabler is about to shoot the woman, shoots down Stabler. Stabler says: "Thanks." He had been about to kill himself. Eileen kneels beside him and whimpers: "Fred, oh Fred!" She now wants nothing more to do with her husband. Gret is brought back from college and sees to it that her father is buried in one of the Indian burial caves, and she stays there. Her mother has long since disappeared somewhere in the Midwest.

In Stabler City there is nothing left that belongs to Gret. She turns Muir Cove into Inspiration Inn. The factories are taken over by a large company. Now the pumps are mass-produced. Stabler's attempt to work with alcoholics is no longer mentioned, although in the bars it is still discussed. By alcoholics. The newspaper is now saying that there are alcoholics who claim that the city was built by alcoholics. Although it was natural for alcoholics to believe that everything of value was the work of their kind, this view, of course, was as grotesque as it was untrue. It was in the worst possible taste to pretend that Frederick Stabler, that great pioneer, had been an alcoholic. Steps should be taken to stop such talk, says the newspaper. But city hall replies that to take such steps would merely serve to keep the rumor alive: it would probably die out more quickly if left to itself. So this is done. The effect: more and more stories about alcoholics emerge. Stabler City becomes a mecca for them. Once again, alcoholics move into town.

Steps must be taken. Steps are taken. A freely elected city council decides democratically that, although alcohol will not be prohibited in Stabler City, it will be ostracized. In the name of Stabler the great water diviner and water extractor, a powerful movement is launched. House after house is rescued from alcohol. The day comes when the newspaper can announce: Stabler City is alcohol-free.

Now production reaches new heights. The first pumps built by Stabler are housed in a museum. One pump is declared to have been the very first; it is gilded and placed on a block of white marble in front of City Hall. The Stabler legend is cleansed and preserved like a costly animal hide. Stabler City sparkles with pride. No finer statistics have ever been known anywhere. Company, press, politicians, all work together. Everything's under control. Those who cannot live without chaos can seek satisfaction elsewhere. For instance, at Inspiration Inn, less than twenty miles from Stabler City. The newspaper regularly makes fun of the horror stories told to her alcohol-befuddled listeners by a shrewd businesswoman who actually passes herself off as a descendant of Stabler's. Gret's inn is doing well. She is satisfied with her life. Her customers give it meaning. All her customers have heard of her and her stories; they need her stories. Without regular trips to Inspiration Inn, work in Stabler City would come to a standstill, Gret maintains. Frederick Stabler would long since have been embalmed to death if Gret did not keep on telling stories about the reality, the true, the unembalmable. In Stabler City, she would say, it was like being aboard a magnificent ship on which everything works perfectly, except that, from fear of infection, the ship will never again touch land.

The result is that some of the people aboard feel a kind of craving for something entirely different. So they come to her. More and more come to her. Even officials from Stabler City come to her. Not officially, but they come. The day will arrive when her father will be celebrated in Stabler City in his *entire* greatness. Before that happens she's not going to die.

The Swiss lady did not once look at John Frey as she projected her terse sentences obliquely upward, as if each sentence stood on its own and had nothing to do with the preceding and following ones. And all the time she was thus talking over and beyond John Frey, she rubbed the gold franc between thumb and forefinger. Contemplating those beautiful, large bony hands, John Frey found himself thinking that they were hands for which nothing could be too difficult. As if she had been bent on entertaining her customer only as long as the stormy sea kept him there, she came to an end as soon as the storm abated. The low tide had exposed the rocky spur in the bay; John Frey paid his bill, thanked her awkwardly, took his leave, and drove back to Petaluma. He made up his mind to visit Stabler City as soon as possible.

He wanted to know more about Frederick Stabler. Why shouldn't he write a biography of this man? He enjoyed writing. For years he had been keeping a chauffeur's diary. It would have seemed wasteful to him to leave the host of impressions he retained from each trip to the vagaries of his memory. Perhaps he was greedy. He wanted to hang onto everything. It was more than a coincidence that he had stumbled upon this man Stabler: it was a challenge. What was he thinking of, a biography! There was much more to be done here! How come he'd only thought of it just now? Rehabilitation—that was his job here! My God, the "Swiss lady" was Stabler! The female clothes. The hands. Gret was Fred. This Gret was waiting to be redeemed. The story was being told to everyone until someone understood everything, all that happened to the Stablers from Trogen to Lancaster County to the *Titanic* to Stabler City. John Frey felt like turning around then and there and driving back and saying: Hi Fred, how are you today? But he couldn't keep

Ed Crowley waiting another day. His Ford had been repaired. Before driving off he asked the mechanic for the exact location of Stabler City. The mechanic had never heard of the place. Certainly nowhere between San Francisco and Eureka, he could guarantee that. It couldn't be more than twenty miles from Muir Cove, said John Frey. Well now, he knew every hill and dale in that direction, said the mechanic, and there was no Stabler City. But then if John didn't believe him, why didn't he go to the local Triple A office or to the police if he liked!

John Frey went to the police. No, there was no Stabler City. Not in California. He could be sure of that. As John Frey drove along 101 toward San Francisco, he recalled how they had laughed at the Wilhelm Tell in Tomales. And he was already a day late. He had hoped to be able to tell Crowley the engineer so much about the urgent redemption of Stabler the engineer that Crowley would feel compensated for the driverless day and promise to include the earliest possible visit to Inspiration Inn in his itinerary. He didn't buy fantasies, Crowley had said. But just the same he would tell Crowley the whole story. Perhaps he could be persuaded to include a visit to the Swiss lady and Inspiration Inn. An area that could do with a few more bridges and roads, Ed. Then Crowley should take the time to listen to what Gret has to tell about her father Fred and Stabler City while rubbing her gold franc piece between thumb and forefinger. Crowley would say on his way to the car: Let's go to Stabler City! Right now! So they would head for Stabler City but never arrive. John Frey was already looking forward to the expression on his chief engineer's face.

Sabina said: "And Aunt Luise came across in men's clothing too." Halm said: "Anyway, when you think of how they all came across—crazy."

Next morning Halm could hardly dress himself. With his left hand he dangled his underpants as low as possible so as to catch his right foot. Sabina had to put on his shoes and socks for him. He could only bend if he could support himself in such a way as not to place any weight on his spine. As they drove toward the huge white Claremont Hotel farther up the hill, Halm felt as if the irregular indentations in the façade of the white, horizon-wide monster were bearing down upon him like the breakers at Santa Cruz. He closed his eyes until he felt that Sabina had turned off before the hotel. Then they drove under the shelter of huge trees almost as far as Crocker Gate. For the first time he walked through the gate with Lena. It was for her sake, too, that he was on campus by eight o'clock. Beside the fountain on the Student Union Plaza a man was playing the violin. The billiard ball of his head was fringed by a ring of curly hair, like that around Rainer's face. "Schubert?" asked Halm. Lena nodded. He picked up a *Campus Gazette* from the bin.

When they reached the path leading off to Coit Hall, he showed Lena the way to Fillmore Hall, to Auster's lecture. He wanted to go straight to his classroom. He couldn't maintain a normal upright posture. He had to walk either with a slight stoop or unnaturally erect, with a hollow back. Since he didn't want to walk with a stoop, he walked unnaturally erect. No doubt that looked ludicrous too. It was advisable to be the first in the classroom. When he wanted to sit down, he had first to hold onto the edge of the table to avoid the point of pain. It was a pain that, when suddenly triggered, contorted the features. And he didn't want to present himself to the assembled class with a grimace of pain. He was the first person in the room. In the *Gazette* he read only one article: about a man who had raped three women in one afternoon. The rapist had been pursued but not caught. At home this would be the very article he would not read. Here he read only this article. It was certainly no subject for conversation.

With much elaboration Halm introduced the subject for the day: how grateful he was to Carol Elrod for her wonderful suggestion that they discuss why each of them here was taking the conversation course. The girl was sitting, as always, diagonally across from him but far back from the table, her right leg drawn up with the foot resting on her left knee; blue shorts and the white terry T-shirt with the low, round neck. Next to her, Jeff, sprawled across the table with weariness, the weight of his drooping body contrasting with her light and effortless posture. Today only five of the registered students were present. This meant that by the start of the second week almost half the students hadn't shown up. Luckily Howard was there. And red-haired Elaine with the two-liner. She always sat with slightly bent head and her eyes turned upward.

So he would like to thank Carol for this splendid theme! Since she finds out everything he does and almost everything he intends to do, she will also find out about this profound homage he is paying her. "Well then, Howard—why does anyone get up so early five days a week just for conversation?" Howard replied that he was no longer a student but a computer engineer and that he hoped his company would soon send him to Germany. And Elaine? Elaine, who must try to project her warm and friendly smile from her permanently lowered face, isn't yet sure what it's going to lead to. So far she sees three options for herself: either she'll eventually go in for comparative languages, or into the banking business, or to a yachting magazine. Halm congratulates her on this abundance of choice.

And Jeff? Jeff hardly looked up from his doodling, which was probably the only thing keeping him awake. He said: "Philosophy, Nietzsche." He pronounced the name Neechee. "Oh," said Halm, and immediately adapted: "Oh, Neechee, I'm glad to hear that!" Of course he was also glad to hear about the computer mission, the comparative languages, the banking business, and the yachting magazine, but with Nietzsche he had a long-standing if not painless association.

So now it was Fran's turn. Fran gave him a hurt look, as if to say, Didn't he know she didn't want to be asked? She had come here voluntarily, but then she wanted to decide for herself whether and when she would contribute. Had she or hadn't she made it clear to him that she was shy, easily scared and so on? And now he's asking her! Crudely, bluntly, brutally! Well, really! All this was conveyed by her worried, hurt, gray-blue gaze. Southern Sweden in the rain, Halm thought. How long has the silence persisted? How many have already fallen into a trance? Apparently all the girl could do was look at him with a worried, hurt expression. So Halm started talking again. Nonsense. He humiliated himself in order to spare her humiliation. If she understood that this was the reason for his rattling on, he'd be happy. He ended by saying they might now go on to discuss which type of linguistic skill was required for each particular purpose. "Let's start with Howard!" Just then, before Howard could reply, the girl said: "I'd like to become an opera singer." "Oh," said Halm, "that's the best we've heard yet!" Might she be the daughter of the dean? His name was Holmquist. That sounded Swedish. His wife was a stage designer. Idiot, he told himself: you know the girl's not called Holmquist, she's called Webb. Fran Webb.

After class, because he didn't want to walk too erect or too stooped, he walked with excruciating back pain toward the Student Union Plaza between the girl and Jeff, who was wheeling his bicycle. He told them he badly needed a cup of coffee in his free period. Whatever happened, today he and the girl must not run into Rainer on the humpback bridge. He'd rather die. So he must disappear as quickly as possible into one of the Student Union cafeterias. Jeff said he'd leave them now, he never drank coffee. And you need it so badly, Halm felt like saying. Besides, he didn't have time, Jeff said as he swung himself onto his racing bike and whizzed down the curving path to the library. Halm kept a little behind Fran's line of vision in case the pain made him grimace.

On the plaza she stopped, she had to go jogging now, she had to jog for half an hour every morning and every afternoon. And swim at least half an hour every afternoon. That was why she would probably never be able to leave California. The deprivation she had suffered in Vienna in this respect had been terrible. Yesterday she had been outside his office in Fillmore Hall, just in case he hadn't known about Labor Day. He grimaced. No, no, she'd been pretty sure that he hadn't been so unworldly as to go to his office on Labor Day. On the other hand she had wanted to give him her essay and ask which text he might suggest for the next one. She pulled a manuscript out of the unstudentlike bag, Halm took it with a vigorous nod—don't nod so vigorously, he thought, and went on nodding—and said, like a student who, having nothing to say merely wants to prove he has learned something: "Th' expense of spirit in a waste of shame/Is lust in action." Or: "you can smile without love but i can only hate." He was not prepared. He hadn't come to a decision. Because he had put the girl with the thirty years' difference in age behind him, he had done nothing more for her. Typical of you, he said to himself. To the girl he said: "Shakespeare." She said: "If you think so." She would come to his office with the result of her preliminary brainstorming, if she might. "Oh yes. Oh yes, of course."

She left, and was immediately among trees. Wherever you go here, you are immediately among trees. But you remain visible. The trees don't form a forest. She walked down the hill, toward the sports ground. Oh, that walk of hers. He mustn't watch her. The Student Union Plaza was the most public place anywhere on campus. There could be nothing as closely under Carol's observation as this plaza. Probably even his expression showed how he was trying to visualize the girl's face at the moment of leaving him. He could, of course, pretend to be listening to the violinist and trying to decide which Schubert piece the man was playing over and over again for an entire morning. As she left him, her face had been quite free of worry, so she hadn't held it against him that he had asked her something in class.

Now that she was walking down the hill toward the sports ground, he no longer needed any coffee but could head straight for Fillmore. He made a slight detour to the man standing in the sunshine playing the violin and threw a dollar into the violin case. They must be about the same age, that man and he. Halm got as far as Carol's door without running into Rainer. Thank God. Carol's presence would force Rainer, if he were to emerge from his office now, into a certain degree of caution or courtesy. Halm reached for the edge of the desk, carefully sat down on the chair, told her about his Saturday's experience in the surf, listing all his bruises and confessing that he couldn't even put on his shoes by himself. Carol told him that the Talmud defines a youth as someone who can take off his shoe while standing on one leg. The surf had been reminding him that that was a thing of the past. Rainer hadn't turned up at all today, he hadn't even phoned. Usually, if he didn't show up he would at least phone. One of Rainer's graduate students was always available to take over for him.

She reminded Halm that he had again forgotten to look in his box. A parcel of books from Felix Auster was waiting for him there. That is the cue for him to mention his reading of Elrod. He gives free rein to his enthusiasm. Carol looks at him suspiciously, saying that T. H. Messmer had closed *Inspiration Inn* forever after twenty pages. Unreadable, as far as he was concerned, Tee-Aitch had said. She could understand that, if she weren't married to Kirk she would never have finished the book. Halm was confused. She was making him look foolish. But he really had enjoyed the book. So O.K., his enthusiasm had been overdone, but he had liked the book. Carol insisted on agreeing with Mr. Tee-Aitch Messmer. Who was that, anyway? Oh, she said, didn't he know him? An author, comes from the same area as Halm, was here two years ago, was never quite as mild-mannered as Mr. Halm. And what does Mr. Halm think of Elissa? Halm waxed enthusiastic again. Carol raised everything in her face that could be raised and as high as possible, and said: "Coward! I believe you're enthusiastic on principle! It's downright embarrassing. You could really drive a person nuts with your calculated benevolence!" And turned around to face the wall like a stubborn sheep. It was time for him to leave. He said no more.

After class he went to the Student Union Plaza and saw Lena sitting on the rim of the fountain, reading; the clownish violinist was still playing the same piece. "Lena," he said. She looked up. "Lena—look at you, on that low rim! No one in the world sits like that, reads like you do, believe me." Lena stood up and looked at him as if he had hurt her. No one else can express an interest as cautiously, and thus as believably, as you do, he wanted to say.

But obviously she didn't believe a word he said. Was he enthusiastic on principle? You with your calculated benevolence! How easy, by contrast, had it been to get along with the Spanish Fly! You took her a few flowers from the garden three times a year and at Christmas a bottle of Armagnac, and she'd be as nice as could be to you. Carol was more complex, precisely one thousand times more complex.

When Lena and Halm got into the car, Sabina asked: "How was it?" Lena wanted her father to answer, he insisted that the question had been directed at her. He was glad Lena was along. He felt sick in his soul. He was suffering from spiritual nausea. He felt like spiritually throwing up. He couldn't listen to Lena. That morning he had discovered that the terrible example offered him by Carol and Kirk was of no help to him. That morning he had been without defense. The girl had affected him as if he had prepared no resistance whatever. The experience of total defenselessness—that must account for the paralysis that had now overcome him. The walk from Coit Hall to the Student Union Plaza, the few sentences, her face close by, the gradual lightening of her expression. Eventully even a kind of smile had forced its way between those lips that seemed to lie heavily one upon the other. This is all so embarrassing, he sees everything all wrong. The girl and his relationship to her could be seen in quite a different light: much calmer, pleasanter, more friendly, more realistic: thirty-three years' difference, if that isn't enough! Surely that should be enough! Stabler had paid Eileen's family $999 for each day that the woman, thirty-three years younger than he, had spent with him.

On the pretext of having to work on his Heine paper, he withdrew right after lunch. He felt an internal dialogue beginning to form again, but he succeeded in preventing the voices from separating into a *He*-Halm and an *I*-Halm. I have no desire to be scolded or provoked by myself. No strength, came a mocking echo from within him! Yes indeed, no strength. You had only to admit everything, and immediately everything became less acute. Sabina came over. She has dug up some ointment containing bee venom and insists on rubbing his back with it right away. It stung. It felt good, he must admit. "Ah, Sabina," he said. "There, there," she said. He would have liked to draw Sabina into his internal dialogue. He felt in no way separated from her. But he could not involve her. It would be the solution. As soon as he drew Sabina into it, the worst would be over. From that moment on they would grow together again to their old harmony, solidarity. So not immediately telling Sabina everything meant he was admitting that he did not want a solution. He wanted the dilemma. The disaster. And how wonderful it would be to spread everything out before Sabina this very moment. Just like seven years ago when they came home from the opera. But it had needed that terrible scene in the lobby for him to be able to speak. Nicole Klingele, who had once been a student of his, had positively yanked him around by the shoulder to introduce her husband to him. After that scene it had been easy to tell Sabina what had happened between himself and Nicole, now Mrs. Schloz-Klingele. And the following summer Sabina and he had managed to put one of his former schoolmates with his young wife behind them. At a gain, so to speak. A gain in harmony. But now he had no taste for such gain. What he had was a taste for loss. My God, how easy it had been to sacrifice Nicole Schloz-Klingele, to deliver himself and her up to Sabina's contempt! How bombastic her costume had been! Spanish, Pierrotesque, vermilion red with enormous white polka dots, with puffed shoulders, then close-fitting to the waist, then ballooning out again and ending in gathers just below the knee. And Nicole's mood had been equally strident. She actually inflated her upper-class Swabian dialect; she had been totally loud and embarrassing. And all that after the second act of *Tristan*! That something like that can be so over and done with! Deeply reassuring.

Fran was not Nicole. But he no longer felt as miserable as he had. He looked at his watch. Since the moment when the girl had turned around and walked off in a way that he felt he couldn't bear, five hours had passed. He had been alone with her for almost exactly five minutes. For every minute of girl, one hour of regeneration. So long as she was close by for only five minutes. For a sixth girl-minute he would probably need an hour and ten minutes for his regeneration, for a seventh girl-minute an hour and twenty minutes. He remained both wrought up and exhausted after she had left. Useless for anything.

The phone rang. Carol was phoning from her home. She was crying. She was so sorry, she said. She was talking and crying almost incoherently. Her crying grew wetter and louder, then sank into a subdued whimper. She begged him to say something, to forgive her. She was always having to make like a tough shiksa. Halm expatiated on how sorry he was to have been the cause of such an outburst. Carol quickly recovered. She realized, she said, that it was possible that he simply didn't understand. But she wasn't about to start in again on Tee-Aitch. And hung up.

He reached—instinctively, as it were—for the girl's essay. She wrote that at the moment she was sitting in her parents' house in Mill Valley, drinking milk and remembering that dark winter in Vienna. In her parents' house, one step was enough to get you anything you wanted. One step, and you were in the shade. One step, and you were in the sun. One step, and your boyfriend was there. One step, and you were with your understanding girlfriend. Being in such a cozy nest made a person lose all sense of self. In dark Vienna, locked up in yourself, you had felt everything as if it were a pain. Even a poem. And especially a poem. Then disaster had struck. Here. In the family. She had had to return. To her father. Her mother had been run over. In San Francisco. On one of the steep streets. She compared the beautiful dark pain in Vienna with the strident actual pain in California. A year later her father had married the woman who had been responsible for her mother's death. And this woman was a fantastic person. This woman was suffering from the disaster she had caused just as much as her father, and her brother, and she herself did. For her the Rilke poem had become the quintessence of her own passivity. At the time, everything had had more influence on her than she had herself. . . .

When Halm walked into Carol's office the next day, she immediately gestured toward Rainer's door, and at that moment he came out, his gown over his arm. With a nod to Halm, he walked past him and out into the corridor. "Wait a moment!" Halm shouted. Rainer stopped and turned around. "What's got into you?" Halm asked. Rainer looked at Halm as if trying to discern something in a dimly lit room. "Right," said Rainer, "I guess you're entitled to a convincing apology, but that would take more time than I have at my disposal on my way to a graduation ceremony." Because Rainer's lower lip was so slack, Halm could see the tip of Rainer's tongue darting restlessly between his teeth. "But if you'd care to forestall my apologies, go ahead!" he said. With darting tongue he waited one more second, then left. After all, he was the boss here. The boss can turn his back on anyone he wants to. Halm felt like sinking through the floor. Carol's laugh startled him. He was standing on the third floor of Fillmore Hall on the campus of Washington University of Oakland, California. He couldn't take any liberties, of that he was keenly aware. He had to serve each person the way that person wished to be served. That was the extent of his strength. He had no say whatever. To yield, that was his role. That he could do, yield. He hoped it would help. He hoped that something he was capable of would be noticed. He longed to be at Inspiration Inn. He desperately needed the cave, the listener, the narrative in which he could hide away. He needed Kirk Elrod. Kirk Elrod was the only person of whom he wasn't afraid.

8

SHE JOINED HIM AFTER every conversation class. Each day he had to find a reason for going from Coit Hall to any place other than Fillmore Hall. True, he still couldn't put on his shoes and socks, but he could walk, although somewhat ludicrously erect. The main thing was not to run into Rainer and his Shakespearean flourish on the humpback bridge over dry Okra Creek with the girl at his side! Not to be standing beside the girl at the elevator door just as Carol was coming out! Halm was glad that Carol wouldn't be there on Thursday. Thursday was Rosh Hashanah. She was a twice-a-year Jew, she had said—on Rosh Hashanah and Yom Kippur.

Friday evening the doorbell rang: Rainer. He put his arms around Halm while still in the doorway. "Can you forgive me?" he whispered moistly. Halm replied: "Nothing would give me greater pleasure!" But Rainer said he couldn't enter the Rinehart house again until Halm had forgiven him. But he had just done so! said Halm. No, Halm would have to forgive him in formal language without jargon or flippancy and in direct speech, first person singular. Halm realized he had a problem. Here he had a chance to use inflated language, was even being called upon to do so, and he couldn't. But he had to, or Rainer would leave. Rainer was standing in front of him, stooping yet taller, his lower lip slack, the tip of his tongue probing miserably between the gaping rows of teeth. Halm felt it would be humiliating to parrot this prescribed sentence. He was evasive. "But I've already forgiven you," he said. "Present tense!" said the other. Needless to say, he was under the influence. He was feeling no pain, yet his perspicuity and perceptiveness seemed to be enhanced by alcohol. Mendacity and truth in Kleist, thought Halm. So he was supposed to tell Rainer that he forgave him for trying to denounce him in front of Sabina. He was supposed to forgive him for saying: You're no good. To forgive the words: You're talking garbage, my boy. Could he forgive that? Couldn't he just as well demand from Rainer the words: I take back what I said? But he didn't dare demand that; after all, Rainer might stick to his guns. Rainer wished to be forgiven for having told the truth. Whatever Rainer said could only be the truth. No more righteous man than he existed.

Rainer was now looking almost imploringly at Halm. The tip of his tongue moved restlessly. Halm already knew that he would give in. He had to utter a sentence that was alien to him. He couldn't even think in such dimensions. To forgive, not to forgive . . . what hyperbole! He would give in. He would, as he saw it, be lying. There seemed to be no other way of coexisting with this truth-athlete. The trouble was, he still couldn't bring himself to utter those words, although he already knew that he wouldn't be spared them. By demanding that I forgive him he is creating a ceremony of submission. I must kneel in the dust; he places his foot on my neck saying he will not remove his foot until I say I forgive him. My God, had they even connived over this, Carol and Rainer? Carol hadn't been quite as pompous in staging her demand for forgiveness over the phone, but then of course she wasn't the boss. And because he hadn't obeyed he'd come in for abuse.

So now he said with an audible groan: "I forgive you."

Rainer thanked him so sincerely that Halm not only was touched but also suspected that his equating forgiveness with submission had in fact been a mistake. Rainer was apparently genuinely sorry that he had told Halm he was no good. Halm was happy. Finally, Rainer! Halm ushered Rainer into the room as if Rainer were a bride. He loved this fellow, this insufferable man of whom one couldn't be too wary. But maybe Rainer really meant well. So come on in, won't you? "Lena, Sabina—here we have the most delightful visitor imaginable!" There was no whisky in the house, Halm had seen to that. Only wine here, he had said. Whisky in California? Ridiculous. Chardonnay from Sonoma, cabernet sauvignon from Napa. He hadn't told Sabina that after the whisky incident in this house he could no longer stand the sight of whisky here, let alone drink it.

He was always happy with wine, said Rainer, with red more than with white. Sabina chose red too. Rainer knew the varieties, the wineries, tasted, praised Sabina, said the wine was "tears of the mountain." Only Lena drank tea. Rainer created an atmosphere of lighthearted splashing around together in warm water, or dozing side by side on the grass. He was relaxed. He stretched out his arms. Today he had again made no headway with his Schubert text interpretation, but he was quite used to that so it wasn't worth getting upset about it, least of all on this red-letter day when they had received a postcard from Jamey, from Brattleboro, where at the moment he was taking part in the Experiment in International Living.

Rainer obviously wanted to share his happiness with the Halms. Thoughtfully, almost tenderly, he asked Lena about her experiences on campus. As if Lena were an internationally lionized philosopher, Rainer asked her with much concern whether Felix Theodor Auster still met her standards. Teddy *had* been someone who had conceptualized present-day pain in precise phraseology: now he was repeating himself. Lena said that so far she hadn't understood much. "I see," said Rainer. And who else did she have? Linda Gallagher, "women's studies." "Oh," said Rainer, "*écriture féminine*," but he wasn't trying to be funny. Roy, the amateur castrator, called Linda the literary nun. How happy he was to have the Halms here! What a great impression Lena had made on his motorcyclist wife! In calling Elissa a motorcyclist, he was always afraid of not uttering that word with as much fervor as he felt. Elissa was the extreme opposite of the literary nun. He had met her at a dance at the Claremont Club to which he had only been invited because Elissa had persuaded her father, who knew the club president, to wangle an invitation. At the time he had been here on a trial basis, and a friend of Elissa's called Bluma had been one of his students. Elissa had only known of him through Bluma when she had wangled the invitation. All she needed was an escort for the club dance. She must have been in a state of shock at the time. Probably she had just discovered that she was pregnant.

In those days Rainer had had no inkling of what it meant for a girl to be related to the McCleaves. Elissa had staged a fairy tale for him. Duration: seven weeks or seven months. Instead of being content one wants more. He was curious to see Elissa's face when she heard that Lena was taking women's studies. Elissa despised such things. Nothing was more alien to her than the desire to distinguish oneself. One could see that, of course, when she's in repose. Cool and contained. One always wanted to get close to her. But it was impossible. For him. There's no way of impressing her, that's the problem. Unless one happens to be a Caribbean black called Othello Jesús de García. Fame, intellect—one could think of nothing that would help one to succeed with her. One has to smell of something, but he doesn't know of what. For example, she never reads. What it takes for Elissa to become interested in a book is shown by the following example: In the forties there was an author here called Mark Cerf. Thomas Mann wrote a foreword to *Tunnel Vision*, Cerf's novel on psychoanalysis. The son of this author, Stanley Cerf, was a professor, wrote poems, without success, married Elissa's friend Bluma who also wrote poems and who actually received a prize from *Harper's Magazine* for a short story. Whereupon she was shot to death by her husband

Stanley. He wounded himself only slightly. Now he is serving a life sentence over in San Quentin, which is almost visible from Euclid Avenue. When Elissa heard *that*, she immediately read the book written by Bluma's father-in-law: *Tunnel Vision*.

Now he saw Elissa only when they had guests. But they talked on the phone, indoors, from upstairs to downstairs. That had the advantage that he could smoke and drink. Tomorrow night, then, when Helmut and he would be playing skat at Kinsman's, Lena would be playing the piano at Elissa's. Halm and Sabina were surprised. She would have told them later, said Lena. "And what are your plans, Sabina?" asked Rainer. Sabina replied: "Don't worry, I'll survive." "I'm glad to hear that," said Rainer. Didn't they too feel moved by Elissa's remark that he, Rainer, was in the process of destroying himself? And not only on account of the nicotine stink in the drapes: she had also mentioned alcohol which, after all, couldn't impair the immaculate state of her tarantula chapel. Those words—that he was in the process of destroying himself—always prevented him from asking for a divorce. At times, when he was a bit fed up with drinking and smoking, it seemed to him that he only went on drinking and smoking so as to be able to hear those words from Elissa.

Stanley Cerf had shot his wife Bluma, twenty years younger than he, through the ear. In cold blood, the prosecutor had said. Some words should be withdrawn from currency on account of their obvious senselessness. Would Lena play the piano tomorrow night even if Othello Jesús de García were there? For she would have to reckon with that. Elissa always went too far. An innocent child from the Old Country and a whore-chasing drama-department Jamaican—enough for Elissa to conjure up an evening. "I'm going to win tomorrow night at skat, you'll see." But he'd love sometime to play four-handed with Lena. Then they'd invite Elissa. Maybe she'd come.

"It's all very difficult," Rainer said, looking at each of the Halms in turn. His grandfather had been a baker, he said. Twenty-three kinds of bread, fresh every day. "One really wouldn't have expected that," he went on quite reproachfully. And by way of confirmation he repeated: "One really wouldn't have expected that." Then to Halm: "Don't take such advantage of the fact that I am at your mercy. You pull strings. You jump to conclusions. You think you're so smart. Sabina—tell him it's enough to love me. All around me, these budding intrigues. Then I defend myself, then nobody admits to having started it. Tomorrow I'll pick you up for the skat. Take care! Goodnight." And turned around once more to say, scathingly: "Pity she's a whore. But, if you don't mind: For interdepartmental use only." Then he turned on his heel, as if about to make a pirouette, and stalked away. The Halms remained together for quite a while, like people who have the advantage. Sabina said that Rainer apparently felt persecuted. "By me?" said Halm. "Yes, by you," she said, "or at least threatened." "Oh well, that's life," said Halm. "Persecutors tend to feel persecuted."

The whole of the next morning, Halm had Sabina give him a refresher driving course. Years ago, after the third rear-ender, he had called it quits. Without either admiring or despising drivers he had said: "I'm no driver." Now, suddenly, he wanted to be one. This country fired him up. With its space and light. He would have liked to be permanently on the road. It seemed as if he yearned to do everything for which at home he had the least inclination. Driving, for instance. Sabina was amazed. He could provide a valid reason. That evening Rainer was going to pick him up for the skat game. There Rainer would go on drinking. The fact that the young instructor from Texas had cleared out for good after his first skat party was an indication of what went on at those evenings. And then to be driven home from Upper Happy Valley by that totally drunken poet and martyr—no, not he.

They drove straight through the ten or twelve individual cities that have grown together along the Bay. They practiced entering the freeway that leads inland through the tunnel, thus presumably also to Happy Valley. He pressed Sabina closely to his side as they walked down from the garage into the house. "And this light, these leaves, this sky, this house, this moment, Sabina! Ah, Sabina—another of those depressingly beautiful days! Whatever is to become of us, Sabina! Do you realize how dark it is in Sillenbuch in January?" Sabina found it wrong to think now of the future. She drew his attention to what was in flower here: hibiscus, bougainvillea, fuchsia. Plants that at home need to be indoors in pots bloom here out of doors, just look. Before they entered the house, Sabina picked a few lemons. Bob's wife from next door had told Sabina that gardening here was fun because there was no winter. Halm wanted to note local phrases in the original. Gardening here is fun. "Good," said Halm, as if at school. In the porch, while reaching for the screen door, he said: "I have absolutely nothing against you, Sabina, nothing whatever." Sabina made the face appropriate to this solemn outburst.

On arriving to pick up Halm, Rainer agreed to let Halm drive, but not the Volvo. He had taken a vow: Never again would he set foot in a foreign car; he owed too much to the American cars. Since his days with the ambulance. Then he'd made deliveries for a florist. Later as a free-lance gardener in Virginia, when he had lived and written from May to October in one of those vans. And for all his dreams there, he wanted to go on thanking those roomy vehicles. So Halm had to pretend that he was able to drive a monster like this too. Driving along, he tested the brake pedal. After the violent shuddering had died away, Rainer looked at him with raised eyebrows. Halm said: "Sorry." The fact that there was no clutch for his left foot was hard for him to grasp that quickly. Why couldn't he bring himself to confess that he had never driven with an automatic gear shift? But with all the fits and starts, Rainer became more and more cheerful. Fear seemed to be unknown to him.

They didn't drive onto the freeway and through the mountain but over the top. He didn't care for tunnel vision, said Rainer. So Halm carefully wound his way up. At the top Rainer said: "This is where Grizzly Peak Boulevard begins, where the Elrods live—they can see all the bridges from San Mateo to Richmond." Beyond the hill the road led down in curves in the shade of the eucalyptus groves. Rainer told him in advance where they would turn right up a valley, park the car, and take a short walk to Inspiration Point. That was where Elrod, who was from Albany, had found his title. "This is where you get the best view," said Rainer when they reached the top. From here one could see the hill they lived on, but from the back, and beyond the hill one could look down on the Bay, on San Francisco, Golden Gate Bridge, the ocean. Halm stood and looked and assumed a devout expression. Rainer grabbed him by his shoulders, swung him around, and said: "Now look." Uninhabited hills stretched all the way to the horizon. Rainer said: "California." A sea of grassy hilltops, dried out by the sun to the verge of a golden shimmer. Below them, the drought-resistant eucalyptus groves. "And look—above the hills the moon has risen to exactly the same height as the sun has sunk over the sea. And we two in the middle between rising and sinking. Satisfied?" Halm nodded. He would have liked to stroke Rainer. But one doesn't do that.

They walked down into the shade, to the car, past crested birds that walked hurriedly back and forth as if in a state of agitation. Rainer said those were not birds, they were ornithologists, a convention probably on music or literature, what misery. But yesterday they had at least received a postcard from Jamey, he'd wanted to tell Helmut that. Halm seized Rainer's arm and gave it a quick, firm squeeze. Actually Rainer should have said Ow! but he didn't seem to have felt anything. "Great, isn't it?" said Rainer. "Marvelous," said Halm. "From Brattleboro," said Rainer. "The boy is taking part in a seminar for the Experiment in International Living there. What d'you say to that?" "Marvelous, I say," replied Halm.

Rainer directed him around increasingly sharp, steep, narrow, wooded, incredible curves and along picturesquely bad roads into Upper Happy Valley. Waiting for them there: Sally, or rather, her mouth in the last rays of the sun. Halm had expected some kind of farmhouse. But what stood there on the only piece of level ground projecting from the steep slope, in a bower of bushes and trees, was a jewel of a house built of pale stone and white beams. The farm lay farther back, out of sight, out of smell. And a little higher on the slope, a cottage, a miniature version of the house: Sally's studio. "They built the whole thing themselves," said Rainer. In the lush, overfed-looking grass between the shrubs, the trees, around the house, again and again: Sally's handiwork. Ceramics lying there as if secreted by the bombastic lawn. Beautiful nightmare fruits. Bulging tumescent shapes, garish and shiny, writhing in and out of one another. Fruits and animals combining into one body. Human parts ending in blossoms. Breasts with bird claws hooked into them. And there was also a real dachshund whose name, Halm was told, was Umlaut on account of the two white strokes over his eyes. He'd already been called that when Roy had been given him by a colleague in Tübingen.

Inside the house everything was white. Although all quite different from the atmosphere at Elissa's, the main impact here too was: awe-inspiring. But since Sally hadn't come indoors with them—she had a bit to do in her studio—Halm didn't feel like expressing fervent admiration for this awesomeness. However, he did have to admire the oak floor laid by Roy himself, as well as the chairs and table he had fashioned.

Leslie Ackerman came in. Roy took the three bottles brought by the three guests and said he was going to put them in the fridge, although it was hardly worth it for the jug wines that Rainer and Leslie always brought along. As soon as he put down the bottle, Leslie Ackerman placed his left hand over his left eye, and he did this so naturally, so unaffectedly, that Halm had to tell himself that by now he scarcely noticed this rather uncommon manner of holding one's hand. Roy shuffled the cards in the virtuoso American way. Rainer said that Roy had earned his living for a whole year up in Reno at a blackjack table. At this point Halm hardly dared admit that he wasn't all that sure of the rules of skat. Rainer noticed this and said: "Deal, listen, bid. We like being four as this always gives one of us a chance to go off for a snack or a drink." Leslie said: "He talks like that because you're here, otherwise he'd say: A chance for a bit of grub and some booze." Roy said that tonight for a change Rainer had better hold back a bit on the booze, it was no fun playing against someone who'd knocked himself out. Rainer said: "Now that asshole is talking like my wife. Let me tell you—I don't go out at night just to listen to your garbage!" Leslie remarked that Roy had only said it out of stinginess because he was scared they would drink more than they'd brought with them. Roy's two-dollar-twenty vino, said Rainer, helped him a lot to kick the habit. "Better anyway than that student piss of yours," said Roy. And to Halm: "Rainer always gives student parties, you know. Each student brings a bottle of the cheapest stuff, half is left over—for us. But before he comes here he goes to the supermarket and pinches price tags and sticks the six-dollar labels on his bottles of student piss."

"Because a price tag's the only thing you guys understand," said Rainer. "Well, high jumper," said Roy, "can you or can't you?" "I can," said Leslie, "and what's more, without lashing an eye bat." "All right, then, show what you've got, asshole," said Roy and started bidding. "Asshole yourself," said Leslie. It seemed to Halm that when Leslie had to say "asshole" it was always a bit of a strain. Yet those Roughnecks had been playing together for fifteen years. When Roy played a ten of spades in the hope that Leslie would have the ace, whereas Halm held the ace, Roy said: "When chickens piss it's hit or miss, but when they shit it's quite a hit." Leslie said: "Get your act together, you mellowed-out flamboyant halfwit." Roy took a trick and muttered fiercely: "High jumper poppycock nonsense." All that Halm could make of it was that this was Roughneck talk. Halm had lost. Roy reached for the sheet of paper on which the names were already written and entered plus or minus points, saying: "I feel plumb good."

Halm again bid successfully for the next game, lost again. Then Leslie dealt, Halm bid successfully, lost. Then he dealt, and left the game for some tidbits, drank the sweetish white wine, and watched the players so as to lose no time in becoming an acceptable skat player again. As soon as he was back in the game, he bid and lost. Each time he reckoned with chances which turned out to be nonexistent. Invariably he drew the suit he had no use for. Each time the others played the very card that revealed his weak point; they played as if his cards were lying face up on the table. He felt totally exposed. It annoyed him to be so predictable. The more often he lost, the more important it was to him to win his bids, so he took greater and greater risks and lost more and more often. When Halm once scored 59, one point short of winning, Roy said: "Shit in his pants just outside the outhouse door, is what my dad used to say." Leslie said: "One of Roy's most valuable assets—his outhouse metaphorics from Tübingen."

Then Halm even lost a game in which he held the four top trumps. Everyone roared with laughter. Roy said: "Shit inside a cannon muzzle, that's no longer such a puzzle. But shit upon a fancy pillow, oh, is he one happy fellow!" But Roy lost the next game, taking hardly any tricks at all. Unfortunately Halm could think of no pithy saying to contribute. Luckily Rainer said in his inimitably soft voice: "Stepped right in the shit, didn't you!" Just then Umlaut the dachshund came in carrying a piece of paper in his mouth. He sat up beside Roy. Roy read out: "Umlaut needs feeding." "You're lucky this time," said Leslie. And, by way of explanation, to Halm: "The last time we were here it said: 'Sally needs fucking.' " Roy said: "But when I came back I won a grand slam right off." "Because you'd just been working on a good slam," said Leslie. Roy: "Don't underestimate my oral proficiency."

Halm felt thoroughly excluded. Nobody addressed an obscenity to him. He didn't belong. He envied the Roughnecks, sitting there on a green island in Upper Happy Valley exchanging obscenities for ten, fifteen, twenty years. Oh Messrs. Kiderlen and Associates, how he shrinks from your obscenity-free language! How wonderful if he could only stay here long enough for Roy to call him an asshole for the first time. Asshole—that was equivalent to tenure. Whichever way they may mean it, they can tolerate each other's company. They make a point of meeting again in the evenings. Back home he hadn't a single colleague whom he would want to see again in the evening. It was all such a mess. Back home.

He drank and played as if there were no tomorrow. Wildly, recklessly. The others, although they were also drinking heavily, took the game seriously. When Roy at one point added up subtotals and remarked that by this time Halm owed the rest of them six dollars and thirty cents, Rainer said, "Maybe now we should increase the stake to one cent per minus point." He thought that might make Halm come to his senses. Leslie: "Or he's losing deliberately because he needs all his luck in love." Whereupon Roy: "But surely not with an undergraduate, Helmut!" That was pointed. They all laughed. Leslie—and his left hand fitted exactly over his left eye—laughed and groaned simultaneously as he repeated: "But surely not with an undergraduate, Helmut!" There are such phrases that, under such circumstances, provoke fresh outbursts of laughter no matter how often they are repeated.

Roy said to Rainer: "You should've told him it's prohibited with an undergraduate." Rainer said that in the semester before last the dumb beauty had tried it on with him, but after two sessions she hadn't shown up anymore. Halm felt obliged to defend himself, especially against Rainer. "Maybe she was scared," said Halm. "How do you mean?" said Rainer. Halm didn't know, so he said: "A person can be afraid of you too." Because Rainer gave him an odd look, he quickly added: "Simply because one has no idea of how kind someone is who lives off the 'tears of the mountain.' " When Rainer's eyes turned stony, Halm said, Now look, there must have been some growing misunderstanding during the last exchanges, or he, Halm, had had too much to drink, couldn't quite follow at the moment. How dearly he would have liked to end his words with "assholes," and in the most cordial tone at that and with pride at being the first among them to use the word in the plural. "Whose lead?" asked Roy, anxious to resume the game. Leslie said: "Sally seems to be staying late in her studio tonight. She must have found someone to feed her." Halm was grateful to Leslie.

The conversation began to surge past him again. He was safe. Although the card game is the most important aspect, it also serves, like the suspension in a car, to enable one to pass over the bumpiest bits of road in comfort. Now the subject was Roy's third marriage. The first one had taken place in Oakland Hills. The second in Orinda, one range farther inland. The third now in Upper Happy Valley, still farther inland. Each time Roy had moved away, leaving the house to the previous wife and building a new house with the new wife. He had either written standard works on the Middle Ages or built houses. The standard works had made him rich, Leslie said. Sally had made him happy, Roy said. Were there any more valleys? asked Rainer. Hidden Valley was the next one, Roy replied. Leslie wanted to know what it was like with an artist. Roy: "I've known for a long time that you'd like to watch. I'll mention it to Sally." Rainer said he admired Roy for the orderly manner in which he conducted his marriages, from the first stage to the last. There was never anything slipshod, never a moment of ambiguity. He was sure that if Roy ever found himself compelled to kill one of his wives, he wouldn't do it without the most scrupulous exertion of his sense of justice. "But I'll be looking to you for the execution!" said Roy, raising his glass to Rainer. "You're most welcome," said Rainer and drank too. If Sally wore the tights she'd had on today, he'd also take part in the execution, said Leslie, and for no special reason removed his hand from his eye. That was exactly the kind of help he would keep away from the place of execution, said Rainer. "No masturbating backstage sycophants," said Roy. Leslie said there was no forming a partnership with a conservative asshole like that.

Roy exclaimed: "I spent the whole afternoon looking for the phrase *Mut zeiget, auch der Mameluck*! How does the sentence run? Where does it come from? Who wrote it?" So now they had turned to *Mameluck*. Each of them believed he had read the line, but no one knew where. Was it Schiller? Or Uhland? Although

Halm hadn't the slightest idea, he joined enthusiastically in the discussion, simply to prevent the conversation from returning to the "undergraduate." Obviously undergraduates were treated like children here. At some point, Kiderlen would rub it in that Halm hadn't taught at a university in California after all but at the college level. Halm had no idea how Kiderlen could find that out, but he was convinced that he would. Kiderlen, without his own doing, had the effect of exposing everything that was clandestine, imprecise, devious, not quite proper in all its inadequacy. In Rainer a similar talent is rampant. But Rainer is a friend.

When they added up, Halm had to pay Roy $6.21, Leslie $1.19, and Rainer 14 cents. It was after midnight. Rainer was humming. Halm let Leslie drive ahead. At some point Leslie turned off to Orinda. Once again they would be driving beside deeply fissured Tilden Park and over the hill. Rainer carried on a monologue but at each intersection promptly indicated which road to take. Halm wondered whether Leslie took his hand from his eye when he was driving. Rainer's speech was labored, slow, as if he was under heavy pressure. He seemed to strain at every word. He could hardly continue. Halm, after all, had had no way of stopping him from rapidly emptying glass after glass. Roy had said: "Tonight he's breaking his own record." They had stopped calling it a jug wine, they were all drinking it, Rainer poured it down his throat.

Halm noticed that Rainer was now verbally attacking someone, working himself up against an opponent, as if he believed that he was having a conversation with him or even a quarrel. Halm felt he should interrupt him, but Rainer had already talked himself too deeply into his clinch. Now and again Halm said: "Rainer!" Whether Rainer heard him or not, there was no way of knowing. Halm shook his head violently, slammed one hand down on the steering wheel, and flicked the high beam on and off, shouting "Rainer!" Surely the fellow could at least remember that he was sitting beside an inexperienced driver who was driving an unfamiliar car through totally unfamiliar territory! But Rainer went on talking, weightily, laboriously, as if in a wrestling ring, although he seemed to know exactly how he would get the better of his opponent. His groping and straining already contained his victory. In any case it wasn't a dialogue with himself in order to clarify his mind about something or somebody: it was a chase, an arrest, a wiping out.

Now he was saying: "Sure, you're not stupid. You think you're smarter than you are. Don't think I can't see through you. You imagine that when you divert attention from yourself you can't be seen. Like a child. Even children can be corrupted. Corrupted children get on my nerves. Even when they're innocent of their corruption. The moral claim derives its acuteness from a sensitivity of an aesthetic nature. You and your empathy. Your empathy is sloppiness. Everyone defends *himself*. But anyone defending corruption in order to defend himself admits that he is corrupt. Like anyone else, I can put up with a bit of corruption. But when someone lives entirely on the tolerance of others, he is asking too much of us. At the moment I feel that too much is being asked of me. Tonight. You attacked me in front of my old friends. Who are my old enemies. A well-known fact. You wanted to poke fun at me so we wouldn't go on discussing your unsavory life-style. I invite you over here, and you show your gratitude by persecuting me. You want to finish me off. You want my job. You ingratiate yourself everywhere. You want to set everybody against me. You spread it around that I drink. I don't believe that you've succeeded in turning my oldest friends, who are also my oldest enemies, away from me. I don't believe that. That doesn't make your attempt any the less despicable. But maybe you actually have succeeded. Perhaps Roy and Leslie now see me through your eyes. With that West German fitness look. Calling upon me to emulate that genius for glossing over. There's plenty of room under the carpet. That's your despicable hope. It pains me. Let me get out, please. Surely you heard that I want out. Fine. As a result of associating with yourself you have come to regard everything as mere empty rhetoric. Such proximity pains me. I don't want to come to a miserable end on account of you, my boy."

He grabbed Halm's arm, thus jerking the steering wheel and making the car swerve sharply. Halm just had time to step on the brake, and the car stopped at a steep angle, slanting, crooked. They had almost overturned. Before Halm could move, Rainer was out the door. Halm watched him run downhill in the light of the headlamps and then disappear behind trees whose dark green, pyramid-shaped branches reached down to the ground. With arms outflung to keep his balance, Rainer vanished into that cluster of regular pyramid shapes. It struck Halm that, up to this moment, he had never believed that Rainer actually meant what he said when he was totally drunk. Halm had actually believed that it was all just a manner of speaking. Necessary, no doubt. Embarrassing, painful, dangerous, threatening, but nothing would happen. Now something had happened. He didn't care for that. For years on end he had withdrawn from the field where something might happen. Systematically. Calmly. In complete order. Inconspicuously. And now this. Ah, Rainer. He would stay here until Rainer returned. In any case, he'd never find his way out of this tangle of roads and hills and valleys. And the night was warm. And this was a car in which one could spend the night.

He settled down, listened to the radio, found the announcer's chitchat agreeable. Why couldn't everyone be as pleasant as the announcer? If he were with the announcer, no such embarrassing scene could ever have taken place. It was clear that Rainer hadn't become an American after all. Always this natter about the superficiality of American friendships. To hell with the Westphalian emotional depth that can lead to something like this. He yearned for that announcer. An evening of skat with three such announcers: that would be the ultimate. All those harmless jokes, those tiny stumblings over words, and, most important of all: not for a second does that announcer take himself seriously. Completely laid back. That would be the place for Halm. "The time is now fourteen minutes to two," said the announcer, making it sound like something for which one should feel truly grateful to him. Halm understood that. He was grateful. It was almost two o'clock. Soon it would be three. Fortunately everything would soon be over. Everything. And to be able to say that in such a droll way! Only an American announcer could do that. And what they were singing pleased him more than what Rainer had said. *I close the door,* sang the singer, who had exactly the same friendly manner as the announcer, *she steps in, I dim the light, she turns to me, I hold her knee, she loosens my tie. . . . She's honey hungry . . . I'm honey hungry and she's mine.* Who could ask for more? Maybe he wouldn't want to hear it sung in German. But here! And now! Then came a hit tune that he couldn't bear to go on listening to. *Young girl, get out of my mind. My love for you is way out of line. Better run, girl, you're much too young, girl. . . .* He switched off. He didn't want Rainer to catch him listening to lyrics like that.

When it grew light and Rainer hadn't returned, he maneuvered the car, although with spinning tires, back onto the road. Then he drove on down the hill, came to a major intersection, saw a sign pointing to Berkeley, and followed it. He drove almost at walking pace. The road went uphill. At last he saw him, the terrible fugitive. He was lying at the side of the road, sound asleep. The grass was of exactly the same color as the curls around his pale, bluish face. The low-crowned yellow hat with the black band lay some way off in the grass. Halm drove as close to him as he could, switched off the engine, and waited. He hoped Rainer would appreciate his being right on the spot. He hoped Rainer no longer remembered what he had said.

When Halm awoke, Rainer was gone. Halm drove slowly uphill, past the turnoff to Inspiration Point, and over the hill to North Berkeley. On Euclid he parked the car in front of the house, walked down onto Contra Costa, and joined Sabina and Lena at the breakfast table. He didn't know what to say. He had to keep everything to himself. The only thing he could admit to was alcohol. Alcohol and the card game, both to excess, Saturday became Sunday, they hadn't been able to pry themselves loose from the handmade chairs in Upper Happy Valley. Admittedly Rainer behaved a bit oddly again, toward the end, but only toward the end, as he always does when alcohol takes over. It's really too bad, but that's how it is. And so predictably. Scarcely imaginable how wonderful it would be here if they had arrived while he was still . . . still different. But that would be paradise. And after that, back to Stauffenberg School? So let's take things as they are.

"So, Lena, how did you get along? And you, Sabina?" Luckily for her, Lena says, she didn't have to play the piano, and Othello Jesús wasn't there either, only Elissa. They'd talked till midnight. "Is it permitted to ask about what?" Lena shakes her head. "Aha," says Halm. And Sabina? Has been making sure, by means of letters and postcards, that they won't have been forgotten by the time they go home. Although Juliane is apparently not prepared to give up that dreadful liaison with a man who, believe it or not, is twenty-two years older than she is, and not only that but married with two kids. Sabina has already written her a second letter. It was too soon to expect an answer. Then Halm must go to bed, Sabina said, but in such a way that he felt he must stay up. He'd had two or three hours of sleep, after all. He'd not been able to tell them that.

Sabina had planned an outing into the wine valleys and to the beach. Perhaps just to the beach, he said. At the moment he'd had enough of the "tears of the mountain." Sabina said she'd be glad of any chance to get out of the house. Surprisingly, Lena raised no objection to the outing. Today, Sabina announced, they would drive south again for a bit, not so far as last time and on a different freeway, then over a kind of pass through the hills and down a valley on the other side leading to the Pacific, to Half Moon Bay. And again her rhetorical "O.K., everyone?"

Sabina was informed about everything that cropped up during the drive. She was prepared. "Our John Frey," Halm commented over his shoulder to Lena. This time Sabina turned off toward the edge of the steep cliff. For a while the Halms sat just looking out over the shining ocean and down into the white frill of foam fringing the broad curve of the bay. Today he didn't even go as far into the water as Sabina and Lena. Repeatedly he called Lena back: she was getting much too close to the breakers. He was genuinely afraid for her. He roared. But Lena gestured that she couldn't hear him. She pointed to the breakers. And went even farther out. He called to Sabina. Sabina laughed. Then he turned around, as pointedly as he possibly could, lay down on the towels, and fell asleep. He heard Lena and Sabina coming, going away again, coming again, going away again. The roar of the surf, the sun, the wind, the warmth of the sand through the towel, his fatigue—although asleep he was constantly aware of it all in the most soothing way. He felt cradled, protected, sheltered. Suddenly he had to look up: close by him, almost on top of him, two enormous gray seagulls with long hooked beaks. "Shoo!" he cried. They walked slowly away. As if disappointed. Offended, too.

On the drive home he tried to tell them a bit more about the skat evening in Upper Happy Valley. There were, after all, a few things he could be enthusiastic about. Sally, the house, the Roughnecks. The rest he kept to himself. "Well, Lena, how did you get along?" Lena said: "Fine." Halm told them that it was important for him to find out as much as possible about Rainer because Rainer was subject to attacks of irrational behavior, and the less one knew about their causes the more one had to suffer. Lena said Rainer's name had never once been mentioned. They had talked only about Jamey and the driving school and that Elissa intended to go into the used-car business. Halm said no more. He pretended to have fallen asleep again. But he wasn't asleep. Lena didn't know that he had become involved in a struggle here. Every detail could be important for him. The more one knew about someone without that person's knowledge, the better armed one was against him. But hadn't it always been that way, that the family hadn't shared in his struggle! Of course, because he couldn't allow them to share. After all, that was part of his struggle, having to wage it clandestinely. From Nietzsche to Mersjohann.

On reaching home he said it was high time he spent a few hours watching TV to attune his ear to American speech. Lena fled instantly to her room. Sabina sat down beside him. They happened to turn on a commercial. With outlandish sounds and even more outlandish grimaces, people were praising some kind of candy bar, as if their purpose were to scare viewers away from those first crisp, then chewy bars that melted in the mouth. Next a girl appeared on the screen, a jogger against a background of trees and grass. Halm leaped up, switched off the set, switched it on again in case Sabina wanted to go on watching—he . . . he was too tired after their long day. Sabina wanted to go on watching for a bit. He went downstairs and to bed. That must have been her. But that was impossible. But it *was* her. But it couldn't have been her. But if it had really been her. A girl running through a shady, idyllic landscape, in slow motion, her legs, her shorts, her T-shirt, her hair, herself. The caption: "Milk. It does a body good." After long, floating leaps and bounds she drank a glass of milk. Did he have such a poor memory for faces? Or was it because of a certain universal quality in her face? Or was it her? She also drank only milk! She went jogging twice a day! Jogging was obviously her top priority! Idiot! As if a commercial spot must have any connection with reality! Yet why shouldn't it happen once in a while?

When Sabina came to bed he wasn't asleep yet. When she was asleep, he was still awake. What tormented him most was that he had not objected when the Roughnecks had called the girl "the dumb beauty." Rainer had been the first and the most frequent to call her this. Why hadn't Halm told them that he had just read an excellent essay by that dumb beauty? A-plus. But had he defended the girl the others would simply have taken it for a confession, not only that he was chasing an undergraduate but that he also was giving her better marks than she deserved: the very thing that must not happen to a teacher. He went on manipulating the scenario until he came to the conclusion that he could consider himself lucky to have caught Rainer out in such a crassly superficial attitude. Merely because a student was of ordinarily pleasant appearance, Rainer was persecuting her with a contempt that excluded all true perception. If that wasn't flagrant injustice! This made him feel good. Also the fact that he would never have called the girl "beautiful" made him feel good. Was she beautiful? Not for a second had he ever called her or thought of her as "beautiful." He still wasn't sure what had made her stand out in his eyes from all the others. But it had not been "beauty." Surely he could believe that of himself. Or couldn't he? Was there anything left that he could still believe of himself?

9

WHEN HE LEFT THE HOUSE on Monday and insisted that from now on he would drive himself, Sabina pretended to be hurt: he was trying to be independent of her, she could see that. He pretended to be caught out. Since they were still in the living room, he caught sight of himself grinning in the mirror. When he grinned he looked unattractive. My God, he knew that, didn't he? Laughing and grinning didn't suit him. But he hadn't realized he looked that repulsive when he grinned. So, remain serious. Lugubrious, that suits you. He hoped he'd never laughed in the presence of the girl. So off to the campus alone today. Lena doesn't want to continue. She quotes Jamey: "Only crackpots study." She'll be picked up by Elissa and taken along to Orinda, to the driving school. Lena feels that she is needed.

Halm drove nervously along Shattuck Avenue through Berkeley to Oakland, turned left up the hill, and drove for a while toward the curving white bulk of the Claremont Hotel. It was in there that Elissa had judged Rainer to be the right man, and Rainer had thought it was the start of a fairy tale. With each thing Halm noticed on the way, he wondered whether it might be a subject for his conversation class. He always had a reserve of political or ideological themes to draw on but he preferred direct experiences. Why shouldn't each student describe his Monday morning route to school? That would demand the kind of words one normally uses, and he would find out where the girl came from this Monday morning. For the girl on crutches it might be embarrassing to have to describe how she got to school. He decided on an abstract theme.

But that morning the handicapped student was absent. He was glad. "So here we go, let's brighten things up a bit." The girl said nothing. Even when his eyes moved only as far as Jeff, he could see that she quickly lowered her eyes to her clasped ankle. She didn't want to be obliged by his gaze to participate. The most surprising account of a morning route came from Jeff. He earns money as a janitor and busboy at the Faculty Club. At night he cleans. In the morning he clears away breakfast and sets the tables for lunch, then jumps onto his racing bike and rides to Coit Hall. So Halm's conversation themes were not to blame for Jeff's yawning and fatigue. Halm looked at Jeff while he was giving his report. Halm had also once had such spiky brown hair. The eyes were familiar to him too. Did he have Halm's eyes? Yes, he had Halm's eyes. Color and shape. But Jeff had always seemed to him like a brother of the girl. Halm looked at the girl, she looked at Jeff. Halm wanted desperately to be able to look into her eyes from as close up as possible. Later, during their consultation. He also had to find out if it really hadn't been she who had floated in slow-motion leaps through the shady grass and then drunk the milk being advertised.

After class, because once again she was accompanying him, he headed not for Fillmore Hall but for the Student Union Plaza. His back was hurting him. The girl only wanted to tell him that she wouldn't be coming for the consultation until the next day, if he didn't mind. He nodded but tried to avoid any suggestion of a smile. After she had left, he walked toward the bridge. For a moment he had seen the girl full-face. She had Jeff's eyes. Jeff's look. And Jeff had Halm's eyes and look. So she had too. Halm's eyes were his only feature that he could not only bear but actually like.

When he sat down on the chair by Carol's desk, she shook her head like a judge who no longer understands the accused. She couldn't be indifferent, she said, to the way he treated his old friend, since this friend happened to be her boss, to whom she was devoted. So much for that! On the other hand she was glad that the sexist skat orgy had turned into a disaster. But why did poor old Rainer always have to bear the brunt! "Tell me, what do you think of Roy and Leslie? Oh no, excuse me, I take back the question, I can do without your predictable ecstatic reaction. Yet I'd really be interested in knowing your opinion of those two." Halm replied that, intimidated as he was by her, he must reluctantly keep his enthusiasm for these two gentlemen to himself. And Carol: He knew as well as she did that, as long as one hasn't said anything bad about a person, one hasn't said anything at all about him. His jejune enthusiasm was all right for the first week. But a person who in the third week divulged as little of his thoughts as he did seemed a positive menace.

Halm said: "Tell me about Rainer." Rainer, said Carol, after being forced by Halm's disgusting behavior to leave his own car, had arrived back at his house, totally exhausted, after trudging for hours through the treacherous dangers of the night. Halm said: "That's his version." Carol: O.K., Halm had been there too. Halm said he would waive a counterversion; besides, he had work to do. "It's gradually becoming insufferable here." Carol crowed with delight: "At last! At last some words from the heart!" As he was about to leave she reminded him of his box. "More material from Felix Theodor Auster!" she cried. "And from Leslie Ackerman and from our mini-Solzhenitsyn, Dempewolf! To be read by Helmut Halm, that's this season's ultimate desire! Your consistent readiness to eulogize, not yet recognized as such, is balm to a campus geared to spiteful whisperings. Read, eulogize, exploit your talent for mendacity, sir!" By the way, simply because the coming weekend coincides with Yom Kippur, Halm and his wife and daughter were not being invited to Grizzly Peak Boulevard, but the following Saturday they were expected to turn up to praise the master of the house and not just to disparage the mistress. Yes, that's the way it was, to her he was mean while he flattered everyone else. When all was said and done, he had an excellent instinct for when he could afford to let himself go and when he had to make an effort. She wasn't about to sing a paean of praise on Messmer's gift for communicating with people, but Halm could learn a thing or two from that intriguing young man. Incidentally she had put a little book by Messmer into his box, she'd be interested to know what he thought of it.

He stuffed whatever he could into his briefcase, saying he would pick up the rest tomorrow. He had parked the car by the wall of the football bowl. He relished the heat. He also relished the thought that all those people he couldn't get along with at home were now asleep. This, even more than the distance, protected him. At that moment he simply had nothing to fear from Messrs. Kiderlen and Rimmele. But this sense of well-being, of having escaped, was enough to trigger a warning: Feel nothing, live for the day, as shallowly as possible. But how could he do that here? This land was an invitation to live big, act big, talk big. The heat, the gas stations, the blacks, the women, the treetops, the luscious gardens, the parched hills, the dogs walking dreamily across the street, and how that's respected, and the light, that light—as Sabina says—which sets everything apart. . . .

In the *Campus Gazette* he read that on Sunday afternoon the rapist had attacked three more women. So Rainer is not the rapist. Rainer is the opposite. Rainer does only that which furthers justice. But for that he would do anything. If there were a law declaring rape to be a punishment, Rainer would take charge of the execution. How can you have such thoughts about your best friend! Punish yourself for this repulsive idea. Phone Rainer at once, the moment you get home, and apologize for your thoughts. But if you phone him he'll think you want to apologize for what happened on the drive home, or earlier . . . and all the time it had really been Rainer . . . disgusting behavior indeed! Some version, that—all one can do is remain silent, shrivel up, long for Kirk Elrod, the only person without power over you.

On the table another of those colorful meals emanating from the Monterey farmers' market. Then he made the coffee. They sat comfortably looking across at San Francisco as it lay quivering in the heat. Sabina couldn't resist picking up one of the magazines that the professor's wife had piled up on a little table beside the sofa. She flipped through the pages. Instinctively, as it were, he groaned a little. She looked up. He made a face appropriate to the groaning. Now, of course, Sabina had to ask whether there was something the matter. He pointed a bit dramatically to his spine. Sabina immediately went off for the bee venom. She made him lie down on the sofa in the sunshine. He confessed how much he enjoyed Sabina massaging him with the ointment.

When she had finished, he drew her down beside him onto the sofa, where there wasn't enough room for two to lie side by side. He pressed Sabina against the back of the sofa and said something suggestive that probably aroused him more than it did Sabina. He didn't say that since her mother's operation they had been living side by side with little or no physical contact. He didn't say that every evening she had used her mother's dainty little slippers as a barrier against him. He didn't say: We're alone, Sabina, the sun is shining on us, and over there floats San Francisco. At that moment a white helicopter made its way across the glittering bay like an exemplary sperm traversing the blue of the sky. He didn't say that either. He fell upon Sabina in a way that reminded him of the rapist. He was stimulated by the grossness of the situation. Their partially bared hips and thighs in the dazzling sunshine. Not enough room. Not enough atmosphere. No atmosphere at all. Sabina endured the unlovely performance with devastating stoicism. It occurred to Halm that by contrast the screams and struggles of those rape victims outside must have acted as sheer stimulation. Perhaps he was trying to prove that Sabina and he could go through with something as terrible as this sexual intercourse in the blazing heat of the midday sun on the most unsuitable sofa in the world without subsequently murdering each other. He managed to produce one single word: "Sorry."

To punish himself, he called up Rainer and talked in such a loud voice that Sabina was bound to hear through the open door how hard it was for him to make this call and how arbitrary were the accusations against which he had once again to defend himself. "Carol claims it was my disgusting behavior that drove you out of your own car!" he shouted into the phone. "I'd like to hear your own explanation for that." For some time he heard nothing. He shouted: "Hallo! Rainer!", whereupon he heard an immensely deep and somehow disembodied voice say: "Yes." Had Rainer understood? Again that deep, murmured, disembodied "yes." Could Rainer explain to him what he had been obliged to listen to from Carol? Silence. Then an equally deep, disembodied, free-floating "No." Yes and No, equally calm, devoid of emphasis. Halm was at a loss. "Hm," he said. He could hear Rainer's heavy breathing. He must be awash in alcohol, thought Halm, and said, making his voice as plaintive and long-suffering as possible: "But who, if not you, is to explain to me why Carol claims that my disgusting behavior drove you out of your car?" Rainer continued his audible heavy breathing, then repeated in that same calm, deep voice: "Yes." Halm said: "O.K. then. Take care." Rainer said: "Yes." And hung up.

Halm went back to Sabina. "The main thing is we're in California," he said. Emigration as emancipation. He must get down to reading Heine. At the moment only the love poems appealed to him: that was how to deal with suffering.

Next day, when Halm stepped onto the gloomy, windowless landing, the girl was already standing outside 407-F. The entire gloomy space was centered on her pink blouse. Grotesque, this girl's figure on this landing that combined all the architectural nightmares of the nineteenth century. To prevent her watching his fingers while he inserted the key in the lock, he pointed to the dark, colorless pile of books beside the fire-escape hole. "Interesting books," he said. She turned to look, he unlocked the door, she went in and sat down. There she was, looking at him out of his own eyes. Why hadn't he noticed that and mentioned it in the first second? Why didn't she notice it? She let the broad strap of her bag slip from her shoulder, the soft, round, aubergine-colored bag lay . . . no, poured itself over her smooth denim thighs. So she always dressed up for their consultation. "Do you like brownies?" she asked, offering him something of a chocolatey nature. He answered hastily: "No, thank you." And then even grinned. Just as well he hadn't become an actor: he would make a mess of every entrance. Every single one. No grinning! And then he goes and grins! Sitting four feet away from her in the glaring neon light and grinning! And refusing brownies! Had he accepted those things from her hand, he might even have touched her hand. Since people don't shake hands here, he will only have one more chance to touch the girl. In December, when he says good-bye. Forever.

She ate brownies. She took a manuscript out of her bag. A white roll held together by a red rubber band. She pulled off the rubber band and unrolled the pages. She had been given an A for this essay. Never before had she received such a mark for an essay. She felt very embarrassed now, she said. She had no gift for essay writing. She wasn't born to it, a certain Mrs. Cerf had told her in high school. Halm said that everyone was born to it. Since her blouse was fairly open he could see how tanned the girl was. Her hair now neon-platinum. So where was he supposed to look? On a bookshelf he saw a sign: DON'T DISTURB. EXAMS IN PROGRESS. That should be hung outside on the door. Under the protection of that sign. . . .

So now on to a new subject. Shakespeare. If you don't mind. Might she read aloud some of her thoughts about the sonnet? Halm, quickly, would she please first read the sonnet aloud? She read it:

Th' expense of spirit in a waste of shame
Is lust in action; and till action, lust
Is perjur'd, murderous, bloody, full of blame,

Savage, extreme, rude, cruel, not to trust;
Enjoy'd no sooner, but despised straight;
Past reason hunted; and no sooner had,
Past reason hated, as a swallow'd bait,
On purpose laid to make the taker mad:
Mad in pursuit, and in possession so;
Had, having, and in quest to have, extreme;
A bliss in proof,—and prov'd, a very woe;
Before, a joy propos'd; behind, a dream:
All this the world well knows; yet none knows well
To shun the heaven that leads men to this hell.

He looked at the indecently soft, purplish bag spread over the denim thighs. He thought: Hölderlin, here we go. How a poem melts on the lips of a native speaker of English! Her very lips seem to melt. Branches caressing their tree with blossoms. The road rises to kiss the knee. I feel a bit dazzled. Probably from being so close. He asked her to read the sonnet once again; he would then supply the German translation after each line. He wanted to interject German into this passionate English. In language as inflated as possible.

Geistverlust in Schamverschleiß
ist Lust, die loslegt, vorher ist Lust
verlogen, mörderisch, blutrünstig, kriminell,
roh, rücksichtslos, primitiv, grausam, unberechenbar;
wahnsinnig begehrt und, kaum gehabt,
wahnsinnig verabscheut, wie ein geschluckter Köder,
gelegt nur, den Geköderten verrückt zu machen,
verrückt im Wollen und im Haben auch;
danach, dabei und davor, rücksichtslos;
das Probieren, Wonne; probiert, das pure Weh';
vorher, ein Freudenbild; nachher, Geträum.
Jeder weiß das, doch keiner weiß,

wie den Himmel meiden, der ihn in diese Hölle
reißt.

Because he interjected his lines with such force, she raised her voice with every line she read. Finally they were both shouting. "Let's do it again, right now!" he said. The second time he followed more accurately on each of her lines than the first time. She had even stopped eating brownies. For a while there was silence, the only sounds being the hum of the air-conditioning and the faint high whine of the neon lighting.

Halm said: "Now let's have it." She read the thoughts that had come to her. As before, she recorded where she had been sitting as she wrote. On the terrace of her parents' house in Mill Valley. (Mill Valley was where Stabler's Eileen had gone for her ice cream, Halm thought.) She had sat under a pergola of wild grape vines, looking into the house: She would rather have sat looking down into the valley that is so overgrown that one can't see very far. Yet all the things one does see there! She wouldn't be able to write a single sentence. Everywhere that lush, pulsating green. Everything so near. She knows that even without looking. Inside the house she sees her friend Susan laughing and talking to Glenn, Fran's boyfriend. But Glenn is sitting where Fran can't see him from her place on the terrace. She wouldn't be able to write if she could see her boyfriend. From time to time Susan conveys by pantomime how the boyfriend happens to be sitting, where he happens to be looking. Although Glenn is aware that Susan is signaling something to Fran, he doesn't realize that he is the subject of these messages. He is the all-American boy. Star of the university's water polo team. Medical student. A person who joins in laughter out of politeness. He means everything he says. And he says everything he means. Thoroughly reliable. Should she long to finish this essay as quickly as possible in order to have her WPP (as she calls her water polo player) back as soon as possible? Or should she sit here and go on writing as long as possible and discover only from Susan's extraordinary gift for pantomime that her WPP is growing restless indoors? They had agreed: he would not be allowed outside until she had finished her essay. She is amused that he is keeping to the bargain. But that's how he is, reliable. If she were to go on writing until ten at night, Glenn would have to leave without having touched her. Tomorrow he has an NCAA game, in the Belmont Plaza pool at Long Beach, so he has to go to bed at ten. He's hoping to be chosen this season as the NCAA Most Valuable Player. Maybe he's just showing off. On the other hand, showing off is not his style. He is terribly serious. He lives only a few hundred yards away. Now she's only writing to annoy him. Let's see whether he stays inside and, when it's time for him to leave, does so without their having even touched. She enjoys tormenting him. But she's not sure whether it really does torment him for her to sit here writing while he stays indoors. Susan is doing too good a job entertaining him. Susan is probably the only one to benefit from this unnatural situation. No, she herself is benefiting too. . . . *till action, lust/Is perjur'd.*

Susan has just signaled that Glenn is beginning to overheat. Maybe Susan is lying. Surely Glenn would never show that he can't carry on without Fran another minute. She has an idea: she'll have Glenn read this Shakespeare sonnet. She's pretty sure he won't understand a word of it. *Had, having, and in quest to have, extreme,* what's all that, he'll say, I can't see any difference. He's always in the same good mood, before, during, after. That's not to say she doesn't have a constant underlying mood herself. She would call it melancholic. Only sometimes when she's running or swimming she's not melancholic. But otherwise always. Always, always, always.

Susan is signaling that the WPP can't wait any longer. She won't stop writing. She can't remember ever having had such an urge to write. She just hopes she won't run out of sentences. Let's see whether he actually leaves the house through the dining room and the kitchen. If he were to leave the way he came, he would pass the terrace door, would see her and she would see him—that would run counter to their agreement. He will reach the hall and the front door through the kitchen. He is serious. Deadly serious. And she can be glad he is. "He's gone!" Susan calls. She could stop now. Tomorrow he'll be flying to Long Beach. She's glad that for two days he won't be here. On the other hand it also makes her sad. She is always just as sad as she is glad. She doesn't understand Shakespeare either. Maybe she shouldn't even try to write an essay on this sonnet. Because of lack of involvement. . . .

She looked up, looked at Halm, out of his eyes. Halm was at a loss. She said anxiously: "But you mustn't believe that that's how it was. Never. It's all my invention." "Or an answer," said Halm. Because he said no more, she spoke. Yesterday she hadn't joined in the conversation about the route to school because on Sunday evening, when she'd been driving over from Mill Valley, she'd had an accident. She reaches the point where the road divides, just before Richmond Bridge, at the San Quentin penitentiary; for a moment she's forgotten, left or right; by the time she remembers she has, in spite of braking, driven up onto the concrete dividers. Both front tires flat, wheels damaged, herself held in by her seat belt and bawling. And obviously she hadn't wanted to talk about that in class. Could he understand that? He nodded because he always nods. What he really ought to have said was: "Too bad you didn't talk about it—landing with a Porsche onto concrete dividers, that's quite something!"

From what she had written, could he see the makings of an essay? It was terrible, she said, the way she depended on him. If he hadn't helped her get an A in her last essay, she would have stopped coming to him. But, since he had, he was stuck with her. That Mrs. Cerf in high school—in handing back her essays she'd always told her in front of the whole class: "You have as much imagination as a BART ticket machine." From then on Fran had referred to Mrs. Cerf exclusively as "Hitler." However, she'll invite her to her Ph.D. party. She had vowed that to herself. But ever since then she has known she can't write essays. Funny, through Halm she has almost plucked up enough courage again. Professor

Mersjohann always wanted her to go for a drive in his dreadful car to discuss her essays. "We'll just cruise around, that stimulates the imagination." She was sure he meant well. But after that she preferred not to consult him at all. Had Halm seen Mersjohann's car? Wasn't it an absolute horror?

Perhaps she was talking away like that because she was afraid of his opinion of her draft. He finally had to interrupt her. He liked her draft, he said. Toward the end she had reached the point from which the path led directly to Shakespeare's theme, and again she had reached this point in the most natural manner. He asked her please not to change anything, merely to go on trying to react to her experiences in words that revealed her to herself more clearly than had her actual experiences. She got up, and her radiance seemed to grow as she stood. She was happy now, she said. After the brownies she had put some chewing gum in her mouth. He hoped she wouldn't produce bubbles that burst on her lips. She chewed as if in slow motion. As if she were dreaming. He wasn't being presumptuous, she did have his eyes. They were also his grandmother's eyes. Close-set, two plumstone shapes, filled with gray-blue. He also got up. The purplish round bag hung once more over the shoulder of her pink blouse. A great drop of purple. He regretted not having been around when the pimples that had left those minute craters at the corners of her mouth had been in bloom.

She left the room; he sat down again. From above, the cold air showered down. Apparently he was no longer capable of remembering sweater and scarf before leaving the Rinehart house. So she had actually left. Thank God. He mulled over the words she had left behind. All-American boy. WPP. Most Valuable Player. Whatever he had thought or imagined about this girl was now really pulverized, destroyed. The problem had ceased to exist. The thirty-three years alone should have been enough. Now, as if more were needed, an all-American water polo player. Once again a *He*-Halm split off from his *I*. *He* refused to be accessible to any logic. *He* still clung to the timeless moment of the duo-recital. A sonnet performed with two mouths. That was all *he* wanted to talk about. *He* refused absolutely to listen to reason. *He* was profoundly stupid. Why do you refuse brownies, you idiot? That was *he*. *I*-Halm cold and contemptuous: I don't like brownies. *He*-Halm: Have you any idea what brownies taste like? *I*-Halm: No. *He*-Halm: There you are then. *I*-Halm: Even so. *He*-Halm: Oh.

Halm rushed out of his office. Outside in the noonday sun, the undulating campus paths, for once almost empty. The people still moving moved slowly. In the grass a few student monuments. Halm also slowed down; he didn't want to be conspicuous. Before reaching the humpback bridge, he saw a couple ahead of him that had to stop every few paces. Finally the pair couldn't move on at all. They stopped, turned toward each other as if steered by some external force, and stood closely face to face. Just as Halm has to walk past them, they sink completely into one another with their mouths. Halm tried to quicken his step.

Next morning the girl joined him again as he left Coit Hall, so he couldn't head for Fillmore. He had to fake a desire for coffee to justify a turn in the direction of Union Plaza. By stopping at the fountain, she indicated that she had to turn off downhill, under the trees. Toward the bowl. He gazed after her. Every day he made up his mind to leave the girl on the plaza before she could leave him. All he had to do, when they had reached the point between fountain and newspaper bin, was to stop for barely a second and walk on, toward the cafeteria. It takes less than a second to say: Well—see you tomorrow. And while one is speaking one is already the person who walks on. Then *she's* left high and dry. But each day there he stood, limp, heavy, as if numbed, incapable of exerting any power. She talked, smiled, said good-bye, turned, left. *He* was left high and dry, staring after her like a dog after its master when it has been given the command: Sit.

He had some coffee or he didn't, in any case got himself a *Gazette* and read—and to him this was the ultimate proof that he wasn't the same person here as he was at home—he read the sports section, he read that the water polo team had won at Long Beach.

Of seven goals, three were credited to Glenn Birdsell. There was even a picture of him, rearing out of the water up to his nipples, the ball held aloft in his right hand as he swung his arm back for a mighty throw. In front of him, a small head in the water, his outmaneuvered opponent, too late to obstruct him. The swim cap made Glenn Birdsell's head small, too. Dominating the picture, in the midst of the foam that he had whirled up, were the bulging muscles of his shoulders and upper arms. He looked almost wonderful.

After lunch Halm first had to pick up the *Gazette* again to study the account of the victory at Long Beach as carefully as if it had been written by Shakespeare. Sabina said: "Now you're even getting interested in water polo." Halm said: "Yes, it's amazing." They drank their coffee and gazed out onto the shimmering Bay. Halm said: "Kiderlen is asleep. Rimmele is asleep. The Spanish Fly is asleep." Sabina has received a letter from Juliane. Juliane has broken off with the man who is twenty-two years older than she. His conversation had degenerated into a string of complaints about his family, from which he couldn't tear himself away. All day long, geriatric care, then more of the same in the evening: that was more than she could take! She was using her newly acquired free time to learn Portuguese. Fantastic how much one could learn in a short time. She planned to go to Brazil. Halm nodded. And that fellow was only twenty-two years older! Geriatric care! Thank you, deardear Juliane!

Now Halm wanted to hear from Sabina that he and Sabina were happy. Now. One couldn't ask for more. Was it enough? For her? Sabina said: "Are you trying to convince yourself of something?" He said he looked forward to California red wine every evening. He went over to Sabina, drew her out of her armchair, and asked for a harmless, uncompromising little kiss. She remained suspicious. "No kiss, then," he said. "Your breath's not all that good," she said. Her down-to-earth tone of concern proved that these words were not spoken in order to ward off a kiss. After all, Sabina was his doctor. Was something the matter? "You," he said. Something that was hurting, she meant. "You," he said. Then he'd go back to his Heine, he said. Back in the study he sat in the uncomfortable armchair and read the light poems about suffering.

Around five he opened the bottle. From six o'clock on he drank the heavy, dusky, roughish wine, which made him feel even better. He became bold, active. He phoned Rainer and invited him and Elissa for Saturday. Since he had now, no matter how unwillingly, put the girl behind him, and for good, he was able to heap cheerful abuse on Rainer and to complain that they hadn't been having any fun together, all they'd had was misunderstandings. He had only come here to please Rainer, so how about it? And Saturday was Sabina's and his wedding anniversary, their twenty-sixth, and the only people he wanted to see were Rainer and Elissa.

The more openly Halm celebrated marriage, the more friendly Rainer became. Since he had decided to postpone putting down his ideas on Schubert's text interpretation until the following week, he'd be happy to come. Whether Elissa would join them, who could tell! He would ask her, provided he managed to reach her, if only by phone, between now and Saturday. But perhaps Lena could deliver the invitation to Elissa? It seemed that Lena was on fantastic terms with Elissa.

On Saturday neither Elissa nor Lena turned up. With the help of an electrician they were putting up a string of lights around the lot on which Elissa intended to sell her used cars. So Rainer, Sabina, and Halm spent the evening alone. Rainer was disconcertingly subdued. Mostly he talked about Lena. Lena was going to bring peace to him and Elissa. Not that he was placing any demands on Lena. Lena was simply his sole, his last hope. Lena was undoubtedly a strong girl pregnant with hope. Perhaps her strength derived from the fact that she wanted nothing for herself. She seemed to manage without accepting from others. But she couldn't bear having to witness a lack, a failure, a misfortune, in others. She didn't interfere, he said, but it was plain to see that whatever happened to others turned into suffering for herself. On the rare occasions when he spoke to Elissa—only by phone, of course—Lena was for the moment her sole topic, that was to say the sole topic that enabled Elissa and him to carry on a harmonious conversation. As soon as they spoke about anything else, it took less than five—less than three—minutes for one of them to bang down the receiver. They could only have long peaceful talks about Lena. Then he asked as briskly as one asks the time: "Who can help us if not the weak?"

Halm was almost offended that Rainer should know so much about Lena. Or was it because Rainer was teaching Sabina and himself so much about their child? Sabina nodded, beamed, seemed unable to get enough of this kind of teaching. So he would try and be satisfied too. It was high time that there should be harmony among them. And at once Halm felt privileged to have such a friend. The fear that Rainer might be about to say something terrible again had almost entirely disappeared. At last he could ask Rainer whether he was still writing poetry. Rainer turned slowly toward Halm like a battleship but then remained quite calm, saying merely that he thanked Halm for the Amfortas question. They would soon both be having dinner with the writer-in-residence, where there'd be ample talk about this vain occupation. Then he started talking about Jamey, a topic with which he continued until he had nothing more to say.

When Rainer reached the point of being able only to snort and gasp like a drowning man, Halm and Sabina drove him in his car to the Tudor and Hansel-and-Gretel house, into which he vanished as into a tomb. Hand in hand they walked down the dark streets and lanes, looking into the fabulous houses where men and women were sitting under lamps and around tables as in illustrations from nineteenth-century novels. Lena did not come home that night. Halm said half to himself: " 'He who cannot lead the way/Also cannot lead astray.'! Do you hear me, Sabina?" "Vaguely," said Sabina. "That's the trouble," he said. On the other hand, he went on, the knowledge that Sabina and he were alone in the house that night was having its effect on him. "What's more, we're in

California. Are there two human beings who must tread a longer path toward each other than you, Sabina, and I, when it comes to staging an encounter which, as lightly as possible, I would like to call: SI? It can go wrong, Sabina. Each time is as risky as the first time. It requires precisely the right dose of humor—a mite too much and all is lost. Goodnight, Sabina," he said. And since she said nothing, he persevered.

He initiated the staging, which was apparently his responsibility, by picking up the dainty little slippers from Sabina's side of the bed, carrying them ceremoniously out of the room, and placing them on the floor outside. Now, he said, he dared approach her. When he was close to her, he asked whether she would consent to being drawn into the passionate whispering that was all part of the scenario. Thanks to the thundering and rattling of the brass triumphal gate against the wall, everything verbal was fortunately submerged in a ludicrous racket. They should have headboards like that in hotel rooms, then the people next door would be as intimidated as he had been in that hotel in Grado. Ever since that night he was no longer such an innocent. Ever since then he'd been governed by the notion that, during SI that does not serve procreation, one is nothing but a hamster on its wheel. One was made to move because one was supposed to do something that nature wished one to do. But in order actually to do it, everything is so arranged that it proceeds as if it were done not under orders but of one's own volition. There was nothing one desired as much as that. There was nothing one would rather do than that. And yet one is merely the agent of the program.

Halm felt he'd been had. And this fusion with love! . . . *swallow'd bait,/On purpose laid to make the taker mad.* In what way, one may wonder, does the self-importance during SI differ from that at a rifle competition? One shoots at targets and pretends that they are bears. But where is that not so? Ah, Sabina, let us alleviate that which we are not to be spared. From this pseudoservice all the way to the so-called final breath. If it has to be, then let it be with you. You know that. What bothers me is all this embellishing.

Isn't it enough to make a person scream, all those linguistic emanations which our culture offers for the sanctification of SI? Maybe one should be "creative" after all—what do you think, Sabina? Sabina knew that was a word that always grated on Halm.

That night Halm told Sabina that what he regretted most about this compulsory reciprocal approaching-attaching-penetrating was that he could only insert such a small part of himself into her. He longed to insert more. Much more. Best of all would be if he could disappear entirely inside her. And forever. So that really was his innermost desire. His very innermost. His very most innermost. And one must give credit to life for endowing no moment more loftily and intensely than that in which the seed is launched. Even if it be illusion, it is without peer. Come.

Each behaved as if satisfied with each other. It is even possible that they were. He was surely more satisfied than Sabina because now he felt totally saved. The girl evaporated and melted away in the face of the solid front put up by Helmut and Sabina as a couple. Halm believed that the staging also required that he bring back her dead mother's dainty little slippers from outside the door and place them under the bed on Sabina's side.

But then when the girl drew the roll of paper with her *Th' expense of spirit* essay out of her purple bag and handed it to him, his breathing did stop again for a moment, and in a kind of unconsciousness for which he did not feel responsible he heard himself saying: "If you like, I'll read it right away, at our table, if you'd care for a glass of milk meanwhile. . . ." So there they sat again as they had in August. As they had with the panther poem. As they had a month ago. Nothing can be longer ago. He read, then he looked up and said: "In the sun the color of your hair is different from in my office." The girl's closed lips shifted slightly. That reminded him that she was expecting to hear something else from him. So he said: "Marvelous, every word of it. Congratulations." He'd love to keep this essay. He was welcome to, she had brought along this copy for him.

Only when she had walked away between the tables—the blue

shorts with their rounded hems stopped just above the level of the tables—did he come to his senses again. He wanted to call after her, run after her, to tell her that his judgment was warped by his downright heroic struggle to be objective. He hadn't been able to read at all. He had skimmed the lines, aware of who was sitting across from him, with no idea as to what he was going to say. So then that enthusiasm had burst out of him. He should have at least told the girl that it seemed as though, here in California, he was capable of producing only one tone of voice—that of enthusiasm. Would she please go and see Carol, who could prove better than anyone else how absurdly small that modicum of reality was in every one of Halm's enthusiastic utterances. It was quite true that he was enthusiastic about her essay, but it was precisely in this enthusiasm that he was aware of his diminished responsibility. Did that stem merely from Carol's criticism?

He must go and see Carol at once. As quickly as his spine would allow. It was only on the chair in front of Carol's desk that he would discover how he was being judged at the moment. Yesterday he hadn't sat on that chair, nor the day before! Perhaps those who had acquired tenure at this university could afford to sit on Carol's chair only once a semester; he could not. Carol again complained about his rare and always fleeting appearances; asked him what he thought of this person or that; mocked his tendency to think well of everybody; almost burst into tears because people considered her abrasive and bad tempered while actually she would much prefer to be stroked. Then came the ultimate mockery: that there were, of course, some people by whom even she, pathetic as she was, couldn't bear to be stroked. She considered this aversion to consolation at any price to be a utopian phosphorescence on the gray face of her watch. Perhaps everything was a fairy tale after all. Perhaps she hadn't been washed up on this shining coast merely to function as a bib for drooling intellectuals. Perhaps one day her prince would come! What did that smart Halm think? That Halm was among the smartest, the craftiest, she knew without having inspected his urine. Saturday, then, at Grizzly Peak Boulevard?

Would his daughter be coming too? One hears the most extraordinary things about her. The divine Elissa, for whom anyone beneath the rank of Montezuma no longer exists, has taken the little angel from Germany with the ruffled wings totally to her high-carat heart. But that such a thing can happen is what keeps the spark of hope alive in the universal rain of ashes. Is her father happy now?

How Carol, who was so fond of talking, still managed to acquire all her information was a mystery to him. As soon as he could, he tore himself away from the beguiling talker, was called back again, and obediently picked up the flood of paper from his box. And because he had responded inadequately to Carol's outburst, and because he felt this was the right moment to mention it, he told her that, whenever he came to his box, he read the name KAROLA VON DER HÜTTE on the next box and every time neglected to ask who that was. Carol raised her hand as if in school, then said impatiently: "There's Messmer for you. He refused to accept that I'm now called Elrod. When he found out my maiden name, he immediately pinned it up there. Kirk mustn't see that." Of all Messmer's deeds, this was so far the most impressive, said Halm.

In his office he read the essay on *Th' expense of spirit in a waste of shame*. He positively scoured the lines for characterizations of her boyfriend. This boyfriend, she writes, *has very unique characteristics. He is bright, clean, handsome, and organized. The only problem with the perfect dream boy is his seriousness and his very reserved sense of humor.* How interesting! And, even more interesting: *He is virtually nonexcitable and has hunched shoulders, drawn up around his ears.* Just a moment: What does this mean? He is virtually nonexcitable. Does she mean "imperturbable," or "not easily aroused"? Certainly she means that he is a fairly calm type. That fits in with *bright, clean, handsome, and organized.* So what we have is a fairly calm type with *hunched shoulders, drawn up around his ears.* So his muscular shoulders rise right up to his ears. That was exactly what Halm had seen in the *Gazette*, as a supertorso enthroned in the foamy water, throwing another "unanswered goal." And yet and yet and yet . . . didn't these lines contain a trace of dissatisfaction on the part of the girl? Wasn't this all-American dream boy just a little too calm? So what. He had put the girl behind him. If he had anything to regret, it was not that this totally impossible relationship with the girl could never acquire even the slightest reality, but that the unattainability of this girl didn't mean all that much to him. Who says so? *I*-Halm. You should know, says *He*-Halm. *I*-Halm: Showoff! *He*-Halm: Cadaver! No further reaction from *I*-Halm. Silence.

The sounds from the air-conditioning and the neon lighting dominated the room with the emptiest of all imaginable chords. Outside resounded Professor Torres's Latin American laugh, gracefully matched today by a girlish soprano. Carol had told him that once, at a dean's party, Torres and Othello Jesús de García, who were standing far apart in the crowded room, had burst out laughing at the same moment, and she, Carol, about halfway between the two, had felt as if she had never been as insulted in her life as by that resounding duet of male smugness.

When Halm and Sabina arrived at Grizzly Peak Boulevard, Carol was wearing a slit skirt. Not to look there when she walked would have been like looking in the direction where there was no lightning during a thunderstorm. Sabina asked at once, and not merely out of courtesy, where Carol had managed to get those magnificent stocks lining the steep path from Grizzly Peak Boulevard all the way up to the house. "From Weimar," said Carol. Her mother had been born in Weimar, and when at the age of sixteen she and her parents were kicked out of there by the Nazis she had taken some stock seeds with her. Sabina said this meant that these were the most authentic stocks she had ever seen: after all, stocks had been Goethe's favorite flowers. "Right!" exclaimed Carol, right, her mother had always said that too. Halm felt that until now he had never for one second taken Carol seriously. Always that tactless manner.

Since the Halms were the first guests, they were given a brief tour. One room was dedicated to Carol's parents. Table, chairs, desk, couch, musical instruments, all as if in a museum. Mr. von der Hütte is a collector of musical instruments. A musician. At the première of *The Threepenny Opera*, he played in the orchestra. For the last seventeen years he has been living with his wife in a nursing home in Mendocino. She looks after him. He had a stroke which left him paralyzed. "My father always had a weakness for volume," Carol said, pointing to the mandolins and lutes as well as to the portrait of her mother that hung behind the instruments and dominated the room. And how beautiful Carol was at this moment as she pointed with her lifted chin and upward-curving fingertip across the instruments to her mother. Her eyes seemed to moisten from the inside and thus become even darker.

"All right, and now have a look at this item—my mother always got the shivers when she picked it up." A small case in the form of an old book; inside, under glass, an ivy leaf, together with a note testifying that in 1862 Carol's great-grandmother, Gretel Dinkelspiel, had personally plucked this leaf from the grave of Goethe's mother in Frankfurt. Halm didn't know what to say. It was enough for Carol to toy with her Berlin dialect for him to feel ill at ease. It sounded not only comical but also terribly grotesque. For the ivy leaf from the Frankfurt cemetery to turn up now on Grizzly Peak Boulevard was equally grotesque. "Item" was what Carol called this memento. Halm felt he ought to make some comment. But he couldn't. Words of sympathy. . . . none of them were suitable. Whatever occurred to him seemed wildly inappropriate. He could think of nothing to say about this ivy leaf from Frankfurt. What would Mr. Kiderlen, who could never do anything wrong, say now? Halm nodded and nodded. Not to be able to say anything gave him a choking feeling.

Fortunately the guests now started to arrive: Leslie Ackerman and his expert on hermaphrodites with her skeletal face and flaxen braids. Rainer and Elissa, and Felix Theodor Auster under his ice-gray frozen flood of hair. Carol announced supper as if she were serving sandwiches; instead, there were Armenian appetizers, boeuf bourgignon, and cream puffs for dessert. Again and again Halm tried to draw the attention of the guests to the food. In vain. Kirk was impatient to know what Halm thought of his books. "Oh yes!" said Carol. "That'll be interesting." Halm worked himself up into his enthusiasm for *Inspiration Inn*. He praised the book and meant the author. Elrod said that everyone praised this book in a way that was insulting to his other books. Felix Theodor Auster said that a conversation about belles lettres should be considered an offense against good manners.

Carol said she didn't want to talk about professorial soufflés or novelistic flapjacks but about things—so, what does our emissary from across the ocean think about the Messmer book? Halm confessed that he hadn't made any headway with it. Carol, cuttingly: "Weakling!" Halm was prompt to admit that. For her that wasn't enough. How about all those other things he doesn't make headway with, slippery opportunist that he is! How about all the things he finds to rave about that she finds absurd! Yet with Messmer's book, he can't make any headway at all! Carol was ablaze. The flickering tendrils of her hair seemed to be speaking with her. Now *she* was rhapsodizing. In contrast to Halm, Messmer had begun immediately to make use of his stay to gather information. He had spent days being guided through all the institutes of the university and then had gone once a day to the center for earthquake research. The San Andreas fault, right next to which, on top of which they were all living here, had fascinated him. All California earthquakes have been caused by the sensitivity of this fault. And Messmer believed that the earth could not tolerate his presence at this its most sensitive point without reacting. Day and night he was waiting for a response from the fault.

Then came the sensation: the response of the fault when he first appeared on Grizzly Peak Boulevard, right here in Carol's house. Messmer turns up at Carol's, and the sewage starts vomiting. The sewage starts vomiting, up here, on September 27, practically two years ago to the day; the drains vomit from every pipe and outlet and, as was established by Messmer's inquiries and our own:

nowhere else, only here in this house, the very moment Messmer set foot in it. Kirk hadn't been at home. He'd been in Long Beach. Watching water polo, thought Halm. "At John Frey's funeral," says Carol. "Aha!" cries Halm. "So there really was a John Frey!" "See? He's managed to make some headway with *your* book!" Carol told Kirk. Kirk said: "Oh yes, John Frey was my friend. He spent his last months in the Veterans' Hospital in Long Beach." And the "Swiss lady"? Halm wanted to ask, but Carol wouldn't be diverted. She had now got to the lingering effects of this sewage vomiting. While she and Messmer were still sitting on the upholstered furniture, looking in dismay and delight at the gigantic mess, the second response came from outside: "The most magnificent thunderstorm I've ever seen! Hundred-degree temperature, with rain, end of September. We never have rain, let alone thunderstorms, in September." She had never seen such lightning, never been so scared by a thunderstorm. As for Messmer, he had immediately called nature's lower and upper rampage a summation of ejaculation and orgasm. Everyone respected Carol's memorial to Messmer except Felix Theodor Auster. "Carol," he said, "you can be proud of having a sewage system that starts vomiting when a fellow like Messmer wants to vent his puny little narcissistic rage."

After dinner they all went out onto the wistaria patio. Halm promptly sat down beside Elissa, who was strikingly pale today. For the first time Halm saw a touch of suffering in her face. At the same time he felt terribly naïve. He would have liked to touch Elissa. To console her. Once again she was wearing something sleeveless. A boyish haircut and such heavy breasts. There is always one woman who exerts the greatest power. That night it was Elissa. So he wanted to sit for as long as possible as close as possible beside her. But hardly had they all sat down, hardly had Halm created a little acoustical enclave with Elissa, when Rainer stood up, groaned, and rushed outside. Leslie Ackerman rose, followed him, came back alone. Carol said: "That's something he just can't stand." "What?" asked Kirk. "Having to watch someone make a play for his wife." "Oh, come on," said Kirk Elrod, "what am *I* supposed to say when you go into ecstasies over Messmer?" Carol gave him such a look that he said: "Honey, I'm sorry," then forcibly changed the subject. "Have I already told you . . . Carol, have I already told the Halms what my second wife's mother said after reading *Inspiration Inn*?" Carol answered: "You haven't told them yet, and, as you see, they're dying to hear about it. I, too, couldn't imagine at the moment what I'd rather do than hear once again what your second wife's mother said after reading *Inspiration Inn*." "*I* could think of something better," cried Auster, "Nietzsche! Our friend is a Nietzsche man. That interests me. When anyone in Europe schedules a Nietzsche lecture these days, he has a full house, no matter who he is—that's what my friends tell me in their letters. I need to have that explained if I'm to understand it. You see, for me Nietzsche is the last major attempt of the philosophical handmaiden to overthrow the priests in order to become the high priestess herself." At last Auster had found his voice. Elrod suffered an attack of cramps, and Carol led him away.

By the end of an evening one no longer knows what one has eaten, what one has heard, what one has talked about. "Sabina, can you remember?" he asked her as she cautiously drove down the hill. She likes Elrod best. So does he. She likes Carol too, though not as much as him. Halm thought: The slit skirt! That had been unfair. Like any advantage. It was beginning to dawn on him what he meant to Carol. A reminder of Messmer. She was scratching at him with increasing fury because, the more violently she scratched, the less Messmer came to light. In Sabina's opinion Carol talked too much and too flippantly about Kirk's age. "But Kirk is the one who always brings up the subject!" said Halm. When Auster asks for some beer with his boeuf, Kirk recalls that three airplanes had been pulling Miller ads across the sky today because a fleet with two carriers, coming from Hawaii, had sailed in under Golden Gate Bridge, bringing ten thousand sailors into town. Ten thousand sailors! How is a man of his age supposed to react to such a sexual invasion, he asks? All day long he hadn't been able to decide what to do. Look across to the city as a voyeurin-imagination, or let down the blinds and read the Bible? So what's Carol to do when he's forever proclaiming the horrors of old age! "But does she really have to say: 'It doesn't have to be ten thousand all at once?' " Sabina asked. "Is that the proper reaction to his suffering over the fleet?" "That's the disadvantage of a house with such a view," said Halm. "One sees too much. In our green crypt in Sillenbuch, no sailor from Hawaii can ever disturb us." "The one I really feel sorry for is Rainer," said Sabina. She must say Carol was right, Helmut should have considered that Rainer didn't have the same washed-out emotional life as everyone else. What did she mean, washed-out emotional life? asked Halm. "He loves," said Sabina. She had never yet met anyone with such acute sensibility and emotional purity as Rainer. He seemed to her like a creature mortally wounded by normal nastiness and depravity. And in the presence of that almost saintly person, that truly suffering human being, he—Helmut—has to stick his nose down the open neck of that strangely cold woman! Sabina was offended. Halm tried diversionary tactics. "Auster is also very nice, of course," he said. Sabina thinks that Auster is like a child who has discovered that one must annoy the grownups if one wants to have their attention. Then she started rhapsodizing again about Rainer. Now Halm understood Carol. A person with that much enthusiasm can get on one's nerves. Yet Sabina's enthusiasm was genuine enough, whereas Carol simply didn't believe in Halm's raptures. It must be very annoying to have to listen to someone's raptures that don't seem genuine even to the person expressing them. Sabina talked about Rainer as if about a better world that survives only in Rainer and is being destroyed with him by a worthless, ruthless counterworld. It was clear that Sabina felt she belonged to Rainer's world whereas Halm belonged to the counterworld. This classification represented something new between them. He said: "Let's hope you're wrong."

As they lay in the big bed under the brass gate, he thought about Elissa. His mind dwelled on that trace of suffering in her face. Like after an earthquake that hasn't quite broken through the surface, he thought. Everything has been shifted a little. Nothing has been destroyed, but nothing is quite intact anymore either. So here one was on the edge of the Andreas fault. In himself, too, nothing was in its old place anymore. These few weeks had changed him. But he could no longer afford change. The weeks had proved that too. If only change were all it was! But he had started on a downhill slide. And before that got out of control he had to call a halt. No more. Everything's fine the way it is. Couldn't be better. That is probably the hardest thing of all: to feel as happy as one is. As one ought to be.

10

WHATEVER FIRST CAME into his mind as he woke up was invariably the most disagreeable thought. The most important was apparently always the most unpleasant. How was he to placate Rainer? He had sat down beside Elissa because he liked to be close to her. He had talked to her about Lena. The warmth with which she spoke about Lena differed from Rainer's. Everyone at the driving school likes Lena. She'd like to keep Lena here for good. Would he consent to that?

They discussed this on Sunday. Sabina said: "Driving school?" Lena said: "Yes, driving school!" Halm said: "At home I wouldn't know what to say if you wanted to work in a driving school, but here in California it looks to me like a lucky break." Lena said: "It is." Although she believed she had Rainer to thank for Elissa's interest. Elissa was afraid of Rainer. She was afraid that he wanted to kill her. Maybe the murder of her friend Bluma was still having an effect on her. When Elissa talks about Rainer, she may suddenly say: "Through the ear, just imagine, shoots her through the ear!" Elissa would like Lena to move in with her. With Lena staying with her, Rainer wouldn't harm her. But Sabina shook her head brusquely. That means: You're both mistaken, you haven't a chance, you might as well give in at once, it's no use talking to me. Halm, on the other hand: For Lena to move to Elissa's for a few weeks, that would be possible, wouldn't it? For Lena to have been discovered in this country by one person or perhaps even two was more important than any European prejudice.

When the front-door bell rang, it was Elissa. Lena had already packed. As Lena was opening the car door she called back that she was also going to cut her hair, that would be better for the crash helmet. Halm and Sabina stood there dumbfounded. Sabina said: "And Juliane wants to go to Brazil!" Halm said: "Have you any better suggestion?" "But that was a sneak attack," said Sabina. Elissa virtually abducted her. Because their own children have run away from them, they steal ours. Halm had to keep her away from the telephone. Since Lena had been working for Elissa, he said, she had become much nicer, and now that her face was no longer quite so tense the scars were tending to disappear. And because it often helps, he said frivolously: "If anyone at home should ask about her, she is at a California school, you simply leave out 'driving.' " In the end Sabina's complaints were confined to Lena's wanting to cut her hair.

The phone rang. Halm hurried to it as fast as his spine would allow. But it was Sabina's brother, Franz. Sabina positively wilted during this conversation. They were living beyond reality here. Now reality was catching up. Greedily or uncompromisingly or pedantically. Sabina came back from the phone, her face working. She was trying to prevent her face from freezing into one expression. It seemed that Franz had come back from a trip and found Father in the hospital. Elmar and Gitte wouldn't be returning from Portugal till next week, Father had been taken to the hospital by Dr. Weichbrod, the headaches had increased, so now it's cancer of the bladder, the operation is scheduled for next week. And Franz even apologized for calling. He had felt he must tell her, although of course there was nothing she could do, but she had to know. Halm said one could divide people into those who apologize too much and those who apologize too little. Sabina said she'd have to go there. Halm wanted to say: And who's going to rub my back and help me put on my socks and shoes? "Hey!" said Sabina. "Yes," said Halm, "I'm just wondering who, when you're not here, is going to tell me whether I have bad breath or not!" "Just phone me!" she said. "I'll do that," he said.

They spent the time before her departure with cooking instructions and trips into San Francisco. He behaved as if it hadn't sunk in that he had to stay here alone. Besides, Sabina might take offense if he agreed that she should go. "Where do you belong?" he asked her repeatedly. Things mustn't be made too easy for her. "Would *you* like Gitte to be looking after you?" she asked. How right she was. In Sabina's arms one could gladly die. Sabina's face showed only what she felt. That's what a dying man would want. He hoped she wouldn't go through his desk at home. The notion that Sabina might discover the letter rejecting his Nietzsche book could only be answered with the wish for a universal disaster. Ah Sabina, who will come out of the kitchen when you're gone, saying: They're certainly practical, these Americans! And the most important thing, Sabina, before this separation: whatever you see of me before you disappear into the plane is nothing compared to what will happen to your husband when you've disappeared. Your husband is so artless. As long as you're here his face will not show the grief of separation. He would have to pretend it. Only when you can no longer see him could you see in his face that he misses you. And how.

He had to ask Carol to invite Rainer to a farewell party. By now, Rainer's only connection with the outside world was through Carol. The Schubert text interpretation had, it seemed, reached a stage at which any interruption might have incalculable consequences. But at the next contact, which always had to be initiated by Rainer, Carol would pass on the latest news of the Halm family. Carol also gave him the telephone number of the driving school. On Wednesday evening Lena came home and stayed. She really had cut her hair as short as Elissa's. She looked as if she had just emerged from the water. Thursday evening Elissa and Rainer came.

Rainer radiated what Carol would have called premeditated benevolence. For Halm, less demanding than Carol, that was enough, although he had to try to ignore the fact that Rainer preferred Sabina and Lena to himself. He was entitled to do so. His motives were always better than anyone else's. Sabina virtually set herself ablaze in front of Rainer, apparently with the aim of demonstrating to Elissa how easy it was to lose oneself in adoration of her husband. Between Rainer and Sabina there was a tacit understanding as between superior human beings who are spending an evening with scoundrels. The endlessly resourceful Sabina not only pocketed Rainer on the strength of her admiration but also elicited a promise from him that from now on he would treat her husband kindly, even if Helmut were to behave—which might happen—in a manner that didn't deserve it. She pleaded for indulgence toward her husband. Almost to excess. Halm looked at Elissa and Lena. He meant to imply: Never mind, the main thing is for us not to quarrel.

And they had to drink. In order that Rainer shouldn't feel that he, Rainer, was drinking to excess, Halm drank almost half as much as Rainer, with the result that the men were soon no longer able to separate a nod from a head shake, their heads simply lolled. And since there was no shouting and no running out of the room, this was the best evening with the Mersjohanns. Halm was touched to the heart by the time he sank into the thundering bed. Elissa had seen to it that Lena drove home with herself and Rainer. So Lena said good-bye to her mother. Sabina took it hard. Lena took it lightly, appeared wise and stoical.

On their last day Halm dragged Sabina around San Francisco. He wanted her to buy something that would remind them of this day. The forecast was for 104 degrees. Even here it wasn't always that warm in October. They found something to be worn around the neck, on a gold chain, an intertwining gold object, a spiral cornucopia or the Aesculapean serpent or a golden sperm. Then he wanted a nightgown. For her. From store to store he became more and more demanding and refused to buy until they had found something in silk which, thanks to its pinkish tone and greenish pattern, raised in him the hope that, when she wore it, Sabina would look as if she were standing naked in a tropical shrub bathed in the glow of the setting sun.

Then they had to have a Chinese meal. Because he knew absolutely nothing about Chinese food, and because he abhorred asking the advice of waiters, even if Sabina were to do it for him, he was presented with a large bowlful of webbed ducks' feet that looked like plastic and tasted like plastic. Sabina had discussed her dish with the waiter and got what she wanted: hot-and-sour soup, shredded beef with bell pepper, and Tsingtao beer. He drank Coors. Sabina had learned from the waiter that Tsingtao beer tasted like German beer, that Coors was American. On the edge of each of their plates there was a fortune cookie. Sabina's strip of paper said: "Your worst fear will be eased." "There you are, Sabina," said Halm, "there's hope for you." "What's yours?" she asked. He cracked open the shell and read: "Tread softly." Carol would say that he didn't need an oracle for that.

Thanks to this exhausting shopping spree, all emotional pressure was avoided. They even managed to survive the forty-minute delay of departure without heavy breathing. Halm said he would be studying Heine day and night. Only when they had almost reached Gate 50, through which Sabina was about to disappear, did some moisture escape from their eyes. At that point he turned and ran. There was no sense in prolonging the moment. In the car he turned up the music to full strength and drove slowly past and over San Francisco, then across the bridge toward home. He couldn't rest his arm in the open window because the sun was too hot. He thought of the stocks that came originally from Weimar and now lined the path from Grizzly Peak Boulevard to Carol's house, mauve and purple. These shades also occurred on Sabina's nightgown. But Father Gottschalk had headaches and cancer of the bladder. So now the girl had lost all her power. An absent Sabina—what better protection? A very noble solution. As soon as Halm was in the house, looking out over San Francisco in the evening light, he realized that he could enjoy the pathos of this solution like music that fell a little short of its pretensions. Even *He*-Halm was quite subdued now, merely mumbling something about the kitsch of this solution but not daring to attack it. *I*-Halm was now unassailable.

On Monday morning when Halm let himself be swept along by the flood of students through Crocker Gate onto the campus, he felt composed. His calm was due not merely to the noble solution produced by Sabina's departure: he had quite simply found a composure appropriate to his situation. Nothing more could happen to him here. Impregnable at last. The breakthrough to his inner self had been accomplished. On Sunday. The deceptive dialogue had ceased. Once again he was a single voice. One can only exist inside or outside oneself. That has now been resolved. That's the way it's going to stay. No longer accessible to everybody. No longer a stumbling assemblage of weak spots. The ideal condition, opaque. A closed being. A stone. Able to see out, but no one can see in. This emotional state might best be called independence. Provided the state continues, that high-sounding word is applicable. The impenetrability (from the outside in) accumulates warmth inside. Of this inner warmth, nothing finds its way out. That's what's new. That's what has to be new. Or become new. Outwardly quite cold. But not antagonizing. Not wanting to provoke any reaction. Simply outwardly cold, inwardly warm. For the first time one has turned toward oneself. Now time will tell whether one can stand one's own company. Everything depends on that.

Halm is cheerful. He no longer feels so inadequate. The acuteness of his self-dissatisfaction was subsiding. His vague outline suited him. He accepted this unprepossessing appearance. He almost approved of himself. Sometimes he had actually thought less of Sabina for not only enduring someone like him but even claiming to like him. Now he was fervently grateful to her for enduring him so gladly. He was as old as he was, that's all there was to it. Growing older means eating less and getting fatter. That's all there is to it.

The man walking toward Coit Hall found beauty in everything he saw. I'm a chastity freak, thought Halm. And lucky to be that. A promising topic of conversation had also occurred to him, he thought. What is the students' attitude toward their given name? From whom had they received it, and with what kind of ritual, what kind of family history is behind it? Would any of them pass on their given name to their child? Although they were almost all present, the given name of any one of them seemed reluctant to pass their lips that Monday morning at nine. He didn't even look toward the girl. Why she attended a conversation class was beyond him. Had she been so sure of finding an essay helper in her instructor? She might well have been. "So, Elaine—who gave you your lovely name, what is the name of your patron saint and what do you know about her?" Elaine knew only that her dad had wished her to be called Elaine. She hadn't been baptized. So much for that.

Halm looked calmly around the room. Why didn't the ever-solicitous Howard speak up? "Jeff, your name surely doesn't appear like that on your ID, does it?" Jeff suppressed a yawn and said his name was Geoffrey; also never been baptized. Now there was really no option but to appeal to Howard as one appeals to a saint. "Howard, is there a Saint Howard?" Howard shrugged. "Were you baptized?" No. "Oh," Halm exclaims as facetiously as possible, "yet another heathen!" Howard mumbles a protest. "I beg your pardon," Halm cries, "not a heathen? What then?" "A Jew," Howard says a little louder, and Halm senses that having to raise his voice and repeat the word more distinctly has tinged his reply with bitterness. Or is that just Halm's imagination? He must press on! But Halm now had to look at Howard. The concern in Howard's expression seemed to have turned to sorrow. History of religion to the rescue! "Jews regard non-Jews as heathen. Hence this classification. I apologize, Howard, for taking you for a heathen!" Howard smiled. Sorrowfully. Halm asked if they all understood the background. Was there another English word for "heathen"? "Pagan," said Elaine. "Right," said Halm. "Gentile," said Howard. "Right," said Halm, "from the Jewish point of view the heathen is a 'gentile,' from the Christian point of view a 'pagan'. . . ." Halm was clutching at straws. The lesson became agonizing. He was sweating. Mentally and physically.

Utterly worn out, he headed after class for the cafeteria. The girl followed him. Might she come to his office at noon, she had something important to tell him? "Why, of course, Fran. But why don't we meet at our little table here in the October sunshine? To a central European it seems so wonderful compared to the icy blast of that neon tomb." After German II he walked, every inch the teacher, to the cafeteria, saw that the girl was sitting at a different table, not their usual one, and mentioned it to her as he sat down, but he was annoyed with himself because this reminder of their earlier meetings had no bearing on the matter—on the contrary. His second remark was no more serviceable. Indicating her Styrofoam cup he said: "I see you always drink milk!" She told him she had never in her life drunk anything but milk. But now he had himself in hand and refrained from asking whether she was the girl who leaps like a gazelle in slow motion through the evening woods, her hair fanning out, and then drinks milk. All he said was: "Imagine that!" He was always so ironical, she said, his irony cut like a knife. O.K., she would provide him with one more excuse for irony: her essay on the Shakespearean sonnet had been given a C-minus. That wicked old Cerf alias Hitler back in high school—she had once given her a C-minus, but nobody had since then. Halm murmured: "Let's have a look."

Her pages were full of red scribblings. Teachers know that students try to decipher every word no matter how wretchedly scribbled: after all, there might be something favorable in there. On Fran's pages there was nothing favorable. *You should tighten up your thesis. This seems a little vague. I get the feeling you are a little bored. Some of your analyses seem a little sloppy. Could say a little more. Your argumentation needs a little more work. Your conclusion lacks depth*. . . . Halm looked at Fran: she happened to be pushing her mass of hair with her right hand from one side of her head to the other, thus for the first time rendering one ear, the right, entirely visible. From it hung a thin ring. As soon as she removed her hand from her head, her hair poured back again. The ear disappeared. It was possible to speak.

Halm said: "We have to repair the damage. He'll find out what kind of people we are." "The professor's nuts," she said. Halm said: "It's my fault. It has to be my fault. C-minus!" She: "The professor only wants stupid clowns who write the way he does." She's going to protest. She'll demand a review. Halm discovered a tiny place, red and swollen, on her right nostril. An incipient pimple. This morning the radio announcer had said, quite excitedly, that there was a chance of rain today. Around her mouth, among the shadings of the old, shallow craters, there were signs of fresh, imminent eruptions. There were some red peaks. Without that volcanic skin activity, her face would have been almost too ordinary. He sometimes had trouble remembering her face.

Now she was once again pushing her hair aside. Suddenly her left ear was exposed. From this ear, too, hung a thin gold ring. Not only did the color of her hair depend on the changing light: the hair itself didn't have the same color for a single centimeter. From blond to brassy to almost greenish brown, a surge of blending colors. At the moment her mass of hair arched away from both sides of her head so that he could see both ears with their thin gold rings deep in the caverns of her hair.

Actually she didn't care about the C-minus, she said, since she was much too melancholic for a C-minus to affect her. "I'm somber," she said. "Sounds nice," he said, "nicer than melancholic." "Gloomy," she added. "Gloomy sounds nice too," he said. "Let's stick with somber," he said. She envied him, she said, he was so consistently bright and hard. Well, he was hardened, he said. Suffering seemed fatuous to him, he said. He could recommend the word to her: fatuous. The girl was wearing chicly disreputable shorts and above them the T-shirt with the Federated Fire Fighter lettering encircling the big yellow F. Halm turned his eyes to the sky. A chance of rain, the announcer had said. She says: "The next essay is on *Much Ado About Nothing* or *Twelfth Night*." She has chosen *Much Ado*. Might she come on Thursday and show him the results of her brainstorming? Yes. Here or in the office? she asked. In the office, said his mouth.

As soon as the girl had left, *I*-Halm refused to admit having said that. How embarrassing, to arrange a meeting with this girl under the roof of Fillmore Hall! Here, in the sight of all, to sit beside her bending over papers, he was entitled to that, he could answer for that, and if there were any onlookers they'd simply have to get used to it. But to sneak away with her in the Fillmore labyrinth into that most hidden of all offices—that is wrong, harmful, uncalled for. You will cancel that tomorrow. *He*-Halm: No! *I*-Halm: Yes!

Halm drove as slowly as possible to Contra Costa Avenue. He wanted to dissociate himself entirely from the events of the last hour. But he was afraid that, if he didn't immediately face what had happened, everything would get even worse. But what actually had happened? His armor, his calm, his impregnability, his composure—all gone. Why did she have to keep shoving her hair back and forth, baring her ears, allow volcanic fields to bloom, talk about being somber. . . . Maybe he feels so dizzy now because, as long as she was there, he hadn't been breathing properly. He had constantly pulled in his stomach. Not deliberately. Automatically. That meant he couldn't endure her presence for much longer than an hour. Always sitting so upright, rigid, stomach drawn in, breathing shallowly. As ridiculous as possible. And then topple off the chair. But dead, if you please, not just fainting. Dying, if you please. Very elegant, to die. A bit too much so. Stay with your own solutions. They're always mediocre, lousy, and stomach-friendly. She needs help with her essays. That's all. And even if she did want more than help with her essays—but that she doesn't want more is beyond doubt—but even if she did want more, which she certainly doesn't, even then nothing would be possible, nothing could be hoped for, because an affair of a few weeks would be infinitely worse than nothing, but luckily nothing *is* possible, because he in his California daze would of course go for the worst. . . .

He let out a deep breath. If she didn't have a national water polo player—which, however, she has—if she were now to ring the front-door bell and, like Umlaut, announce: I need feeding—what sentimental kitsch! Then you'd have to slam the door in her face. . . . Everything that went through his mind in connection with this girl was nonsense. It was his job to see that she disappeared from his thoughts. So, out with you, please, you stupid, spoiled Porsche-creature! Hasn't Carol supplied all that was necessary for this exorcism? Fortunately Professor Rinehart has Shakespeare on his bookshelf. He'll settle down comfortably, with something to nibble on, and read *Much Ado About Nothing*. Outside, the glittering Bay; beyond it, not softened by any haze today, the city, hard and bright. Can one ask for more? One can't ask for more. You're lucky. Indeed you are.

He plodded through the idle chatter of the characters in *Much Ado*. Of course one's never critical of Shakespeare. Perhaps he never even wrote this play. Halm sat there, from time to time looking out into the dazzling day. No chance of rain. The secondary couple, Benedick and Beatrice, is of course the principal couple in the play. Has the girl suggested this play because Benedick and Beatrice unceasingly attack one another polemically, merely because they can't confess so-called love for one another? After all, what happens to the primary couple, Hero and Claudio, isn't worth an essay. Regardless of what she has in mind, he can only advise her to write about Benedick and Beatrice: the tone of hostility as a declaration of love. Language as the exact opposite in emotion. The explicitness of the unsaid in the said. Revealing merely by hiding. Perhaps then she would at least have an inkling of all that he was not saying. If he was not allowed to say anything, he could use this bickering couple to signal that he was saying nothing and all that he was not saying. Why has she chosen this play?

He must have some fresh air. His head feels like a balloon. Pressure as if he'd drunk too much tea. Overstimulated and exhausted—that described his condition. If only he could at least shake hands with her once a day. But that's not the custom here. How many hours does he now need to recover from one hour with her? The ratio is becoming more and more unfavorable. If he doesn't manage to reach a state of firmness, this condition of stimulation and exhaustion can become permanent. The knowledge that absolutely nothing of what he felt was justifiable spread through him like poison, a weight, depression. To sit on the patio step, to stare down onto the little bit of lawn, to avoid all movement, to reject all clarity, to ask for all-encompassing fog, the end. How little use his composure had been. The need for justification should be eliminated. It's all hypocrisy anyway. If your scruples are stronger than your urge for . . . for recklessness, it doesn't mean that your conscience is alert. It means that your vital urges are weak. Conscience is the weakling's punishment for his weakness. The vital person feels justified. In comparison to his urges, the restraints of conscience are so weak that they can be ignored.

Under the giant redwood tree, that was itself like a house, he saw the black-and-white cat. He jumped up, brought out plate and dish as Sabina had told him to, placed them where they had been before, and sat down, this time not on the steps leading from the patio onto the lawn but on the ones leading from the house to the patio. He sat without moving, called "Here, puss!", sighed, and chirped in motherly fashion. The cat did not move. He rose and approached her as slowly as the hand of a clock, but she disappeared into the bamboo thicket at the far end of the lawn. O.K., suit yourself. But next morning, before driving off, he walked down and found plate and bowl empty, so he refilled them.

Fortunately he was the first in Room 101 today, for as he sat down he noticed, drawn on the table, a fairly large picture of what, for a brief second, he took to be a butterfly; then he realized that what he had taken for the body of the butterfly was a sexual organ; and the wings were not wings but testicles. This absurd penis/butterfly was flying toward a somewhat less absurd-looking labyrinth intended to represent a female sexual area. By the time he had grasped all this, Elaine was coming in with her two-liner, but he was just able to fish some papers out of his briefcase and cover the drawing before Elaine reached the table. When they were all seated, Jeff mumbled something that Halm couldn't make out, but all the others did and laughed. Halm assumed a casual air and said that of course he would like to join in the laughter, could Jeff repeat his joke for him? Jeff looked at Halm out of Halm's eyes and said: "Forget it."

When the class was over, Halm placed his briefcase on the table before removing the papers covering the drawing. He pushed it onto the papers, pulled the papers out from under the briefcase, put them away in the briefcase, stood up and didn't remove the briefcase from the table until he turned toward the door. Outdoors he found himself suddenly joined by Jeff and the girl. But at the first turning the girl left them. Jeff said: "She really likes you. She claims that when you smile you look like Marlon Brando, and he's Fran's favorite actor."

When Halm could finally close the door of his office behind him, he felt relieved. He spent his free hour sitting under the cold air shower unable to move. He thought: When a person's no longer capable of transporting a sweater and a scarf from his home to his office, he is no longer *compos mentis*. After his German II class, when he dropped into Carol's chair and sighed as vaguely as possible, she said: "I see our butterfly has finally had enough." His instinct was to run away. But he had to look at Carol and, what was more, with a searching, threatening furious look. . . . "What's the matter—did I put my foot in my mouth again?" At last she seemed really to be a little afraid of him. He relaxed and dug out his piece of paper. On it was the new title of his Heine lecture: "One of the Asra Clan." "Oh," she said, "when they love, they perish." "Aha!" he said, "an expert!" "And who is that 'One'?" she asked. "And the Schubert camp?" he said. "Is silent," she said. On Saturday, he said, she and Kirk as his guests—was such a thing conceivable? "Even practicable," she replied. Was he intending to invite Teddy Auster as well? Teddy had complained about Halm.

Congratulations! At last Halm had succeeded in breaking through his opportunistic affability at one point! For once he had shown his true colors! Sorry though she was that dear old Teddy happened to be the victim, she was glad for Halm's sake.

Halm didn't understand a word and asked for an explanation. Well, after all, he was reading and praising everything in sight, Teddy was the only one to suffer his silence. But that wasn't true! He hadn't read everything by Zipser or Dempewolf, or by Ackerman, or by Roy, so obviously he hadn't praised everything either. Only Carol's gift for caricature had made of him this ninny of servility. Maybe he did tend to be a bit servile, he admitted that. On the other hand, he had by no means read everything yet by his favorite author, Kirk Elrod. He wouldn't get anything done here. This country occupied him day and night. "This country," she said, allowing her protruding upper teeth to disappear behind her beautiful lower lip. He yearned to be able to take up Auster's works. "Conservative Irritation as Found in Heine"—how he was looking forward to that!

Carol pointed to his box: as disappointed as Teddy was, he refused to be discouraged, there was some new material in there again. Halm stashed it all away and said: "Good-bye Karola von der Hütte!", pretended to be in a hurry and continued hurrying until he was sitting in his car. At that moment a white BMW roared past him down the street; in it the girl. He started the engine and drove home as slowly as possible. He'd rub that in when he next saw Carol. To call a BMW a Porsche! The only thing that was correct was the color. Probably you were led astray by alliteration, Carol dear! Papa's practice plus Pacific Heights equals Porsche. He had to pay her back for the butterfly. Or was it just a coincidence? Or her work? Had she drawn it? Between seven and eight in the morning? Or was he already known here as Butterfly? Nickname: Butterfly. At home: Kiwi. Marlon Brando. . . . And the answer suddenly popped into his mind: Malvolio. They're playing a game and you're Malvolio. They advise you to wear yellow stockings, cross-gartered. That was why she had chosen

Much Ado rather than *Twelfth Night,* which would have seemed too blatant to her. They want to have their little game. When he smiles he looks like Marlon Brando! Just as in *Twelfth Night* they make the poor steward Malvolio believe that his mistress is in love with him and that she commends his yellow stockings, cross-gartered! And he's supposed to smile! And Halm knew how stupid he looked when he smiled.

As soon as he reached home, he began seeking out the Malvolio places in *Twelfth Night. If thou entertainest my love, let it appear in thy smiling; thy smiles become thee well.* When you smile you look like Marlon Brando! And he's Fran's favorite actor! They're probably thinking up something for tomorrow that'll fit in with *yellow stockings . . . ever cross-gartered. Twelfth Night* would be too blatant, too obvious—that might betray their Brando-Malvolio game. *Much Ado,* on the other hand, is ideal. With the Beatrice text she signals that she thinks quite differently from the way she speaks; but not, of course, in reality, merely as a challenge to him to reveal himself so that in the end, like Malvolio, he can be made to look like a fool. But they're mistaken in him, these California kids. He's determined not to smile anymore. They're trying to trap him with the hope of looking like Marlon Brando! He knows what they're up to. Yes, indeed! A little less would have been more. He's not about to make himself look ridiculous with Benedick tirades. He was always so ironical, she had said, his irony was cutting. . . . That was her way of forcing him into the Benedick role. When your voice becomes so angry as to sound comical, I can hear the melting love lines! That was her method of training him in order no doubt to make him perform for her friends. What he must now on no account betray was that he had seen through the ploy. He must act as though he knew nothing, understood nothing, had no plan: in other words, was completely invulnerable.

Carol cannot be aware of any of this. The drawing is by Jeff. Howard knows nothing about it either. Elaine does. Her two-liner is all of a piece with displays of that kind. He felt it was now no longer necessary to steer the consultation from the office back to the cafeteria. He was calm. Yes, he was! The Bay out there, glistening silver. Of San Francisco, not a trace. For the first time. A white bank of churning clouds reflecting the glistening of the Bay, turning grayer as it rose. As soon as one looks down at the Bay again one is dazzled, blinded.

Halm sat down in front of the TV. He really must acquire a complete understanding of the language. Perhaps if he had understood Jeff's joke he would have tumbled to everything right away. In other words, he can't afford not to understand some things. Needless to say, the girl was once again leaping like a gazelle in slow motion through the sunset among the trees, drinking milk and saying: "It does a body good." He had the feeling of being deeper into America on the screen than on campus. Someone being interviewed about television said: "Life is better on TV than at your front door." He agreed with that now. The news of a plan to install a telephone on Golden Gate Bridge so as to give suicides one last chance to make a phone call that might reverse everything, inspired him with the idea of suggesting suicide as a topic of conversation. He'd show them! Marlon Brando-Malvolio indeed! But he would be calm. Television soothed him. All those disasters smoldering everywhere, ready to flare up. That handsome president with his pious, calculatedly impressive demeanor. Halm need no longer take himself seriously. There could be nothing less important than himself here and now. Whatever he did or did not do was a matter of total indifference.

He finished off his bottle of wine and, his head buzzing, went down to the bedroom to telephone Sabina. But the very way Sabina answered the phone told him that on this particular night she couldn't help him. Father Gottschalk has had his operation. This morning. By her time it was now two in the afternoon. They won't allow her to return to the hospital until tomorrow afternoon, so there's nothing to report yet. She took it for granted he was calling because he was worried about her father. Oh Sabina, he is full of "tears of the mountain," he couldn't say a word. Naked and drunk, he lay with his ear to the phone, listening to Sabina's breathless voice of misery. He said: "I'll call again, Sabina. Well then. . . ." How he was supposed to fall asleep now, all upset as he was, he didn't know. He decided to stay awake. That helped. He must have fallen asleep fairly quickly.

Next morning he brought in the plate and bowl from the patio, refilled them, and set them out again, then went back to the steps by the house and waited. The cat emerged from her tree house and walked gingerly up the patio steps. With each step forward, she seemed to take root and so had to strain and stretch to detach herself again. And she didn't drag herself straight to the food and milk but, hard though it was for her, to him, to his bare toes. He wanted to remove a piece of sticky tape from her thick black-and-white fur, but his hand scared her, and she ran away, back onto the lawn.

It was time to leave. He wanted to be there early enough to wipe the drawing off the table without witnesses. He took along a damp cloth. A pity, really, about the penis/butterfly flying toward the female grotto. Last night, while listening to the seemingly endless debates over a Korean passenger plane that had been shot down by the Soviets, he had learned a new expression: heat-seeking missile. He wiped away the penis/airplane, leaving the grotto, although he covered this with his papers. He didn't want the kids to know right off that he was well able to take care of himself. After class he spent so long packing up his things that he was the last to leave the room. Outside the building the girl was waiting for him; he headed for Fillmore, she walked beside him. Rainer was almost certainly not on campus, which meant that he could approach the humpback bridge without anxiety. He hoped that they wouldn't run into that persistent old dog again, the one that keeps on trying to solder himself onto the young boxer bitch. Oh, Otto, Otto, where are you! The girl told him she hadn't yet been able to read *Much Ado* so was there any point in her coming to his office? He leaves it up to her. All right, she'll come.

He must go and see Carol. Sit on that chair. Dear Carol, at last he can give her some pleasure! No raptures today! At last a sort of antipathy! Toward your president, or rather that handsomely made-up ghost of a president in Washington. She must excuse him for saying: "Your president." God knows you didn't vote for him. Carol sighs, rolls up her eyes, hides her teeth behind the ramparts of her lips. Halm was to be pitied: this president was one of the best America had ever had. She, Carol, her husband Kirk, all their relatives and friends, had voted for this president and never for a second regretted it. The only people still opposed to this wonderful man were a few card-carrying highbrows and some kinks. No Rainer here to murmur an interpretation for him. Halm is immediately unsure of himself. He simply had no idea. He promptly admits that he had been drinking last night. He asked for time to reconsider. He would continue to observe the president and report back to her. The Schubert camp . . . ? Silence. After he had stuffed the papers from his box into his briefcase and nodded again to Carol, she wished him "a busy office hour." Since repartee is far from being his forte, he didn't know how to reply. You're mistaken! he should have called out. I've got over it!

After German II the girl was waiting for him outside Coit Hall and walked back with him over the bridge. But there were other entrances to the Fillmore building besides the one through the main lobby. At this hour they were bound to run into Carol on her way to lunch. So immediately after the bridge he turned right and made a detour in order to enter the building from the side. The girl said nothing. True, there was no elevator there, only stairs and long corridors on his floor. He pointedly took the stairs without effort, hiding his breathlessness. But before he and she could vanish behind the door to 407, Carol came toward them along the corridor. She must have been waiting somewhere, observing everything, and deliberately contriving this so far most embarrassing of all encounters. Then at the last moment her powers seemed to desert her. She wasn't even equal to a joke. She could only nod, then could be heard quickening her step. She must have run away.

As soon as he was sitting in the neon light across from the girl, he wished he could have apologized for everything he had been thinking during the last twenty-four hours. She looked so totally different from the way she had in his imagination. He still had no photo of her. Sabina was the photographer, not he. Today her hair, platinum white and, lower down, brassy green in the neon light, fell onto a dark-blue blouse. And she was wearing pants today, of a gray so pale and intense she might be said to be wearing silver pants. Since she hadn't read the play, she said, any ideas that came to him as he read it were not much use to her. By the time she got around to reading it, she would have forgotten whatever he could tell her. She could remember music much more easily than language. A tune she had once heard she would never forget. Now he regretted that he couldn't sing. She was convinced, she said, that he must have a good voice. Must have had, she said. He said that, since he always read with a pencil, he could let her have some of his comments on paper. And handed her the sheets. She was delighted. "You're so . . . ," she said, not knowing how to end the sentence. Twice she said "so." He was on the point of saying: so stupid. But he said: "So hardworking, yes, I do work hard, I always have done." But that wasn't what she had wanted to say: what was it? "So kind," she said, and looked at him as if she had just won a point against him in an athletic competition. He had the feeling that she was proud of having dared to say it. However, she had already risen, so he also rose; she held out her hand. That was an experience. She was already outside, and he still held her hand in his. "Wait," he could have called out. "Fran, you've forgotten your hand!"

When he was back at home and staring at the wall of cloud that still held San Francisco captive, his fear of being ridiculed as Butterfly or Brando-Malvolio seemed childish to him. Whatever plans the girl had in mind for him, he would acquiesce. If she wanted to make him look ridiculous, let her. For him it was enough that her thoughts were occupied with him. The telephone rang. He rushed to it. It must be her. He was quite sure it was her. At last. It was Carol, who said, although not at once: "Sorry, I dialed the wrong number." And didn't immediately hang up. He had more than enough time to say: Carol! You did dial the right number! But that was just what he couldn't say. He hung up before it became embarrassing. He hadn't said anything. He couldn't think of anything to say. He had wanted to convey that he hadn't known it was Carol. When it was too late he realized how that must have hurt her: even her voice he hadn't recognized. He ought to call her. Most likely it hadn't been a mistake that she had called him. She wanted to talk to him. In his mind's eye he saw her showing him her father's collection of musical instruments and the portrait of her mother. How her eyes had grown even darker. How she had stood there with her flickering tendrils of hair. Why didn't he phone her back right away? She was his only confidante here. The only one to whom he could talk. And the one he was fondest of. He was sure she was the only one who liked him a little, even if only because he reminded her, albeit to his disadvantage, of Messmer. But he couldn't phone her.

What he could do was drive into town and buy what he needed to try out some running or jogging in Tilden Park. He had studied the map and found the entrance he was looking for; then he slowly ran downhill, uphill, downhill, beside the stream, through tunnels and passageways of trees, and finally walked slowly around the big loop that led him back to his starting point. His boyhood friend Klaus, who some years earlier had tried unsuccessfully to persuade him to undertake such exercise, would be gloating now. Luckily there were no spectators here. In this park, everybody ran, walked, or stood any way they liked. Everyone seemed completely tolerant of everyone else. That was Halm's impression. You nodded or didn't nod, but no matter how people passed one another everything took place in an atmosphere of complete approval. He had already noticed something of the kind on city streets and roads; that was what had given him the courage to mingle with these joggers. Unthinkable to be acting like that in Sillenbuch. Mrs. Niedlich, Mr. Reichert, Mrs. Patzschke. . . . Here there was always more terrain than people. Finally he even did the kind of forward bends that students in their sports gear did on campus in front of certain instruction boards as if this were part of a religion. If Messrs. Kiderlen and Rimmele could see him. . . . He noticed how the exercise seemed to help his back that had been wrenched by the breakers.

After a shower he opened his bottle of wine but corked it again without filling his glass. He wanted to see whether he could manage without wine. For a whole evening. This California red had not taken long to impart a red tinge to his nose. Rainer's nose was already more blue than red. Halm was embarrassed about his nose in front of his students. He wasn't a maniac, after all. Should he, in order to prepare himself for more jogging, reduce his smoking? Not smoke at all this evening. Yes indeed. Just Heine and TV. He stuck to that.

Next morning the cat came more quickly up onto the terrace and over the steps where he was waiting with bare feet. She didn't waste any time looking sideways at the food on the terrace. First she wanted to be stroked. In a frenzy she flung herself onto her back and into his hand. A white cat with a black blanket. At one point the black reached almost all the way around her. But her paws are pure white. Her face is mainly white but looks out as if from between the folds of a black curtain. Sprouting from her black ears, white hairs quiver like the feathers of a young bird. At last she's had enough stroking, now she can eat and drink. Halm noticed that one of the pugs next door was watching him from the open window like a person. Halm waved and left.

11

FOR THE NEXT FEW DAYS he didn't dare sit down on Carol's chair. He knew that this amounted to an admission of a guilt he didn't acknowledge. Carol had so timed her arrival that she saw him disappear with the girl into the 407 labyrinth. It was she who was responsible for the appearance of ambiguity. He should drop into her chair with a laugh! Masterly, her ability to put one in the wrong. Come to think of it, she never says a single word that doesn't serve to prove what an injustice is being done to her. Usually she presents the proof in such a way that, just after tossing a spiteful remark at one's head, she laughs. Then, still laughing, she suddenly plunges into a heartrending sadness from which she tonelessly implies how much nicer it would be if for once she were given a chance to be pleasant, instead of constantly being forced into the role of a rough-tongued witch. No doubt that explained why her husband, who knew her longing better than anyone else, called her "Honeybunch." Halm would have liked to call her "Lambikins." Or "Byron." But with her Berlin-Baltic aversion to bombast, she would probably have met this with scorn, even if a minute later she began once again to long for something of the kind.

As he came through the door she said: "By tomorrow I'd have had you dragged in here by the police." She indicated his box bulging with papers. He replied that, although he couldn't afford to achieve concentration by locking himself away like Rainer, he did at least have to devote every free second to his Heine lecture. "So you do have a few free seconds—how nice!" she said. "Catty Carol," he said. "Honey-sweet Halm," she retorted. Now he really loved her. How to let her know this? "In your eyes one has always, without knowing it, done something wrong," he said. "Don't fool yourself, my dear sir," she said. "Aha, done something wrong again!" he said fondly. But she went on: "Did Mr. Kiderlen reach you?" It sounded as if she knew exactly how much this would upset Halm. Mustn't panic now. She had given Kiderlen his number, she said. A charming man apparently, that colleague of his, and how sophisticated, such impeccable Oxford English: he had to decline her offer to speak German since it was he who was intruding here by telephone, so it was only right that he use the language spoken where he was intruding. He said this as if he would do exactly the same if he were calling Tokyo. "And why, may I ask, did he call here?" "So he didn't phone you?" "No!" cried Halm, "and I was home all the time!" "Except for a few evening runs in Tilden Park," said Carol through almost closed lips. By the way, he always chose the entrance by the roundabout, and, while the terrain there was rugged and romantic, she would recommend the Nimitz Way entrance, a few miles farther on; nothing could be more sublime than those high-level trails and eucalyptus groves at sunset.

Halm was so confused that he was unable to ask how she had learned all this. Worse still, he ignored her remark as if his jogging were something he had to hide. He felt guilty about a bit of running! When talking to Sabina on the phone he hadn't said anything about his new life-style either.

So tell me, what did Kiderlen want? Carol assumes surprise. Halm asks so angrily, whereas Kiderlen had inquired so warmly after Halm! "But why, for God's sake!" Halm shouts. He's at the end of his tether. Oh well, first Kiderlen had inquired after Halm, how he was getting along here, so she had been able to reassure the caller, whom naturally she had taken for a concerned friend; Halm knew how to make himself popular with the right people; she hoped this was the kind of answer Halm wished her to give. In any case, the caller had laughed a bit and said that at home Halm had been more inclined to make himself unpopular with the right people. They had chatted for a while like that about Halm until Kiderlen had said that the reason for his call was a sad one: Rimmele had died. Failed to return from a Sunday hike, found under a juniper bush on the Swabian Alb. Halm was shocked. Kiderlen had regretted Halm's absence at this time. No one on the faculty was more greatly needed now than Halm. He, Kiderlen, would, of course, now have to run the school temporarily as Rimmele's deputy, but how he was to manage that without Halm was a mystery to him. So, regards to Halm, and he hoped he'd soon be back. As soon as the negative element was lacking, it was greatly missed.

Carol said she wished somebody would talk like that about her. Kiderlen had talked about a Halm she didn't know, since here he always appeared to be the boundless enthusiast. But she preferred Kiderlen's Halm to the campus Halm. "I find it hard to believe," said Halm. Just then a voice from the door said hello. The girl. That was all he needed. The girl ignored him and asked Carol whether she mightn't come an hour earlier, that would give them more time *and* more light. Carol told her she would try. And the apparition was gone. Carol said, and Halm had the feeling she was savoring every word: "She has a marvelous home, hasn't she?" Halm said in a strained voice: "How should I know?" Carol: "That's right, you prefer to meet in the total discretion of your charming office. But Fran's Maybeck house in Oakland Hills would be more romantic. Belongs to her father, of course. Your taste is impeccable, Mr. Halm. Fran Webb is a precious little person. Even I, by no means inclined to enthusiasm, don't hesitate to call her a jewel. Even when she opens her beautiful mouth, she is still bearable."

Oh, if only he kept a diary! Then he would now be able to prove to Carol, quoting date and hour, that, when the conversation had turned in this office to Fran Webb, Carol had once said: "Yes, she's nice enough as long as she doesn't open her mouth." And now this! For his sake? Or was he only imagining this? No, no, no! She has made a conquest of Fran, for his sake. Anyway the girl had always been enthusiastic about Carol, so it couldn't have been difficult for her to win Fran over completely as a friend.

He must change the subject immediately. Would she mind if he tried to invite the Mersjohanns too for Saturday? He'd like to see his daughter again, and without Elissa there wasn't much chance. And another thing too: if during the next two weeks he didn't seek out the finest spot on campus, the chair in front of Carol's desk, the only reason would be that he could no longer face the day of his Heine lecture without doing something about it. Just compare the work being done in the Schubert camp, while in his own case—nothing. He was really beginning to feel uncomfortable at the thought of October 29. That would be the most important day of his stay here, the crucial one.

Even if he hadn't already known it, his conversation with Carol had shown that there was nothing between him and the girl. By this time even Carol would have established by means of on-the-spot investigation that there was no shred of evidence. Perhaps that's why she suddenly finds the girl "precious." Carol's swift conquest of the girl has destroyed the very last remnant of any prospect. Not prospect—the last remnant of illusion. A shrewd move, Carol. Brilliant. She has the stuff of a world chess champion. No, she should become foreign minister. Chats with Kiderlen. So who is it who now holds in her hands all the threads he hangs by? Carol. Perhaps it was she who called Kiderlen. He wouldn't find that out until after his return. If she had done all this to impress him, then . . . then she really did impress him. That Carol! Since Sabina left, she's the only person he can talk to. Those chats with the girl are more like bloodletting than conversation.

He put some snacks within reach and read over the Heine lines he had been jotting down over the weeks. *The butterfly is in love with the rose,/And flutters about her all day. . . . The rose spreads its perfume—but is it aware of its perfume? . . . When you wander slowly by/And your gown just touches me, My heart cries out in joy and follows/Ardently your lovely wake. . . . Has she never even shown you/That your hot avowals moved her? . . . Because I love you—I must flee/And shun your countenance. . . . Lightly swinging bells are ringing/With a soft insistence. . . . My adored and golden-haired one,/Every day I'm sure to meet her,/When beneath the chestnut branches/In the Tuileries she wanders. . . . /She is Laura! Yes, like Petrarch,/I can hold platonic revels/With this name, and clasp its beauty— /He, himself, did nothing more.*

He had filled pages and pages with such lines. There was only one poem he had copied out in full:

The Asra

Daily came the lone and lovely
Sultan's daughter, slowly wandering
In the evening to the fountain
Where the plashing waters whitened.

Daily stood the youthful captive
In the evening by the fountain
Where the plashing waters whitened—
Daily growing pale and paler.

Till one dusk the strolling Princess
Stopped, and suddenly addressed him:
"Tell me now thy name, and tell me
Of thy country and thy kindred."

And the slave replied, "My name is
Mohamet; I come from Yemen.
And my people are the Asra,
Who, whene'er they love, must perish."

The lines, which had appealed to him because of their associations, had grown familiar as he copied them, and now, as he reread them, became part of himself. He felt at ease with them. He found that he had to adjust his title again: "Laura and Asra." That was his title. He wanted to argue his case in a Heine tone. There was nothing he liked better than dealing with so-called pain in this manner. Full of envy, full of confessed envy, was how he wanted to portray Heine's self-expression. Of all the premises of this self-expression he would name "youth" as the most important. Although he himself must at one time have been younger than he is now, he was never as young as Heine had been when he wrote those poems. He would describe those Heine poems as something that moves in the sunshine as seen by someone sitting in the shade. That is where a flash of brilliance can be appreciated. That would bring him to his theme: an Asra may speak only when he is asked. He creates for himself an "unknown," a "Laura." He exults. That's the point. He dies in exultation. Halm wanted to depict an Asra-Laura relationship that was to appear just as melodramatic as it was comic. And the comedy was to spring solely from the melodrama. And the comedy was to be the most unintended imaginable. He was interested only in unintended comedy. The most comic aspect of Halm's Asra: he doesn't even die.

Would this approach force her to laugh and cry? That was his goal. That alone. Nothing else. He would speak only to her. This "fountain": that of the sultan's daughter and the one at Student Union Plaza, Heine's meter, trochees, leaping like the jets of water in the fountain. . . . What a chance to tell her what he could never tell her either in his icy neon crypt or at the cafeteria table, or at the real fountain! Even that wouldn't do any good. It couldn't. So what could there be? There could be nothing. But for that very reason he had to say it. Say just that. That there can be nothing—that is his theme. He couldn't remember ever having been so motivated in preparing a lecture. And he fell into a state of almost idealistic rapture at the thought that, exactly parallel with him, the girl was describing the same situation with the aid of Beatrice and

Benedick. On an extra page that he intended to give her the next day he jotted down four lines of Heine that applied more to the Beatrice-Benedick world than to that of Asra and Laura:

They loved one another, though neither
Would speak to the other thereof;
They looked at each other like strangers
The while they were dying of love.

Let her comment on that! He was determined not to expect anything from her. He had nothing to hope for. So disappointment was out of the question. In spite of now spending more evenings in front of the TV set, he tried not to succumb to movielike emotionalism. Although, after observing Carol's conquest of the girl, he identified himself with the loneliness of Western heroes at their lowest point. But when they proceeded to ride toward their solutions, he stayed behind, a solitary witness, as it were, against the cinematic falsifiers who transformed the need for a solution into fact.

Halm was glad when Carol called to suggest that they meet on Saturday at Grizzly Peak Boulevard rather than at the Rinehart house. He was no good as a cook. He would have wasted a whole Saturday buying a lot of stuff and arranging it attractively on plates.

He drove to the Chinese flower shop and put together a bouquet of tiger lilies and green ferns that Sabina would have regarded as too contrived. Carol, today all in lacy black, liked it. Auster couldn't come after all, for a sensational reason: the man who for decades has been proclaiming that there was nothing as ridiculous as a married philosopher, has flown to Reno for the weekend, to get married. Let the kids have their fun, murmured Rainer.

All evening, Halm stayed as far away as possible from Elissa. He was concerned only with Lena. With her short hair she looked as though she belonged to Elissa's troupe. Jamey had written again, said Lena. A postcard. From Staunton, Virginia. The card showed the basement of the Woodrow Wilson house where General Lee had once had his office. Lee's horse Traveler was also shown, stuffed and looking very lifelike. Lena had told all this only to her father, but Rainer, having picked up Jamey's name, had been listening. In a pitiful wail indicating extreme misery he called out to Elissa: "And why don't *I* get to see a card like that?" Elissa said in surprise: "Lena?" Lena, instantly and in a high clear voice of utter certainty: Yesterday, when she went down to Rainer's room to play four-handed piano with him, she had taken along the postcard to show him. She describes his pleasure over it. "And that was when?" he asks. "Yesterday," says Lena. "Yesterday!" says Rainer in a tone of contempt. As if to say: What nonsense! Quite impossible! "Yesterday," says Lena evenly, "we played the F-minor Fantasy." "Oh, the F-minor Fantasy!" says Rainer, "Oh, that was yesterday, oh I see, you mean *that* card, the one from Staunton, with Traveler on it! Of course, if you mean that one, Lena did bring it along when she came down, and so on and so on! Now I have two women in my house who are above all supicion. The Hansel and Gretel house on Euclid will soon be known as the House of Virtue and Certainty! If things go on like this! If!" And looked around the group like a kindly paterfamilias who has just told a moving and ingenious fairy tale. They all breathed a sigh of relief.

Carol still wanted to talk about Teddy, who was marrying a Chicana. No one had suspected that Teddy was still harboring secret socialist sentiments and was giving evening lectures at the Bay Area Socialist School in San Francisco on Mission Street, and then he gets mixed up with a Chicana! She said that the way one would have said it in Stuttgart: With a gypsy! In this case she was apparently a Mexican. Twenty-eight, said Carol. At the moment they were discussing whether this marriage would make the woman eligible for a pension. Chances were poor. She should've married someone from the English department, said Elrod. Halm saw his opportunity. After his last visit to Grizzly Peak he had been furious with himself, he said, for not having managed to learn more about *Inspiration Inn*. So there really had been a John Frey? Kirk had mentioned a visit to the Veterans' Hospital in Long Beach? Yes, Frey hadn't recognized his old friend Kirk. But, when Kirk had hummed one of the old songs that Frey used to sing, John had not only smiled but hummed along. "Do you remember the tune?" asked Halm. Elrod hummed it. " 'From Lucerne and on to Weggis,' " said Halm. And where is Stabler City? "You must ask John Frey that," said Elrod. It was John who had told him the story. "And you didn't ask him?" asked Halm. Kirk replied that evidently John had told the story better than he had retold it—in any case he'd never wanted to know more than John had told him.

Rainer said that yesterday he had handed in his driver's license, for good, because he felt that driving was no longer for him, and it had turned out that for the last three years he had been driving without insurance. "Uh-oh!" said Carol, "that's a dig at me, I should've noticed that." "Not at all, Carol, I merely meant to say that one doesn't always have to know everything," said Rainer. Halm would even have liked to know whether what was visible through Carol's lacy black dress was Carol or whether there was some deceptive material in between. Instead he asked Rainer whether the Asra poem had been set to music. Rainer, to the others: "There are also some people who ask more than they want to know. My dear friend: two weeks from today you will be instructing us about Heine! If Annemarie, that scion of a Stuttgart family, had known that her endowment would enrich a Helmut Halm from Stuttgart by five hundred dollars!" Carol muttered: "That old scarecrow!" Rainer said: "I'll ask you to take that back." Carol said: "Stuff it!" Rainer went on to say that Annemarie's death sentence had been her mother's suicide. "Does an eighty-six-year-old, who has made herself the raison d'être of her sixty-one-year-old daughter, have to commit suicide? I have never in my life found anything more inexplicable than what mothers do." "I feel the same way about fathers," said Carol. "Annemarie," said Rainer, "not our smartest but our most warmhearted and fair-minded colleague, could no longer go on living after her mother had died. Once a month she had all her door locks replaced. When I phoned the police after finding Annemarie dead, the police refused to take that address seriously because they had been called there too often for nothing." Carol, dryly: "Please don't forget to add that she was permanently plastered." "Oh, she was drunk? And permanently? Well, I must say I seem to have no eye for that sort of thing!" Rainer exclaimed.

"She was one of us," said Kirk Elrod, "no doubt about that." "And the stingiest creature ever to assume human form," said Carol. Rainer in his murmuring tone: "Carol, it's just that she never learned how to spend money. In her family, she once told me, only her father was allowed to spend money. For everyone else, spending money was a mortal sin." Carol: "When she needed treatment for her glaucoma she didn't go to the clinic because there was a bus strike. She would wait until the buses were running again. Or I was to drive her. I told her: 'Can't you take a taxi?' After all, I knew she had millions in her bank account. It was all left to various organizations." Rainer said: "A hundred thousand came to us." "For Heine," added Carol. "And Halm," said Rainer. "She always thought of me as being anti-Semitic," said Carol. "Oh well," said Rainer, "anyone with a Baltic semiaristocrat for a father is under suspicion until proven otherwise. How are things going in Mendocino?" "No change," said Carol, "she goes on nursing him and carrying him about, he goes on complaining, and she says, 'What are you complaining about considering how well off we are?' " He weighs barely a hundred pounds, her mother had told her last week on the phone, so her burden was getting lighter from month to month. And she had laughed. "And that's been going on for fifteen years," said Rainer. "Seventeen," said Carol. "Oh," said Rainer, "then it's two years since I last asked you about your parents, forgive me."

As they walked down between the flowering stocks to Grizzly Peak Boulevard, Halm thought of Sabina and Goethe, of Annemarie and Heine, of Mrs. Dinkelspiel and of Mr. and Mrs. von der Hütte. That Lena was driving with Elissa bothered him. When might he see her again, he asked? "Sometime," she said casually.

Elissa waited beside the open car door until Lena had got in. Rainer was already in the car, on the backseat. In the end Halm and Carol found themselves alone on the street. Elrod, who had suffered no attack today, had stayed indoors. "Goodnight, Helmut," said Carol. "Goodnight, Carol," said Halm and got in and drove off. Her gaze lingered after him.

Now he felt he must phone Sabina, although they had agreed: not before Sunday. He kept trying for three hours before she answered. "Well, Sabina, how's everything?" he asked casually because he wanted to go right on telling her highlights about himself, Lena, Heine, and California. But Sabina said in that breathless voice: "He's not well at all. He's been in pain ever since waking up after the operation. They keep trying new drugs." She asked about Lena, wanting to know more than Halm could tell her. She exclaimed that he didn't seem to be looking after Lena at all. Now Halm asked after Otto. Not well either. It was her impression that he was never going to recover from his experience with Mrs. Niedlich. "Perhaps we've been away too long," said Halm. "Please, bring Lena back!" she cried. He must promise. The conversation became labored. They were talking at cross-purposes. In California it was just getting light, in Sillenbuch dark.

Halm postponed the discussion of the *Much Ado* essay until the afternoon. They met at the cafeteria table. He was free until six, when he had to go to the Faculty Club to say good-bye to a fellow German who was flying home the day after tomorrow. She was free until five, when she had an appointment with Carol. But only a short one, after that she would be free again. He read her essay, she drank milk. At the very beginning he came across a word he didn't know: "repartee." She explained to him. In Shakespeare's play, she wrote, Benedick and Beatrice behave exactly as people do today when it comes to expressing mutual affection. By means of wit and repartee, a person who is in love, hence vulnerable, tries to protect himself. When Beatrice was alone she was an entirely different person from what she was in Benedick's presence: forthright, serious, and romantic.

Halm decided to try out something with his students at home: not to translate but to understand. When one translates, one is left not with the text that has been translated but with the translation. This was how it seemed to him now as they sat at this table, because of his desire to regard the girl as an untranslatable Beatrice. She was forthright, serious, and romantic. He had no wish to know what that was in any other language. As soon as Benedick appears, they start all over again with repartee and spite. It was, wrote the girl, so much easier to communicate indirectly rather than directly. Only when Benedick was alone, when Beatrice was alone, could each express his or her emotion poetically. But, wrote the girl, she found the language of concealment they used in their belligerent dialogue more interesting than the all-revealing language of their poetic monologues. She almost regretted that to the malicious intrigue which divided the primary couple Shakespeare had added a benevolent intrigue that informed each of them of the love of the other. She would have preferred it if, without the intervention of superimposed, all-disclosing benevolence, each would personally have to discover love in the belligerent tone of the other. If such a thing were at all possible. Which she didn't know. Perhaps one was too apprehensive to do without help from outside. In plays as well as in real life.

"Is that really the way it is?" asked Halm. What he meant was, whether there could be such a thing as a benevolent intrigue in real life? Had she ever experienced that? Oh, she cried, she was experiencing it right now! Since discussing Halm with Carol, she understood him much better. "I see," said Halm, looking down at the essay paper. He didn't dare indicate how much he would have liked to know what Carol had told her about him. Should he tell her that latterly Carol has been speaking of her with enthusiasm? In that case he would have also had to say that only a few weeks ago Carol had been parroting that unkind phrase, "the dumb beauty." Better for him to continue reading: "Loneliness finds expression in the language of hostility," she had written. The couple positively screamed. Shouldn't they have been allowed to go on screaming until they both dropped dead at each other's feet? What was the point of mutual understanding? Merely to open the way to a lifelong misunderstanding on a lower plane? Granted that, at the crucial moment, the benevolent intrigue of the environment can point to works of literature in which two lonely ones have betrayed themselves as loving ones, but perhaps everything would still go on in the adversarial tone if Benedick were not to cry: "Peace; I will stop your mouth. (*Kissing her*)" It is only this final wordless action, rendering all further words superfluous, that brings the couple fully and finally together. After that Beatrice has no further text. Her mouth has been stopped. When happiness begins, every play comes to an end. "Strike up, pipers." They dance off.

She felt divided, she wrote, when she thought about this sequence of events. Naturally the unwinding of such a plot satisfied the desire that has been aroused by it. But because everything here progressed with such unwavering smoothness, she ended up feeling slightly more deserted in the insignificant complexity of her mere life. It is as satisfying as it is impossible for two perfectly matching hostilities to meet and confront one another until they become a *single* bliss. She at any rate, more often than not, must fear that she will go astray. Her tone usually met with no response. To experience someone else adjusting to the tone one has cautiously offered—even if it is a tone of hostility—must be like the emerging of an oasis on the desert horizon. What was so irrational and exciting about the Benedick-Beatrice confrontation was the total unison of their hostility. That must be fabulous. That's what one longs for. You open your mouth and say *a*, the other says *z*; you say *b*, he says *y*; you *c*, he *x*; you *d*, he *w*; you *e*, he *v*; you *f*, he *u*; you *g*, he *t*; you *h*, he *s*; you *i*, he *r*; you *k*, he *p*; you *l*, he *o*; you *m*, he *n*. In *m* and *n* they meet, recognize one another, they fuse. MNMN. No further ado necessary. No further ado. No ado. Just nothing. Thus she concluded her essay.

Halm looked back to the place where *m* and *n* come together and fuse. Surely she must have meant HalM and FraN! Enough, Malvolio! *Thy smiles become thee well*. You may not know exactly what Marlon Brando looks like when he smiles, but you do know what you look like when you smile! Nobody, man or woman, is going to fool you with: Your smile suits you, Helmut dear. So he told her this essay was her best so far. He marked a couple of places and how they could be improved, then went on to praise her ideas. She wouldn't accept that. After all, it was he who had given her the stimulus, the direction, the courage, above all the courage. For a while, each tried hard to convince the other. Each wanted to heap praise on the other. Neither wanted to accept it from the other. The result was again a kind of closeness. Although it was only sentences, breath patterns, with which they attacked each other, if a spiritual plane exists, something developed between them. It was a celebration, a rejoicing. She had succeeded in something. And he applauded her vigorously for that while at the same time thinking also of *his* deadline, of *his* forthcoming appearance, of *his* response to Beatrice and Benedick. Next week, he said, Asra and Laura, a similar couple. Unfortunately he hadn't yet got very far, he felt so . . . paralyzed.

And as if he had to prove the opposite, he stood up, said good-bye, and left. As he had done before, some weeks ago, he as good as abandoned her among her spread-out papers. If he hadn't used that stupid, absurdly inaccurate, totally trite word "paralyzed" to describe himself, he would still be sitting there, his life would take a different course. . . . Who is in charge in moments like this? It's not the kind of reaction a person has when he jumps aside to avoid a rapidly approaching car! But it must be something of the kind, otherwise he wouldn't now find himself hurrying along the campus paths. Hurrying where? Slow down. You've been out of her sight for a long time. You could at least have asked for a copy of that excellent essay. She'd probably brought one along. Now she's disappointed that you didn't ask for it.

He hurried uphill, at each fork taking the steeper branch. He was sweating. He had never been to the upper periphery of the campus, where the student residences were. At the moment he simply couldn't have endured a level path, much less a downhill one. He had to go uphill. At last he could come to a halt. He had to. He was out of breath. In front of him, in a gentle hollow, a few girls sat in a circle at equal distances from all the trees. He counted them. He started with the one wearing a T-shirt, she was easy to remember. He counted ten girls. All sitting in the lotus position. Around them, bicycles, clothing, dogs. As one imagines a gathering of gods. Seeing the kids sitting like that in the grass, the effort of getting here did not seem in vain. Loudspeakers boomed from the residences. At the moment not one of the girls was laughing. But the gravity on all their faces had nothing ponderous about it. Perhaps they were merely concentrating on what they were discussing among themselves, in the warm October sunshine, sitting on the grass, in California, in a gentle hollow.

How long was it permissible for him to stand here gazing at this girl-Olympus? The previous Sunday the rapist had for the first time found his victims on campus. Another three girls had been raped. Now one of the dogs had become bored with hanging around and had begun to pester a red-setter bitch. She would have nothing to do with him. But he is strong, highly motivated; a few times he succeeds in inserting himself, but never for very long. She shakes him off. The chase continues. But now Halm really had to leave. What else does he expect to see here? He walked up as far as the residences. On the little fire escape platforms some girls were exposing their thighs to the sun. On all sides a cacophony of youth comes pouring out of the dorms. Why must it be Fran? In the face of this display of girls he had to ask himself this question. Why not Fran? Fran was probably the most typical of all. She was the personification. That was why it was so difficult to remember her. She typified everything female that existed on campus. As a person she was not important. . . . Thus his thoughts went round and round. Thus he tried to cope. Thus he spent his time until he could enter the huge log house to drink a farewell glass of wine with Mr. Zipser.

Too bad that Zipser had to go back so soon. Maybe they'd meet again in Leipzig or Stuttgart. What Halm regretted most, he said, was that he hadn't taken the time to reconcile Fritz Dempewolf with Zipser, or rather with the German Democratic Republic. "So good-bye for now, my dear Zipser!"

Heavy with wine, Halm walked across the campus down to the old car parked beside the wall of the stadium. A pity he wouldn't be seeing Zipser again that soon, probably never again. How discreet Zipser became when the discussion turned to the difficulties of life in his country! Tomorrow he had to fly via New York to Rome, from there take an eastern bloc plane to Prague, and then home. He had been told to fly with TAROM, but he would rather have renounced California. He has had some experience with TAROM. . . . Halm felt pampered, no longer capable of enduring hardship. Zipser judged everything in terms of how it furthered his work. It was due to sloppiness in East Berlin that he had arrived here without a visa. In Prague he had had to behave like a raving maniac, which is not his nature. In New York IREX had to vouch for him. And tomorrow, still without a visa, the same thing in reverse.

Halm drove home as slowly as possible, home to the TV set. He was in no shape to continue working on his lecture: the wine, in fact this entire day. He turned onto Contra Costa Avenue as if into a safe harbor. As he approached the garage and was about to press the electronic button for the garage door, he caught sight in the dusk of the white car standing at the curb, a BMW, *the* BMW. It flashed its turning signal, swung directly in front of Halm onto the road, braked, came to a halt on the road. Halm also turned back onto the road, drove toward the brake lights, which went out; the BMW started moving, Halm followed. He had no choice. The first curve was a hairpin bend. Through a tunnel of trees, by now quite dark, they crawled ahead as far as the traffic circle; the BMW turned onto the street leading straight up the hill. Halm followed. He recalled the TV advertising slogan for BMWs: "The ultimate driving machine." On TV the white BMW then stopped outside a palace. That seemed to be applying to him. If the white 528, on reaching the top, were at some point to turn distinctly to the right, it could only be heading for Oakland Hills, for Hill Court. And Hill Court—that was its palace. But how does she know that he knows that she drives a BMW? He couldn't see her now. He would have to switch on the high beam. Even then the headrest would conceal her head. Luckily she was driving a BMW and not a Porsche. Carol, you won't be forgiven for trying to destroy this girl with clichés. At the top she unfortunately turned left. Of course, she's heading for the park. Fine, he has his running shoes in the trunk. There followed a seemingly endless drive. Curve after curve downhill, then again curve after curve uphill. As far as he's concerned, this can go on for decades, forever as far as he's concerned. Oh, Fran. So she has noticed more, much more, than he ever suspected. How unobservant he was. He has one experience after another and fails to perceive that others also have experiences. Twice he has seen her drive by in her BMW. So how in the world does he know that while he has always seen her she has never seen him? Perhaps she has seen him nine times without his noticing her. What a good thing he has taken up driving again!

He was carried away by their stately gliding through the dark. This afternoon, that rejoicing. Now this stately progress. At last that suffocating sense of exclusion was over. That holding back, that sense of asphyxiation. Take this slow driving, for instance. She wants the old Volvo to keep up with her. Or the old driver. Him too, if you please! Then she signaled, a parking area showed up to the left under some trees; she turned in, he followed, she stopped, he stopped behind her. Now get out of your car. But he couldn't. He hadn't initiated any of this, hadn't wanted it, he simply lacked. . . .

Now the door of the other car opened and out came, and toward Halm came: Carol. She swung her hips as she walked, as if carried along by music. She was smiling. This was the Nimitz Way entrance, did he remember? Starting from here and following along the ridge there was a path, she didn't know for how many miles, through eucalyptus groves and over bare hilltops, with views over Golden Gate out onto the Pacific and, when you turned around, over all the golden hills far into the hinterland. So if he was planning to continue with his jogging, she urged him not to be put off by the slightly longer approach and to start from here from the Nimitz Way entrance. It really looked as though he had to intervene, or Carol would never be able to stop. He had also got out of the car. To top it all there was a full moon over the hills. And all the cars, that's to say people, in sight—they were all so-called lovers. Carol said she had also shown this spot to Messmer. "Ah yes, Messmer," said Halm, "my peerless predecessor." "Try harder," she said.

"Since when have you been driving a BMW?" he asked her in an inquisitorial tone. "Come on, don't pretend," she said. Did she mean it wasn't hers? he asked. Are you kidding? Surely he knew it was Fran's car, didn't he? Fran's! Now just a moment, Fran drives a Porsche. Also white. But a Porsche. Papa, Practice, Pacific Heights, Porsche: according to Carol's information! She: "Why not a BMW?" And there he'd been thinking, he said, when he saw her down on Contra Costa, what do you know? Carol's test-driving a new model and wants my advice! Nimitz Gate and jogging was the last thing he would have thought of right then, or he'd have asked her to wait while he changed, but on the other hand it would have been a bit late in the day. "So you never believed for a second that Fran was luring you away?" she asked. "Carol, my dear, I have to disappoint you. When you turned onto the street down there, I could see you almost in full profile, and you certainly never told me that Fran drives a BMW—so much for that." "Too bad," she said. "My little ploy has failed!" "Let's celebrate that!" he said.

He was all agog, as if some great event were imminent. She must lead the way again. To a Chinese restaurant, please! She knew of one. He hoped their fortune cookies wouldn't yield any embarrassing sayings. He must smooth over the evening with a veneer of complete harmony. How wonderful Carol was! That must emerge from everything he said and did. She was wonderful. By means of her wonderful ploy on this wonderful October evening in this wonderful country, Carol had proved in the most wonderful manner that he probably—how was he to put it?—that he probably did love that girl Fran. Otherwise it would have been totally impossible for him to stay on such calm and friendly terms with that glorious Carol who, despite her Are you kidding?, still radiated an aura of English-German Romanticism. He was lucky with his fortune cookie. Out of sheer inadvertence he had eaten his oracle with the cookie, and Carol's oracle miraculously said: "There is a true and sincere friendship between you."

Now he could ask her point-blank: "By the way, do you still hear from your friend Messmer?" She swallowed the bait. In other words: there was no one she would rather talk about than Messmer. Admittedly it sounded like one continuous tirade about him, but then that was Carol as Beatrice. Halm could now understand that better than a few weeks ago. He wished he had also reached the point where he could let loose a torrent of invective about Fran.

Later, when they were standing outside again in the moonlight beside their cars, Carol's last words, before she opened the door of the BMW, were: "Well, now I have to return the car to Fran, I hope she isn't asleep yet." He watched her drive off, he waved, the white BMW disappeared; now once again the other woman was sitting in it. Should he phone Carol when she might be expected to have reached home? Don't you dare! *He*-Halm formulated the suspicion that *I*-Halm was equally uninterested in both and was merely using the one to mask the other, and the other to nullify the effect of the first. *I*-Halm did not argue. He wanted peace from this tumult. He needed peace. Well, now I have to return the car to Fran, I hope she isn't asleep yet. Up there, over there, in Oakland Hills, Hill Court, a Maybeck house, Carol had said, he'd have to look it up sometime, a Maybeck house, that sounded good. I hope she isn't asleep yet. He carefully poured the wine back into the bottle. He had been mistaken. He needed some milk. And some TV.

12

THAT A PERSON SHOULD do as he pleased impressed Halm. On the outside, architecturally speaking, the Rineharts' house, with its roof shape and tiles, was remotely Spanish. The garden between street and house was Japanese. Then on the inside that mirror-encrusted, English-Japanese department-store Versailles. Vulgar pomp. Halm felt good when he walked barefoot across the golden carpet prairie. He found himself growing more and more able to face his mirror reflections. Daily jogging. Wine and nicotine approaching zero. Since Sabina was no longer feeding him, his meals had ceased to be meals. He nibbled at snacks. Ate fruit. It felt as if he were eating up an entire harvest. And now he drank milk. He was spending between four and five dollars a day on himself. The fact that he could write his Heine lecture in ten days but live off the proceeds for a hundred days, enhanced his satisfaction. Certain people wouldn't have recognized him. He felt as if he had arrived at a high plateau. He had never felt as light before. If only he could have taken Rainer with him. But when he enthused about his new life, Rainer looked at him as if from an immeasurable distance. Once he said: "Cut the propaganda, for God's sake." Halm felt annoyed. Rainer was right. He was being just as pushy as his ex-friend Buch, who apparently couldn't enjoy anything without succumbing to the compulsion of trying to force it on other people too.

Every morning he walked barefoot down the stairs, across the patio, onto the lawn, and made movements that were alien to him. Gradually all mental activity ceased, the movements remained. So-called experiences were left to his bare feet on the dewy grass. In the evening, as he ran through the gullies and slopes of the Tilden solitude, he surrendered everything to his muscles, his lungs, and so on. In the morning, when he steps through the patio door, the cat immediately comes running from her little wilderness, follows him to plate and bowl, watches them being filled, but then, instead of eating, accompanies him down the patio steps onto the lawn. In time with his two bare feet, she performs gymnastics down the steps. She is always a tenth of a second ahead of the foot on the next step, is already lying exactly where he wants to step: so he has to adjust to her. But as soon as he has put his foot down, she attacks it, flings herself upon it, insinuates herself; when the second foot arrives, can't decide between the two, forms a link between both feet; notices when one foot wants to move on, hurls herself down in front of it, and is there below it that tenth of a second earlier so as to be able instantly to hurl herself upon it again. How is one supposed ever to arrive at the bottom of such a feline scale! But when he does finally arrive at the bottom and steps onto the wet lawn in order to let the dewy grass complete what the cat has started with his feet, she streaks off. In two or three leaps she is up beside plate and bowl: now she can eat and drink. Hunger and thirst do not come to her until she has had his feet. But he gets something out of it too. Every day a little more. When he arrives on campus wearing shoes, they contain feet that have experienced the passionate caresses of a young part-Angora cat.

It is hardly a theme for his conversation class. But he feels so alive that he refuses all preparation. Now he would have been embarrassed to arrive in the classroom with a plan to assume the role of a superior person. If we are alive now, that must somehow proclaim itself, hence be capable of being put into words. And why? Because we are together in one room. That is the sensation. No one is alone at this moment. How does each person affect the others? Jeff, am I disturbing you in your doodling, or are you doing it only to justify your sprawling across the table or perhaps just to keep yourself awake? Believe me, this is of interest to your conversation instructor. Elaine, how about you? Tell us what you think of us. Gail, I'm so glad to see you among us again. We read the interview with you in the *Campus Gazette,* Gail. You've been elected spokesperson for the handicapped students. Let us in on it. What happened? From the interview we learned that you've suffered from this paralysis for only two years, as the result of diving head first from a balcony into a snowpile many feet deep, that the snowpile had frozen into solid blocks—at Lake Tahoe, where your parents have a cottage. Do we include each other in our sensations of the moment, today, now—or have we nothing in common? All of you, and he, your instructor?

Every day he had to hurry back as fast as possible to the Rineharts' house and work on his Asra presentation, that paradoxical role. As Asra who speaks up, who doesn't die. "Our lecturer has a fever," said Rainer, whenever they met. On Saturday there would be people from Sonoma and Palo Alto in the audience. Apparently Halm's topic "One of the Tribe of Asra," was proving attractive. "Oh, it's already called something else," said Halm. "So what's it called now?" asked Rainer. Halm was reluctant. The new title would instantly betray everything to Rainer. For the first time Halm sensed that he required courage to perform the Asra role on Saturday. Faced with Rainer he lacked this courage. Since by now everything had been printed, he said, he wanted even Rainer not to be confronted with the new title until Saturday. "Oho, so we're to be confronted, are we?" said Rainer.

Halm was almost glad that Carol was staying away all week. She was in Mendocino; her father's condition was far from good. But he ran into Kirk Elrod twice. On each occasion, Kirk wanted to drag him off to the Faculty Club for a drink. Halm said: "Impossible, my lecture!" Kirk said: "Publish or perish, you have adapted perfectly." Whether it was Dempewolf, Roy or Leslie Ackerman, or Felix Theodor Auster just returned from Reno, he postponed everything—invitations for skat, reading, conversation—until after his own lecture. As a result he found himself in a kind of mood that stood him in good stead when he sat at Professor Rinehart's sticky and therefore uncluttered desk. At least, that's what he thought. He felt it was going well. As he wrote, many things cropped up of which he hadn't thought during the preparation. And after working for eight hours and jogging for one hour, he would eat his fruit and vegetables in front of the television; especially if, before that, following Sabina's instructions, he had talked to Lena on the phone and heard from her that she had meanwhile obtained her driver's license, for the motorbike as well as for the car.

They chatted comfortably with each other, feeling sorry for the poor relatives in Europe where fog has clamped its mushy teeth down on the Sillenbuch north slope and won't release its hold until the end of February. Hospital, cemetery, Kiderlen, a permanently despondent Otto . . . what else? Mind you, things at the Hansel and Gretel house are also quite alarming. Even the tarantula has problems. It has refused the last two cicadas. They had perished in the crystal landscape. Elissa is wondering whether there might be a conspiracy against her tarantula. She is already afraid for Jamey's souvenir bird, P. One must be prepared for anything to happen, she says, whereas Lena is quite sure that only the bearable can happen. She can present it in such a way that Elissa's suspicious anxiety can subside for minutes on end. That's Lena's main task there: to reassure Elissa that no plot is being hatched on the lower floor of the house. Lena hopes she is not mistaken. "Oh, Lena," says Halm, "all the things you'll be taking on in America!" But she likes what she's doing. He's going to tell Sabina that. "See you soon, child! Don't forget me." "I'm trying to!" "Cheeky!" Obviously the Traugott effect was fading. The best thing would always be to travel into another language. With the words for it, the worst is left behind. And there are so many languages.

Halm settled down in front of the TV. He is fascinated by the way people kiss here. He had already observed this on campus, but on television, now that he was alone, he could do so more closely. Amazing the way the women here let their mouths drop open, the way the men then sank their mouths over the open mouths of the women. No wonder that, on studying the program, he marked the title "An Unusual Love" and proceeded to watch it. His own case in TV format. On the familiar coast Highway 1 a red VW beetle, a convertible, the blond at the wheel, stops near Pacific College, a careless cyclist rides into the car door as it opens, he turns out to be an instructor in marine biology at the college, the blond attends the same college, he asks her for a date, she's always too busy, has a part-time job, he helps her with an essay, she gets a B, he could take out a girl who drives a Porsche but he takes her out for some ice cream, but instead of having the ice cream he kisses her, she goes to his place, lets the spaghetti splatter onto the floor, tells him she's working at a health bar, that she's a prostitute, four times a day; after all this she leaves, he is appointed deputy chairman, an oil tanker is stranded, the students salvage oil-drenched creatures from the surf, still further impediments must arise, but then he discovers the movie explanation: her father hated her mother, tried to have sex with the daughter, she was twelve at the time; when she is seventeen her boyfriend sends her out onto the streets, but now she is saved, both are saved, united in the torrential California rain, The End.

The VW driver was more like Fran than he was like the instructor. He was suitable for TV only as a spectator. After a movie like that he felt not exactly sullied but soiled, besmirched, befouled. On the one hand one is glad that television is not like life, but on the other hand one blames it for not being so. Can one expect TV to be like life? In that case nobody would watch it. "Life on TV is better than at your front door."

Then back to the verbal depiction of the pain of the Heine poem. Reading the printed program for Saturday gave him palpitations. His lecture came last. Before his lecture, Roy would sing Schumann's *Dichterliebe* cycle, accompanied by Mrs. Ackerman, the hermaphrodite researcher with the beautiful skull face framed by the thick blond braids. Imagine Roy singing! Wasn't it Sally who had that bottomless vibrating voice? Should Halm wear a tie? Yes. Because there would be a song recital. And your Asra text requires apparel that's inappropriate to the text.

And on the Friday before this Saturday, around noon, at the table where they had both ordered milk, the girl drew from her purplish bag her essay on *Much Ado:* she had been given a C-minus. He thought of the B given the student on TV. As his students in Stuttgart would have said: Knocked for a loop. Halm hid his face as undramatically as possible. That bastard! That idiot! That asshole! What's his name? W. Martin Littlewood. Where does he live? Where's his office? That's the limit! It's deliberate! And if it isn't deliberate, then it denotes an incompatibility that shouldn't be expressed by marking! "He'll be hearing from me," said Halm. All these question marks! She showed him the pages scribbled over in red. On five pages, seventy-seven question marks, she'd counted them, that makes 15.4 question marks per page. I ask you, can there be any essay fit to be bombarded with 15.4 question marks per page?

Halm shook his head more vehemently than ever in his life. "Fran, don't worry. You are the victim of deliberate malice on the part of a teacher. He is in love with you. He is having his revenge. I'm quite sure of it. You can believe me. There are teachers who are as weak as that. There are teachers who are weaker than any student can imagine. How old is he?" "Old," she says, "pretty old, around fifty." Halm, with lightning speed: "Then it's revenge! Personal, in any case. After fifty, some people get like that! Believe me!" Would Fran mind lending him the essay? He'd like to have a closer look at all those question marks, that saturation bombardment, that graveyard of question marks.

He puts the pages in his briefcase and is at a complete loss. He has the feeling of having fled his pursuers as far as the extreme edge of this continent and of now standing at the brink of a sheer cliff. So it has all been for nothing. But how could everything not have been for nothing? Idiot. The language doesn't contain words harsh enough to teach you a lesson; you need a treatment going beyond that. If only he had nerves strong enough to bear such a silence! And he couldn't endure her anxious south Swedish rain-gaze either. Didn't her gaze seem to ask if there was something the matter with him? The mark is his disaster, right. He has steered her toward the secondary theme of Benedick and Beatrice. She has practically ignored the primary action around Hero and Claudio. On his advice. He is to blame, to blame, to blame. His colleague had obviously been totally baffled, could only resort to question marks. According to him, she had not even discovered the four stages in the couple's choice of words! And the one thing that had fascinated Halm, the spellbinding movement of *a* and *z* toward each other to fuse in *m* and *n* had been positively peppered with question marks by this WML.

With a great effort Halm got up and said he would obtain satisfaction for Fran. No, she said, she didn't want that, that would be impossible, as soon as Halm intervened she'd be done for, she must manage on her own, she would manage, Professor Littlewood was a generator of clowns. Wherever one came across a clown he could be traced to Littlewood's hand. She hated clowns. Clowns were extortioners. She hated extortioners. Littlewood was an extortioner. But she'd take care of him. As easy as that. And she snapped her fingers. No problem. Today she would run twice as far and swim three times as far as usual—so where did that leave that generator of clowns, W. Martin Littlewood? "Have a nice weekend," she said, and her face glowed with such warmth that he wanted to cover his eyes with his hands. How were these eyes to perceive anything of lesser radiance in the future? Yes, a nice weekend, he wished her that too. But we'll see each other before then. She turned, walked left past the cafeteria, down the steps, under the trees, was gone.

Pretty empty, a Friday like this, now. He'd follow her example: run twice as far. He drove to the Nimitz Way entrance and jogged along Carol's high trail. A vast expanse of sky glowed above the Pacific. The pylons of Golden Gate Bridge stood up to their hips in purple mist. The longer he ran, the darker it grew, the lighter did San Francisco become before its backdrop of hills. On his way back, the moon filled the eastern sky and the empty hilly country. The west was dominated by San Francisco's splashes of light, glittering green-gold, a restless cluster of jewels. And himself facing it all. That gave him a momentary sense of composure. His gaze kept returning to the sky, below which the ocean must be lying. The Heine day wouldn't begin until eleven. He'll start off, as befits Heine, as early as six for the coast. North of San Francisco, run directly alongside the breakers. Perhaps he would discover Muir Cove.

As always when he planned something, he went beyond what he had intended. He was ready by five-thirty. A little more time-conscious than usual, he abandoned his feet to the downward-somersaulting cat. He drove his car quietly out of the sleeping street; once beyond it, he pressed down the accelerator in the direction of Albany, El Cerrito, Richmond Bridge. He was on the lookout for the place where the streets meet, or, for those driving in the opposite direction, separate, where the girl had driven onto the concrete dividers. He saw the concrete strips. A pretty brutal way to divide a street like that. At home there would be a hundred blinking lights to indicate the curve, and there would be boards and painted fences. Here everything was left to the drivers.

He found the exit, even found Pelican Inn where John Frey had parked his car. But the road led still farther down into the bay. He drove until potholes and ditches forced him to stop. In front of him the bay, that could scarcely be called wide, starkly framed by steep slopes, to the north by rocks. And a rocky spur divided the curve of the bay into two bays. John Frey had been able to climb over this spur, he couldn't. Beyond the rocky spur shone pale yellow mud slides, pale rock walls, and carpets of thick-leaved plants creeping over the rocks. Stretching from one end of the bay to the other, the surf. For a moment Halm sees the white breakers as a row of teeth in an enormous mouth laughing in the morning sun. Far out above the ocean, a bank of clouds. He walked up the path, which on the map was marked Coastal Edge Trail; at the top he continued south, jogging along through high, dense scrub. Around deeply indented bays. Below him, always the Pacific, rocks and bays assaulted by the surf. And because he enjoyed moving around, albeit with foreign feet, in this other language, he thought as he looked down on the invading surf as it sprayed its white foam into the bays: coast-fucking Pacific. Some of the little bays looked like rocky chambers and halls. He saw a hundred places where the Swiss lady might have found an abode. Perhaps John Frey had walked along here and been infected by the limitless opportunities for hiding in the area. At least a weekend in such a Pacific bathroom! Since Mr. Kiderlen had telephoned Carol and pretended to be cordially inclined toward Halm, it had become advisable to look around for such hideaways. So far he had seen nothing that promised a refuge equal to these tiny bays, guarded by that ocean with those breakers.

Halm ran and stopped and gazed, and ran on again. The air all around him was scented. He thrust his hand into the dry scrub and it came out full of brittle stuff. He sniffed it: he recognized the scent from Sabina's perfume or from her kitchen, but he couldn't identify it. So the result of all his contemptible education was that, in spite of that all-pervading scent, he lacked the thing that was the most important to him, merely because he couldn't think of the word: its name. Also because he wanted to tell Sabina which herbs, stretching all the way to the horizon, he had been running through. When Sabina wasn't along, he couldn't experience anything, without, in the experience, already formulating it for Sabina's benefit so he could tell her about it. When he couldn't identify the hibiscus growing up the wall beside the patio door of the Rinehart house, Sabina had said: "All you can recognize is snowdrops, right?" He put the handful of crumbling herbs into the zipper pocket of his running shorts. Here Sabina would be running too. Here one had to run. The only danger: not being able to stop. To turn back, unimaginable. Imaginable, however, essential in fact: to go on running until one could run no farther. At some point one was bound to find oneself on the last hill before the

Golden Gate, across from San Francisco. He felt he was acquiring a bit of a tan for his Asra presentation. Sea breezes and sunshine would paint a little Yemen on his face.

Suddenly he looked down on a cut that widened out away from the sea. A real little valley, with even a green meadow, and fair-sized shrubs and little trees. Under those trees, a car, so weathered as to be almost part of the scenery. He climbed down. A dog ran toward him, barking. A bearded man emerged from the island of bushes and trees and called to Micky to come back. Oh for God's sake, no . . . Klaus Buch! To Halm it seemed the little valley was rocking, trying to revolve around him but unable to achieve momentum, but it jerked and swayed. This had to happen to him! He flees to the end of the world into the arms of that arch-interferer, that super-adventurer, that miserable ex-friend Buch always out to get the better of him! And who said in Rainer Mersjohann's accent: "I'm real, all right."

Was anything wrong, the man asked? Oh no, thank you. Fortunately, in spite of that deep tan, that shaggy beard, and that virility, it wasn't Klaus Buch but someone who immediately recognized Halm as a German because he was one himself. His name was Harold Maier-Friese. With a gesture that embraced his little valley he said: "Here you see the end of the German student movement. If you've come here deliberately, to track me down, let's say, you must be from the German Secret Service." Halm denied that was the case. He was in a bad mood today, the other man said, because he had been robbed the day before. While he had been out at sea, fishing. Everything gone. The quasi-honest earnings from making and selling belts. Nowhere did the lack of political training have a more disastrous effect than on a thief. A thief always robs the wrong person. Even his *Auto-Erotic Care Book* by Miss Snow of Pacific Heights was gone. It wasn't you by any chance, was it? Halm solemnly denied this. "Oh well, never hurts to ask, does it? So, on your way, friend, jogging is healthier than Christianity and less harmful than Marxism." And he disappeared into his trees and bushes.

This incident gave Halm the strength to turn back. Had it not been for this veteran, he would probably have disappeared somewhere here. Like that fellow—he had made it. Robbed, it was true, and in a bad mood, yet in what an enviable mood! Otto, how about that, just we two here. . . . So back along the brittle, scented hillsides. He would never see all this again. So make the most of it. At the Pelican Inn, which looked as if Shakespeare had sat there before John Frey, he had some coffee. He wanted to say: Milk . . . it does. . . . But he said nothing, drank his coffee black. His head felt enormous. His whole body felt on fire.

On the way back he was overtaken by clouds. On Richmond Bridge he was glad the Volvo wasn't that light a car. Gusts of wind tugged at his steering, and even before he reached Contra Costa it started to rain. Not drops but sheets of rain. Finely dispersed water drifted through the air as a solid tissue of wetness.

He changed his clothes and, as always, was overpunctual, the first to arrive at the Faculty Club. Delay due to a rainstorm was always provided for in his calculations. He hated making himself conspicuous by arriving late. He listened to the lectures preceding him with a kind of exemplary attention. This meant that he could virtually not listen at all but sit and look like someone who is listening. He was tense. Thirty at most in the audience. Rainer introduced each speaker. He was a master of the light tone expected in such introductions. I'm sorry we couldn't arrange the weather. A German department could least afford these days to invite people to a symposium without laying on good weather for them. We have learned from Avis that we must try harder. . . .

Halm hadn't seen the girl yet. Probably she would come only for his lecture. With a big smile she had wished him a nice weekend. That was routine. She just happened not to have remembered that on Saturday he would be presenting "Asra and Laura." So far he hadn't seen a single one of his own students. No doubt they would all turn up only for *his* lecture. That was flattering. During the last break he drank two more cups of coffee; he had been drinking coffee during each break. His head was on fire. When

Roy and Sally had approached Halm, Roy had exclaimed: "Sally, look, Helmut as a baked tomato, what a subject for you!" Sally displayed her gleaming smile. Now Halm knew what he looked like. Obviously not like an Asra from the Yemen. And everyone who knew him remarked on his sunburn. Carol said: "Oh, did you fall asleep in the solarium?" Rainer said: "Never go to the beach without a hat, my boy."

On returning to the little auditorium with Rainer, he thought there were now a few more in the audience. In passing he caught the gleam of the girl's blond hair. He and Rainer sat down. Joyce Ackerman and Roy Kinsman went to the front. Joyce accompanied, Roy sang. The roughest of the Roughnecks sang the *Dichterliebe* cycle. A different Roy. Leaning into the emotional curves of Heine and Schumann. For the first time that day Halm was listening. I'll be damned, he thought. The castrator of pigs and husband of Sally! The master of asshole-language! And now he finds and winds and binds tones that make Heine and Schumann float and flow away. I'll be damned. Halm glanced at Sally, who was sitting beside him. Today she was all in white; only lips, nails, and shoes were bright red. The lips not only moistly red but positively swelling with pride and pleasure. Surely something was about to flow out from those banks of moisture. He remembered the umbrella she had been carrying: the handle was a dog from between whose legs the umbrella shaft protruded as its sexual organ. Undoubtedly her own work.

So, where are we now in this *Dichterliebe*? Halm couldn't remember ever having heard these songs before. For that you had to come to California. He hoped Fran understood the words. *Ich grolle nicht*. . . . Oh Roy, imagine being able to convey so much meaning! An all-encompassing mood felt by fifty people to the same degree. A single breath in the room, that of Heine-Schumann-Roy. Each one a poet.

And in the great sea sink it
  Beneath the proudest wave;

For such a mighty coffin
Should have a mighty grave.

Perhaps this touched Halm so deeply because that morning he had been jogging along the Coastal Edge Trail.

You know what makes my coffin
So great, so hard to bear?
It holds my love within it,
And my too heavy care.

That's how it's done. That's how it was done. Simply a pretty story, four lines, meter and rhyme, and down it goes, once more an emotion has been sunk in a lead container and it can no longer radiate. Apparently Schumann is terribly serious about it. Was Heine equally serious? And Roy takes it even more seriously than Schumann. Can he possibly survive that? During the applause the old Roy gradually reemerges. The grin with which he accompanied his asshole-language returned hesitantly. Last of all, gestures like a boxer. The old Roy.

"Hey, Helmut, it's your turn!" Rainer whispered in Halm's ear. The audience had stopped clapping, Halm mounted the two steps and walked to the lectern that stood off to one side. He placed his manuscript on the lectern, removed the paper clip from the pages, and suddenly felt unable to begin immediately. Possibly he'd been listening so hard that he hadn't gone on breathing regularly. He had been too closely attuned to Roy's breathing rhythm. But probably Roy had drawn breath a few times without Halm's noticing it. Halm didn't know how he was ever going to get his breath back. The possibility of breathing in, of inhaling again, seemed to be totally cut off, blocked. How long had he been standing there without air? Should he flail his arms? Open his mouth wide? It was affecting his legs. He could feel himself collapsing. He heard a noise that seemed to approach but then immediately moved away again. About fifty nurses bent over him with open mouths. He was lying on a stretcher. Next thing he was being loaded into a vehicle which shook and swayed and moved off, and so on.

In the hospital he was able to ask the doctor what was going on. The doctor replied: A sort of collapse. Could Halm think of any explanation? "I've stopped drinking," said Halm in the style of the local tongue-in-cheek introductions. But alone in the room he felt gripped by a kind of rigidity. He was incapable of any movement. His now totally petrified imagination permitted only two or three images. On the floor, heavy, paralyzed. Finding it hard to breathe. He must remember to tell the doctor this. He had told him that, apart from a persistent buzzing in his ears, there was nothing bothering him.

Although he told Sabina about it in a way that would prevent the slightest shock, she was so shocked that she stammered like her brother Elmar. She shouted and stammered. So he outshouted her and started all over again with his phrases designed to gloss over anything bad. Gradually she came to believe him. Perhaps her nerves were to blame for her overreaction. Her father's pain: the doctors had run out of ideas, the nurses had ceased to believe in that pain, no one had ever heard of such pain, but now tell me, how could that have happened, because I wasn't there, I shouldn't have left you, I've known it all along, it was the worst mistake I ever made, even if this hadn't happened, I would have told you today, I should have stayed with you, I wanted to turn back right away, never mind the cost, after a few days I wanted to go back again, but if you could see Father, see him lying there, can you understand? Yes, yes, for God's sake, Sabina, stay there, stay there! This minor attack, it's nothing, nothing at all compared to what your poor father's going through. . . .

It was becoming a twenty-dollar conversation. Halm's collapse at the lectern gradually turned into evidence of his inability to live without Sabina. But it wasn't like Turin, Sabina. They even exchanged details about hospital rooms there and here. No one could fall down in this room, said Halm, unless the door happened to be open, and then he'd be lying in the corridor. And the corridor was in turn so crowded that anyone falling down had no chance of reaching the floor. Probably he'd fall anyway onto the black cleaning woman droning away day and night with her vacuum cleaner. . . . She could hear he was feeling better. It was really getting too expensive.

The conversation with Sabina did him good. He wished he could secretly take off right now, but he wasn't allowed to leave until Monday afternoon. Rainer arrived with Lena. Rainer shook his head, raised his Saint John's hands, and said: "Oh boy!" But he had had the lecture copied and distributed immediately, which meant that, since the intention of the endowment had been fulfilled by the dissemination of an opinion on a poem by Heinrich Heine, Helmut could be paid off with five hundred Annemarie-dollars. And that's never the least important part, is it! Halm tried to stroke Rainer. He told the despondent, worried Lena that he was well, probably too well, that was what his body couldn't take, it had rebelled against being deprived of its accustomed, long-suffering, tough sickliness. Jogging by the sea! Not with this body! It doesn't have to accept that! There'd been no such bargain! This running around here was getting worse and worse! What next! So back to the easygoing old ways, and the body is immediately reconciled and behaves again. Rainer agreed with this diagnosis. But I'll teach it, said Halm. Now we're really going to see some training! They'd soon find out who was the boss. Now he had tasted blood! His project for his old age was going to be sports. If there was to be no book on Nietzsche, there would at least be an unparalleled physical renaissance. "Your father has suffered badly from exposure to the hot California sun," said Rainer. "It was the change in the weather," said Halm. Without that plus coffee plus coffee plus coffee it would never have happened. "Don't forget the *Dichterliebe*," said Rainer. The one who was really to blame, said Halm, was Lena, who had chosen to spend the weekend with Elissa in Sacramento. If Lena had been there he would have had to collapse before Lena's very eyes, and that he simply couldn't have managed. Now Lena stroked him as he had stroked Rainer. "At least you produced a manuscript," said Rainer. "A whimsical whimsy, whatever, you can be satisfied, the minor experience has passed through the filter of verbal expression, you're a fine fellow again. Lena, drive up to the enchanted house, tell the iridescent mother-of-pearl lady that your father and I are having an aperitif here and will be coming up later for the season's most modest supper, and, if it doesn't suddenly stop raining, will go on drinking with the thirsty earth as long as the discretion of the night and the tears of the mountain last."

13

WHEN HALM APPEARED next morning at the patio door, the cat came bounding up from the garden. She wanted to consecrate not only the steps from the patio to the lawn but also those from the house onto the patio by her rubbing ritual. His bare feet were not allowed to take a single step without being guided by her pliant caresses. She had obviously missed him for two days. Once again she was not interested in eating and drinking until she had done everything with his feet that could be done with them. Today for the first time she bit his toes. Merely to express her interest. Was he meant to learn something from the three-month-old cat? Something spiritual perhaps. Or should one say: Something bygone, something lost?

Thus invigorated he walks through Crocker Gate, picks up the *Gazette* from the bin, and is shocked to see the headline: HEART ATTACK STRIKES SPEAKER DURING LECTURE. And with the article a picture of him, prostrate on the floor. He walks immediately to the nearest shelter and reads the report of one B. Bushstone:

> A *visiting German lecturer from Stuttgart collapsed from an apparent heart attack on Saturday at the Faculty Club.*

A University spokesman would not divulge the condition of the speaker, Helmut Halm. Halm was about to begin his lecture when, around 5:45 P.M., he started "feeling ill," according to Carol Elrod, secretary of the German Department, who was present. The Oakland Hospital Rescue Squad was called while he was laid on a stretcher, with his feet and head propped up. The 55-year-old Halm, his shirt opened, remained conscious and lucid through the incident, while German Prof. Rainer Mersjohann stood nearby, occasionally dousing Halm's head with water. Halm complained he had trouble breathing and felt a "tingling in my fingers." The Rescue Squad arrived at the scene around eleven minutes later. The attendant took Halm's blood pressure, which he said was "a little high." The attendant tried to calm Halm, who was by now beginning to breathe rapidly almost to the point of hyperventilation. A brown paper bag was placed over his mouth, forcing him to breathe his own carbon dioxide and slowing down his breathing rate.

Halm became more conscious, and the attendant said: "More than likely the cause of the blackout was the excitement." Halm was wheeled from the Faculty Club to the waiting ambulance around 6:25 P.M.

Halm felt a cold shiver down his back. He would never read this report again. It was enough to cut off one's breathing all over again. And how absurd he looked lying there! Like some obese victim. It would have been even worse if they had photographed him while he still had the paper bag over his mouth. He was annoyed by the sentence that "excitement" had been responsible for his "blackout." That sounded as though a lecture at this university was something so exciting for him that it brought about his collapse.

The students clapped and stamped their feet and congratulated him on his rapid recovery. The topic of conversation for the day: collapse, fainting, death, and reportage. Everyone participated except the girl. Today Gail led the discussion. She described how she had been standing in the balcony of the vacation house; below her, in the deep snow, her boyfriend, who had just called out: "Unless your dad jumps first, you'll never have the guts!" Then she jumped and hit the frozen blocks of snow, and then there was this explosion of light that she will never forget. She never saw her boyfriend again. He immediately volunteered for Third World aid in Africa.

Halm was waiting for someone to say something about "Asra and Laura." After all, Rainer had handed the lecture to everyone who had been there. Did he have to acknowledge that not a single one of the students from his conversation course had bothered to go to the Faculty Club? A nice weekend, that was all. So the blond whom he had glimpsed from behind in passing hadn't been the girl. *Ich grolle nicht*, I bear no grudge, he sang to himself, emphasizing the *nicht* with as much agony as Roy had shown. And yet he was, must be, very glad that she hadn't seen him lying there like an obese corpse. Only Howard, that good fellow, said he would have loved to come but that, since he no longer stopped to look at any announcement board, he hadn't known about it. Heine, that would have interested him.

After class she asked whether she might see him at noon. Since it was raining again he suggested they meet in 407-F. "I like the rain," she said, and simply walked along beside him. She even walked with him under his umbrella. So he would run into Rainer on the humpback bridge while sharing his umbrella with her, below them possibly the revived, romantically surging Okra Creek! That mustn't happen. He stopped, said he was out of pencil refills, he had to go to the stationery store at Student Union Plaza. And left her standing in the rain. Didn't she have an umbrella? But then she loved the rain. And the rain had turned to a mere drizzle. And this November rain wasn't yet a cold rain. Thus he justified himself after leaving her. Besides, it felt good to maltreat her a bit. At last, just a bit. Later in his office, he could continue to maltreat her. Perhaps he would kill her. Suddenly he felt closer to Rainer and the rapist than to anyone else. And he actually wished that Rainer were the rapist. And Rainer would take him along. And they would lie in wait for the girl. And then. . . . That was as far as he got. He was an inhibited person. But those are the very ones who are the rapists. They need those shock-situations to get rid of some of their inhibitions.

At five after twelve he sat in his office waiting for the girl. She comes in wearing black boots. And she has a cold. Every sound saturated. Every word filled to bursting. What now issues from her mouth has a sluggish power. So today he has to endure her as a lady. From the black boots and designer jeans up to a black, lightweight open woolen jacket and a shimmering pink blouse. Hanging over her shoulder the round, obscenely soft, purplish bag. So 407-F is really a torture chamber. Which is why they've put him in here, why they send in to him as often as possible their Number One Torture Lady to break every bone in his body until he is left behind as a wretched, barely breathing, almost unconscious broken fragment. She is the continuation of the breakers. But she doesn't kill, she tortures. You have to kill yourself. Or kill her. He took measure. Strangle her. That was the only thing he could imagine, the only thing he could see himself doing. He didn't think he could shed blood. But he could strangle her. She had enough neck for him to use both hands. And then press that softness together until it became firmer and then quite hard—he could actually imagine the sensation in his hands. He hasn't wanted this, but he has to do it. Above all: the movements that occur in strangling need not seem as ridiculous as everything that serves sexual surrender more directly.

He finally stood up and held out his hand. She would remember from Vienna that Europeans shake hands five times a day. She smiled knowledgeably as she shook his hand. Then he let go of her hand somewhat abruptly and indicated by gesture and expression that he had quite forgotten where they were, even adding: "Oh I forgot, we're in California!" With that he was put back into his role of essay helper; there could be no further thought of strangling. He postponed it. I'll kill you one of these days, he thought. Don't smile like that, child, don't give yourself such ladylike airs. You have a neck that lends itself to squeezing. The fine gold chain around that neck marked the lower limit for the right hand, then the left hand above the right. . . . Later. He wanted to look away from her and noted that his eyes took with them what he saw. And instantly he knew that he had experienced exactly the same thing at the Faculty Club during the instant before his collapse: all the heads had been retained in his eyes, they moved with his eyes from left to right, from right to left, then upward—and by that time he was falling. The next image had been that of the fifty nurses.

He sat down. Here it would be *one* nurse. A torture nurse. He sat. When he looked into her eyes it was not only his own—or rather, those of his maternal grandmother, from whom he was said to have his—but also those of the cat, the attacker of feet and toes, which looked back at him, hence more than ever his grandmother's; for the older she grew the more pinched her mouth became and the more clearly her face had come to resemble that of a cat. Suddenly he could very well imagine this girl as an old woman. Also as a young man. From heroic times. Leif should be her Viking name.

If he didn't mind, she'd just like to leave this paperback containing *The Hamlet* by William Faulkner. She had to choose a character, which one would he suggest. . . . Oh, my dear girl. If one is as much of a failure as he is, one wants to be left in peace. This challenge to a further round also sets the seal on its course. But he can't defend himself. That would look as if he had been helping her merely in exchange for something, but now, after seeing that there was nothing in it for him, he turns tail. He wants her to see his eagerness as a newly blossoming cherry tree, each blossom pure and white to its very heart! He would astonish her! She would wonder whether she had ever met such a cherry-blossom man! Such an old fool. Futile to figure out further defense ploys. Put an end to the illusion that, as long as he was here, he could erect a defense against this girl. Nothing will happen, but only because she has no inkling of what is going on inside him. Not even as Brando-Malvolio does she want to show him up. That would require her to have some inkling of his feelings. She has none. Otherwise surely she would have told him why she didn't go to his Laura-Asra lecture. Surely it was almost to be expected that she would be interested in his Laura-Asra presentation. After all that had happened. She wasn't the least bit interested. As if that weren't enough! At the same time—don't forget—you must be glad she didn't come. Although it is the worst that could happen, it is also the best. Din that into yourself: the worst is still the best. If he had helped her achieve one A after another—maybe then, overwhelmed by her success, she would have given him an impetuous hug. Earlier, the few minutes under his umbrella had been wonderful. They had had to harmonize their movements. They had succeeded. For two or three minutes they had moved as if they belonged together.

So by when did she want him to have read it and give her some advice? This week she is fully occupied with studying for her opera course, exams begin next Monday. Friday maybe? "Very funny," he said. It was *He*-Halm who said that. Halm jumped up and said: "Nothing's funny at all." She also stood up. Finally she left. He couldn't immediately run after her. One has to stop oneself doing what one wants and do what one doesn't want. Sublime, austere friction, a positively spiritual generation of heat. At the upper level it hums on the frequency of inaudibility: *Ich grolle nicht*. The worried theoretician of self-suppression of the Viennese/Victorian school has judged this too negatively. If only you could write down music! The chords of friction that are now spreading through your mind with grotesque solemnity—and well aware of their grotesque solemnity—prove that the unwelcome can produce a bombastic vitality, a rejoicing in fact. Didn't Heine have a word for it? "Rejoicing in pain"? He thought so. And food still tastes good. You simply have to admit that. And if you are alone, you grin. And nowhere are there such good toothpicks as in America. Serious, simple wooden toothpicks from Maine. What a pleasure to be able to use such toothpicks after a meal. How satisfying. The quintessence of deliverance. All those who through some blockage are in danger of succumbing to a negation-routine or a utopia-idea should be presented with many little packages of Maine toothpicks. But right now he had to go and sit on Carol's chair and listen to her version of his collapse.

Luckily Carol wasn't there. She was with her father and mother in Mendocino. Halm drove home. At the sight of the TV set he capitulated. He switched it on. In broad daylight. And that wasn't a mistake. Everything the screen offered felt good to him now. It felt good that a David Bowie should have faced a half-empty Oakland Coliseum with no more than 35,000 fans. It felt good to hear the Goebbels-like or demented TV preacher Dr. Scott say: What I like doing best is spending money for Jesus—give me ten million dollars a day, I'll spend them, every day. It felt good to see striking teachers demonstrating on the streets of Oakland. It did him good to hear that a five-hundred-million-dollar diet company had gone broke. It felt good that the whole area should at the moment be scared of a spider called the brown recluse that had already killed a fifty-year-old man. It felt good to hear that someone on the coast was mutilating pelicans with a knife. It felt good that nothing good was happening anywhere. Best of all was when the president appeared on the screen. Carol was right: there could be nothing more heartwarming than this delightfully made-up, forever laughing ghost of a president. Only the president's wife is more heartwarming than he. She is the quintessence, she's the absolute That's-the-way-it-is. How good it feels that everything is the way it is.

In this lighthearted mood he walked next morning through Crocker Gate. He needed no reason for his happy frame of mind. In this exhilarated mood for which no causes were required he took his seat facing the sex-grotto drawing that was gradually blurring into a purely decorative object. Moreover, he had lost almost all fear that his topics would founder on lack of interest. Howard had long been the true leader of this conversation. Howard simply allowed no topic to founder. And when gnomish Jeff mumbled something from his semirecumbent position that Halm didn't understand but that made all the others laugh, Howard would say with amiable severity that Jeff had better not bring his drug talk with him to the class. Halm looked forward to Elaine's bowed head and her turned-up doll's eyes with their fluttering, tangled eyelashes. He looked forward to Gail swinging herself in on her crutches. He looked forward to Art, the giant who constantly moved his giant mouth and then decided to say nothing, making it look as if he didn't want to say anything right now; nothing could be more appropriate, more inspired, than having brought that giant mouth to the point of being able to speak and then following the command issuing from that giant interior: say nothing. He looked forward to Cynthia smiling shyly out of the nineteenth century—Cynthia who, when she spoke, uttered everything she wanted to say with a wonderful calm, but always with an expression implying that it embarrassed her. And he also looked forward to the mute girl from Mill Valley.

Moreover, just before the rain started, the dahlia buds had opened, the ones growing on the side of the garden next to the house with the pug dogs; now their pale mauve was shining through the rain. On her last day Sabina had said: "You'll still be here to see the dahlias in bloom." But when, to top it all, Schubert was being announced on the radio, he rushed over to turn it off before the quartet had a chance. Besides, he had his homework to do: Faulkner, *The Hamlet*. Already the second sentence was enough to defeat him. O.K., so it was a sentence that probably anyone had to read twice. The author apparently took pride in writing sentences which, if one really wanted to get at their meaning, had to be read twice. And apparently he took even more pride in knowing that the reader actually would read the second sentence twice. By the time the reader had got as far as halfway through the third sentence, which was much more difficult than the second, he would jump back to the second, to the beginning of the second sentence, and would carefully reread it until he was more or less sure of what it meant. So, my dear third sentence, now let's see whether you can present the slightest obstacle to someone who has mastered the second sentence. Probably your entire orneriness derives solely from the fact that the reader stumbles into you after fleeing from the second sentence. Naturally you can demolish that kind of a reader with the greatest of ease. But a reader who has thoroughly conquered the second sentence—what hold, I ask you, do you have over him? Very little. But still quite a bit. On the other hand, the fourth sentence already betrayed the fact that the author had not succeeded in turning every sentence into a tangle that would show up the impotence and feebleness of the reader who is bent on pressing forward. He read the fourth sentence as if it were nothing. However, unless he devoted breath and being entirely to this world of the printed word, he would not—he could already foresee—be able to gain a foothold in this Mississippi region, since everything took place within Yoknapatawpha County.

Aware, then, that in not yielding an inch he was becoming stronger and stronger, he savored the thought that his adversaries at home were now asleep. The rain was a great help, too. This rain that could only count up to three. Only up to three and back and up to three and back. When the wind grew in violence, Halm sat behind his glass aquarium pane, staring out at trees and bushes, the green sea between the nearby roofs that swayed and billowed as wildly as a real ocean. The roofs stood out like rocks among the billows. The wind increased until it howled and whistled. One can't help watching a storm in a foreign country. There is no telling how far it can go here. The trees looked agitated. The wind sounded against the house as if demanding entry. It took a real grip on the house. And the house actually groaned under its grasp. In Sillenbuch the wind doesn't have that grasp. And the sheets of rain that it drove along became denser and denser. From time to time water splashed onto the patio as if it were being dumped from a great height.

So as not to be entirely cut off from everything, he switched on the TV again. The storm was described as the first big one this fall. Nine inches of snow in the Nevada mountains. The waves of the Pacific have by now reached a height of almost twenty-five feet. The sheets of rain blocked out all visibility. All one could hear was water. It trickled, drummed, splashed. The rain was storming the house as if it could conquer it. The cat, too, with no experience yet of fall and winter, was unlikely to survive all this without some trepidation. He would have taken her into the house now, but she was no longer to be seen. If, as is to be feared, the peak of the high tide should coincide with the peak of the storm, says the TV, things may become unpleasant here and there. For the time being one should avoid the scenic coast road. At such times it always loses a few sections to nature.

He brushed his yams and squash with oil, placed them in a casserole into the oven, and turned the oven up to 350. To judge by the sounds, the water was already inside the house. It only gurgles like that when it's already inside. But he'd rather be swept down the steep slope together with the house than put up any resistance. No doubt Mr. Rinehart was well insured. According to Sabina, the neighbor on the right was a retired insurance broker. Even a retired insurance broker doesn't give up until his neighbor has been insured against absolutely everything.

Where was Lena now, he wondered? He found it a strain to call her only twice a week. In weather like this, one is dependent on how well one can live with oneself. And one should have learned that by now. Since Sabina had left, everything in the house exuded loneliness. Objects had lost their meaning. The chairs had lost their relationship to the table. An atmosphere of indifference had spread throughout. At night he lay listening to the sounds. What did they signify? With Sabina around he didn't seem to find that necessary. That must mean he was used to her ears keeping watch for him. Don't panic now, just because it's getting dark. When it gets dark, prudence increases. So does imprudence. So nothing changes. Except that it's getting dark. It was on a night like this that John Frey had listened to the Swiss lady. Halm listened to Faulkner. Suddenly the power failed.

Next morning there was still a power outage. So off to class unshaven. That provided him with a good conversation theme. Those who have no fireplace can come to Halm's this evening. Professor Halm will personally light a fire. With Professor Rinehart's wood. By candlelight he sat all evening beside his fire waiting for visitors. He believed that someone would come. He believed that soon the doorbell would ring, he would go to the front door, and there she would be standing in her black boots and all that. He knew for certain that she wouldn't come. But he believed that she would come. Hence his excitement, his exhilaration. Repeated every day. Every evening. How that girl dressed since the rain and the wind had taken over! Before that she had never worn anything but those shorts made with curving sides, now and then the rakishly shabby warm-up pants, and always those washed-out running shoes. Now she was always dressed to the nines. Swathed in scarves that were fit for composing an opera. Her shoes endeavored to look plain yet conveyed that they were anything but. Halm stopped resisting. Time-processing, that's what you have to do. Putting the present behind you, transforming every second, as soon as it arrives, into the farthest possible past. Devouring the seconds, as it were, out of the hand of the present. Gobbling them up. Swallowing them. No consequences. Finished.

What Sabina had to do was more difficult. Father Gottschalk, that most peaceful of men, had been driven mad by his pain and had had to be placed in a private room. He bit the hands of the nurses who were trying to wash or feed him, and as soon as doctors entered the room he threw anything within reach at their heads. Sabina was the only person he could tolerate. He heaped abuse on her too, but he didn't bite her or throw things at her. Sabina took his abuse seriously, suffered his sufferings with him. She couldn't imagine how there could be any Christmas this year, said Sabina. And how's Helmut? He must tell her honestly! Does he still feel giddy? She'll come over at once, she really will, she knows where she belongs, she can't help her father anymore, it's just that she can't just leave him lying there like that. And Lena! Yes, Lena's in better shape than any of us. And Juliane? Juliane is doing better.

But unfortunately she won't change her mind: she still wants to go to Brazil. "But why Brazil?" he asks. "Nobody knows," says Sabina, as if they were talking about a disease whose causes are still mysterious. "To Brazil, of all places!" he said. "And Otto?" "He can't lie down anymore. His heart, most likely. Now he always sits as upright as possible. Then his front paws slide from under him, then he has to pick himself up again, then everything slides away again. There's a struggle beginning there too," says Sabina. "Well then, Sabina," he says and disconnected himself from the continent of death agonies.

He had to go out to his little Angora friend. Once again she was shining pinkly from the depths of the garden. He had to get her used to the fact that he now came down with his bare feet in slippers. After the heavy rain, the air hadn't yet warmed up again. But she persisted until he stepped out of his slippers and responded to her caresses with his foot. She was entitled to expect that. He and she were a couple. Just then he saw a disreputable old tomcat approaching from the pug house. Looking greedy, mangy, experienced. So Halm had to stay until his little friend had finished her meal. The huge tomcat, rakishly dirty and rather shorthaired, came closer and closer. Halm chased him away. The tomcat runs off but not toward the pug house, rather toward the patio door, which Halm has left open. If any cat is to be allowed inside, then only his. So Halm makes a swift movement toward the door, frightening his little friend, who jumps away, also toward the door, but he doesn't notice this since he's concentrating on the tomcat, whom he must get hold of or chase away. Only when the slippered foot treads on something soft and there is a scream does he realize that he has trodden on his little friend with the hard sole of his slipper. And off she sped, down onto the grass, and away.

He couldn't wait. His other mistress wanted to know by Friday which of those Yoknapatawpha characters sitting around on verandas, in carriages, on horseback, lent himself best to an essay. To Halm, everything in this book was wonderful. Closer to Homer than to himself. He couldn't rid his mind of those chewing, spitting, ruminating characters. Yet had to struggle so with the reading. His dream of understanding without translating was being severely tested. It was probably an illusion after all. He was no longer reading merely for his taskmistress. With Faulkner's book he traveled deeper and deeper into this America. The poor, thin, lurid skin of the present was nothing compared to the power of the past. He owed much to the girl. Without her he would never have penetrated to these more dreamy than active heroes of the Mississippi region. Didn't she sit around in his conversation class like one of those characters? She never opened her mouth, always pulled up her right foot, laid it across her left knee, clasped her ankle, her eyes on whoever was speaking, and it was impossible to tell whether she heard what was being said. Her way of looking implied that it was enough to look at someone. But which character was he to recommend from out of that dust- and sun-drenched tapestry of characters? They were all the same size. None among them can stand out. There are no small ones and no big ones. That this was so, without the need to spell it out, seemed American to him.

But then, after page 102, a character appeared that changed the atmosphere: Labove, who worked at the sawmill and on his father's small farm, and, from his earnings, was able to study in Oxford, forty miles away. He is aiming high: to go into politics, to become governor, but while still a student he is hired as a teacher in the hamlet that is the setting of the novel. He stays on for five years, he has long since passed his exams in Oxford, he could be an attorney, but he stays on. Because of Eula. He is her teacher. Eventually he tries to rape her in the classroom; he fails and now disappears, forever. The novel is concerned not with Labove but with Eula, the muncher of cold sweet potatoes, the indolent daughter of the largest property owner, Mr. Verner, who either rides around the place on a fat white horse or—preferably—lies in a hammock from where he rules his property in a desultory way. But Labove, who is twice as old as Eula, endows her with names that are otherwise unknown here. He sees her as Venus, himself as Vulcan, and so on. The five years turn into a single sweeping trend, a wave that mounts higher and higher until it culminates in a cold, vertical, hard crash in a single sentence: "Stop pawing me," she said. "You old headless horseman Ichabod Crane." In order to render the mythically indolent Eula, that sweet-potato muncher whose powers resided in her passivity, large, superlarge, insanely large, the author builds up Labove's ambition-oriented existence, an existence rooted in deprivation and stubbornness and geared ruthlessly, day and night, toward its goal. As soon as Eula's breasts loom large on the scene, this existence is swept into a uterine maelstrom and crushed. While wrestling with her he whispers a mishmash of Greek and Latin poetry and American Mississippi obscenities into her ear. But she flings him off and onto the ground and utters that one sentence: "Stop pawing me, you old headless horseman Ichabod Crane." Labove was skinny rather than gaunt, hence the allusion to "crane." According to the books, "Ichabod" was a male Hebrew name but in the vernacular had acquired an adjectival quality, meaning something like "inglorious." Although "headless" can mean "brainless," "foolish," what is it doing in this sentence? One would have to ask a woman about that. Halm phoned Joyce Ackerman and learned within minutes that Faulkner's Eula had taken it from Washington Irving. In *The Legend of Sleepy Hollow*, written in 1819, the horseman who haunts Ichabod Crane really does ride along without a head. Halm didn't know how to translate that.

He would suggest to Fran that she write about Eula. Eula is larger than Labove. Labove is only there to increase her size, to intensify the cruelty of the effect when, after further male approaches, she is forced to become the wife of that mollusklike careerist Snopes who spreads himself around like mildew.

Next morning Roy Kinsman grabbed his arm, led him down the corridor to Leslie Ackerman's office, and from there telephoned Rainer, asking him to come at once to Leslie's office. He told the group that they had eaten and drunk him out of house and home, now he had been waiting week after week for an invitation so that he might avenge himself on at least one of them. It was Leslie's turn. All right then, Saturday. Actually Halm had wanted to go for a drive with Lena. But skat had priority. Carol gave a pained sigh. How she could bare those protruding teeth when she was disgusted! Until she buried the splendid array behind her heavy lower lip. Rainer's lower lip, on the other hand, drooped farther and farther. Standing close to him one could hear his heavy breathing. When he was asked how the Schubert text interpretation was coming along, the restless tip of his tongue ceased its back-and-forth between his teeth, and Rainer nodded as if he had been asked a question to be answered with yes or no and he was hereby saying yes.

Friday, the day before the skat Saturday, the girl turned up in the neon crypt. Meanwhile the ice shower had become a stream of mild warm air, rendering sweater and scarf unnecessary. Nevertheless the children's drawings were a daily reminder of the Neuschwanstein posters he had meant to bring along to protect himself from them. This Friday the *Gazette* had two headlines: the rapist had finally been caught—the rain storms that had softened up the ground had been his undoing—and the university senate condemns in the strongest possible terms any kind of teacher-student romance. Harvard University statistics are quoted showing that 34 percent of all college coeds and 47 percent of all university coeds had been exposed to sexual harassment. There you are, 34 percent of undergraduates! So you see, my dear skat partners, it isn't all that uncommon. Quite apart from the fact that he'd never reached that point. He didn't dare use this as a conversation topic. He would rather have it explained to him by Carol during his free period.

She referred him to his box. In it he found a pamphlet, on glossy paper, dramatically printed in full color, on sexual harassment and how to combat it. "You can thank your stars you didn't make more of a nuisance of yourself toward me," said Carol. She too, as one of the females deserving of protection, was covered by this all-encompassing chastity campaign. However, what he was up to with Fran—well, she wouldn't report him although he was obviously laying the groundwork for a case that would be included in the 34 percent of undergraduate harassment. "What do you mean, 'laying the groundwork'?" he asked without a smile. She would be glad to read it out to him. If, without looking it up, she rightly interpreted what she had read, he was not yet ripe for a "formal grievance procedure," but. . . . Just a minute, here was the paragraph applying to his stage: "an informal pregrievance complaint resolution process." In other words, something like that could be launched against him any second. So it looks to her. The only female he had been harassing here, he said, was herself, he was awaiting her denunciation. Sure, the only thing ever expected from her was that kind of crap, she said; she was forever being expected to play policeman, whereas she'd much rather be the criminal or at least the victim.

He asked after her parents. Tomorrow, while he would be at that male orgy, she would be in Mendocino again. After lugging her husband around for seventeen years, her mother's arms were hurting. Although her father now really did weigh only ninety-one pounds. Halm was glad to be able to tell her that at the moment Sabina had a similar battle on her hands. "Have a good trip back from Mendocino. So long! Dear Carol!" Then as quickly as possible to his office.

Just as he was reading in the pamphlet about the various categories that sexual harassment of students by the faculty could be divided into, she walked in, chewing. Again—naturally—boots of such soft leather that they fell in folds. The finest silver-gray silk blouse under a needlessly elegant double-breasted black jacket. Lohengrin and Swan in one. And then she resumed shoving her hair from one side to the other so that it gradually flowed back again on its own. Labove had gone mad. And in the process he knew he was going mad. And already was too far gone to do anything about it. And then Eula called Labove's drowning in her maelstrom simply "pawing." Looking at Eula, Labove had been able to imagine wounding her seriously enough to draw blood. Labove wasn't yet thirty; at fifty-five strangling is as far as one can go.

So, before suggesting anything, he'd like to hear which character in this tapestry appealed most to her. The girl pursed her lips and said: "Labove." "I see," said Halm, "Labove—why him in particular?" She finds Labove attractive. She had never heard of anyone having such a problem finding the money to go to university. Farm, sawmill, wielding a shovel in college, football, teaching in some godforsaken hole forty miles from the university, kids aged seven to nineteen in *one* classroom. At last he has got through it all. Could be an attorney. His career could begin. Meteoric rise. He intends to become governor. Then he goes for the girl. He has known for a long time that he is on a ruinous course. At some point he will be as insane as a man must be to go for a girl like that. Then it will all be over. His career. His life. Everything. It will all have been for nothing. Or rather, for that girl. She finds that impressive. Somehow.

Halm said: "Yes. Of course. But Labove is only a secondary character. What do you think of Eula?" Fine, as long as Labove is around. Without Labove, Eula is not as attractive as with Labove. In her opinion. "But surely," he said, "Eula is the quintessence of the entire historic and prehistoric fate of woman. First the fullness of female power itself, then the classic wretched female fate: wouldn't that be a good subject for an essay?" She, easily: "Why not choose Labove?" "Hm," said Halm. "Studies of rapists have shown that the destruction of what was desired stops the desire." She said with a smile. Halm looked into her eyes, which were as familiar to him as his own. "How do you mean?" he asks. She shrugs her shoulders. Says no more. Because he doesn't know what else to say, he asks whether she has read that the local rapist has been caught. She: Had he read that stupid resolution of the senate's on sexual harassment? He nods. She says: When she's finished her work for the opera course she'll start writing about Labove, she may have some questions for Halm about the rapist, might she ask them? "Anytime," he says weakly. Whenever she made even the slightest movement, silver lights rippled across the silken blouse. And the solemn portals of her jacket swayed. Would he be free

Tuesday evening, she asked? She'd like to go to the opera with him. Not to a real one, she was sorry to say, but her opera professor was showing the class *Walküre* on Tuesday evening, a Bayreuth performance on cassettes. Steiner Auditorium, seven o'clock, Room 96. He acted as if it were nothing, to be invited by her, to listen to *Walküre* in the evening, beside her in the dark. He replied: "Tuesday? Next week?" Hmmmm. On Thursday Professor Mersjohann is flying to Houston for the symposium on music and poetry. Provided Rainer did not come with some dramatic request, say to try out on Halm his lecture on Schubert text interpretation, provided no such hindrance arose he would come, with pleasure in fact, *Walküre*, why not?

Since she had issued this invitation, he no longer thought of raping her. But after she had left he again had that feeling of having done everything wrong. He had let her go. An argument arose in him as never before. Who had let her go? You! What was I to do? Rape her. Harass her, at least. Why didn't you harass her? Good God, hadn't she pointedly grinned over that stupid senate resolution? She admires Labove! And even Eula hadn't screamed when Labove tried it. Of course, because she saw no necessity. She didn't even report him. What to Labove meant staking his entire existence, to her meant nothing worth mentioning. Yet it is Labove whom the girl admires, not Eula. She admired the gamble, the courage, the risk, the madness. But then Labove did have that madness, you don't. He was mad. He knew it. You are normal. And you know it. That was an appalling realization. A devastating one. To be so incapable of madness! This fear! Not fear of punishment! Sexual harassment . . . ridiculous. He was only afraid of the words: "Stop pawing me." To hear those words from her would, he feared, be more than he could endure. Obviously he wouldn't react like Labove. His hands thought of a neck. But the neck had gone. Perhaps she had sensed what was going on inside him, so had quickly suggested Tuesday evening. And indeed that suggestion had solved everything. It was easy enough to postpone everything until Tuesday evening. Wonderful, to be looking forward to that

Tuesday evening. A prospect such as he had never had. Why hadn't he accepted unconditionally? Actually he had said he might come or he might not. That was a mistake. But it didn't prevent anything. And no one would be able to prevent him now. Not even ten Rainer Mersjohanns! Th' expense of spirit in a waste of shame is lust in action; and till action, lust is perjur'd, murderous, bloody, full of blame, savage, extreme, rude, cruel, not to trust. Let's hope so, thought Halm.

Come to think of it, had he ever accosted a girl, a woman? Had he ever indicated any intention before being assured by a signal from the woman that, if he approached her, he wouldn't be rejected? For others that had been no problem in their youthful days, they would accost one woman after another until it worked with one of them, whereas it seemed that he had always labored under the fixed idea that a rejection would be unbearable. Hence also, as soon as he had Sabina, his radical specialization in this one woman. Sabina was everything to him, and to him everything was Sabina and apart from Sabina there was nothing. Oh well yes, Nicole Klingele. And later, when her name had changed to Schloz-Klingele, she had swung him around by the arm in the foyer, in her eagerness to introduce her handsome, moustachioed husband to him and him to her husband. "Swe-e-etie!" she had screeched. It had sounded as if she were torturing the word. So this was her favorite teacher. . . . A scene containing every conceivable embarrassing element. The very essence of complacency, puffed up in red silk. And a few years before that scene he had believed for two whole weeks, believed day and night, that he could not, must not live without this Nicole.

To think now about what he had done in those fourteen days and nights should be salutary. Nicole was not so different from Eula. They had wrestled for a whole night. In a hotel in Baden-Baden. Nicole had had to audition for a violinist. Brahms. Something with a girl's name. Agathe? Brahms had composed it somewhere in the area. During the first half of the night Halm had called Nicole "Agathe." She wanted to be a violinist. After the audition, which had not had the desired effect, she had come to the hotel and was so dismayed over the ramshackle beds, the threadbare armchairs, the grimy flowered wallpaper, that he immediately went down to the front desk and implored the clerk to recommend some other place. "Of course, if you're looking for something first class," said the porter, "we happen to be second class." Halm did not say: "Fourth class, that's what you are." He knew that everyone must pretend to rank himself differently from the ways others rank him. Roaring with laughter they threw themselves onto the bed in the "first class" place, which luckily wasn't first class. Then began a wrestling match of ten hours and a thousand rounds, which Nicole won. The first five hundred rounds, the Agathe rounds, were exciting. Since he was wrestling with a nineteen-year-old in what was by his standards a luxurious Baden-Baden hotel room, in a bed that could serve other purposes than closing one's eyes and falling asleep; since this girl had more or less encouraged him to travel and spend the night together—at least he hadn't been able to put any other construction on her unsolicited message; since she had taken off all her clothes except for a narrow strip of material; since she had embraced and kissed her teacher in a manner which he was forced to regard as an invitation to go all the way; since she had also called him "Swe-e-etie": he was convinced that, although her vocabulary should not have pleased him, the most astounding night of his life had begun. He still remembered—he would, unfortunately, remember for all time—that, after settling between her ample breasts, he had thought: This is the most sublime, the most beautiful experience you will ever have. This is the greatest, he had thought, resorting to the language of his students. But during the second five hundred rounds, the Nicole rounds, it gradually became clear that he was not consuming an exquisitely prepared appetizer prior to a still more exquisite main course, but that Miss Klingele intended to let matters rest with the appetizer. He in turn was past grasping this, or he believed that he mustn't grasp it; in any case he struggled on, and the longer he struggled the more clearly the struggle turned into just that. And that was the one he lost.

Miss Klingele was almost taller than he was and markedly

stronger; moreover she was ruthless and—in his view—unfair: physically and mentally. Her remarks as the night wore on revealed to him the value of the virginity of a Stuttgart millionaire's daughter. He really must understand: too precious to be casually sacrificed to a schoolteacher no matter how revered. Papa had a car dealership which he obviously operated with a devotion far exceeding mere business interest. His make of car was his faith. Money was never mentioned in the family. Each year ever more perfect models: that, coupled with the happiness and career of his one and only Nicole, constituted Mr. Klingele's entire raison d'être. Mr. Klingele, so revered by his daughter, was devout, devout in terms of his make of car, his family, and the world. After that night Halm could have written Klingele's biography. By dawn Halm should really have been grateful for the privilege of spending a whole night touching and appreciating the Klingele personifications and their worth. In the name of her family's self-esteem Nicole put it to him fairly unequivocally that he should feel such gratitude. Who had ever been allowed to come as close to her as he! She enumerated them. There had been exactly five. He, the sixth. Had he not suffered acute pain from various internal and external factors during this battle that had been lost in the forefield, he would have been more than willing to show her this gratitude, for only now could he appreciate her in her absolute innocence.

But he was not in good shape. He insisted on an early departure. Without breakfast. Wanting to get home as quickly as possible, to Sabina. From now on, immune. More immune than Siegfried after his bath in Fafner's blood. No linden leaf had interfered with his total immersion in Nicole-acid. He was immune all over. And when, after the Swe-e-etie scene in the foyer of the opera house, he had been able to share the whole experience with Sabina, he could regard himself as redeemed. And now? Tuesday, another opera scenario. . . . No, finished, over, amen. Anything learned from Nicole Schloz-Klingele must not be applied to Fran Webb.

At the school dance, Nicole had asked him to dance with her. Her way of dancing with him made him suddenly see himself as a hitherto undiscovered champion dancer. Sabina hadn't gone with him to this school dance. The moment had long since passed when a teacher should have stopped dancing on and on with a female student. If he and Nicole, by then almost out of control, hadn't knocked over a table, they might well never have been able to stop. Nicole had been wearing something pale green, multilayered, with many flounces. Such a thing could never have happened to a Kiderlen. There was no more to be said about it. Sabina had been told about it, and that was the perfect way of putting an end to it. Now, if you don't mind, no influence whatever from the past on this Tuesday evening! For once, if you don't mind, an evening simply as it is! For once a date without those paralyzing, frustrating Stations-of-the-Cross from the past! Let Tuesday evening be nothing but the present! Past and future, those forces of frustration, are suspended! Curtain up for *Walküre*!

But before that there was still skat on Saturday night at Leslie Ackerman's. Halm drove to the Hansel and Gretel Tudor house on Euclid Avenue, Rainer handed him the key for the Chevy. "The Chevy man can," thought Halm, annoyed that his consciousness was daily becoming more and more permeated with advertising slogans. He could offer no resistance to the TV spots and spells. "A penny for your thoughts," said Rainer. "I've written a book on Nietzsche that nobody wants," said Halm, "and I've just discovered why." "Congratulations," said Rainer.

Beyond Orinda the road went steeply uphill, then immediately just as steeply downhill, the last hundred yards an asphalt strip that was vertical rather than merely steep, and at the summit, on the oasislike, densely green hilltop, lived the Ackermans. Another impressive middle-class home. This time mainly by way of porcelain. Porcelain everywhere. Frames large and small, display areas either on shelves, or in wall niches, all for porcelain. "Makes your eyes bulge, doesn't it?" said Mersjohann. "Leslie, show him the high altar," he said to their host, who modestly declined. The sports trophies were the real sacred objects of the house, said Rainer. Halm said that, apart from Neuschwanstein, he knew of nothing with such a sublime location as this house on its California hilltop. Joyce, that youthful female skull framed by its thick blond braids, said that the house had been built way up there by the former chairman of the Communist Party of California. After all, he had wanted to be fully protected. "From the KGB," said Leslie, genuflecting. "But then why did he sell?" asked Halm. "His wife developed an allergy to grass," said Leslie. "Due to the alienation of those ground-rent theoreticians from the grassroots," Rainer murmured.

They played skat in a room opening off the one in which Joyce sat over her doctoral thesis on literary hermaphroditism. She could listen in to everything. This did not tone down the Roughnecks' vocabulary in the slightest. It began just as soon as the wine each had brought was handed to their host. Roy had just delivered himself of a Schumann-Heine pang that needed a gigantic coffin to contain it, and now, when Rainer produced two bottles that he called "tears of the mountain," he said: "Tonight you can drink your student's piss yourself," which prompted Leslie to cap it with: "Tonight he hasn't even bothered to stick stolen price labels onto his catheter loot—just look, mercilessly honest: two-seventy, three-fifty." Roy: "Three-fifty is a forgery!"

Halm lost again. The three Roughnecks whooped and jeered. Roy put it more concretely: Now that Helmut has to save up so he can afford the best attorney for his trial. This term, on campus, Halm's name was being spelled "harassment." Joyce came in quickly from the next room: That was unfair, here was someone wanting to live it up for once on a California campus, and he gets caught up in some kind of chastity campaign. "I'm glad that at least he isn't the rapist," Rainer said under his breath. Halm joined in the laughter as best he could. Then he tried to get out from under. "Does one say har*ass* or *har*ass?" "I've just the answer," said Leslie. A fellow student, in Seattle, had mispronounced that word, and the professor told him that as an assignment he was to clarify the pronunciation by the next class. The student, at the next class: I looked under har*ass* and found it's pronounced *har*ass. Leslie emphasized the first pronunciation to make it sound like "her ass." Joyce, still in the doorway: If this campaign had taken place when she was one of Leslie's students, either his career or their romance would have been finished. The first time she had gone to Leslie's office for advice on her reading list, he had given her a funny look and said: "You know better than I do which of your gaps need filling." Well, at that particular moment she hadn't been able to imagine that her gaps could be filled with reading, said Joyce. The thick blond braids are actually connected by her blond glasses, thought Halm. The conversation had already moved on to Auster and his Chicana. How repulsive when he puts his blotchy, old man's hand on her immaculate forearm. "He's forty-one years ahead of her," said Roy. Halm wasn't sure whether they weren't really aiming at him with those comments. Leslie remarked that the twenty-one years between himself and Joyce had been almost doubled by Teddy Auster. Rainer said that Leslie spoke as if they were discussing a high jump. "Give me four bubs," Roy said to Leslie, who was dealing. "You'll have to get two of them from Joyce," said Leslie bravely. Joyce laughed.

Halm made a serious effort. The others respected him more when they lost than when he recklessly bid for one game after another and lost. In the end he owed only $1.23, whereas Rainer had to pay $4.17 to Roy alone.

Outside the Hansel and Gretel house Rainer wouldn't let Halm change over into the Volvo, insisting that Halm accompany him into the house. Down to Rainer's floor. Elissa and Lena were off at the farewell party for the final course of the year. Sometime during the next two weeks, said Rainer, Elissa would disappear. Ostensibly to look for Jamey. Yet Jamey addressed all his postcards to him, not to Elissa. A card had just arrived for the hundred-and-twentieth anniversary of Lincoln's Gettysburg Address. From Gettysburg, Pennsylvania. Lately he had often been sending cards on the occasion of national holidays. Usually from the scene of whatever was being celebrated. That's where she might find her son. . . . But she isn't searching for her son. She is searching for herself. In the beds of blacks and Chicanos. . . .

Halm couldn't desert Rainer in that condition. Suddenly Rainer took Halm's hand, pressed it, and said he had a suggestion to make: Halm could stay on here. He would get him a position. There was still time to fix up the matter of a pension so that Halm wouldn't lose anything. Halm thought at once of the *Walküre* evening. And right away Rainer surprised him a second time: He knew that Sabina didn't care for California, but, regardless, Halm must get away from Sabina. Nothing worse than a marriage ground down by all that was left unsaid. No matter who broke the contract and who was responsible for breaking it. Questions of blame were secondary; what was equally intolerable for both was the betrayal. What's a murder compared to betrayal? A blessing. A murder does not really injure us. A murder lets us remain what we are. It destroys our physical selves without touching our spiritual substance. Betrayal destroys our spiritual substance. Halm was in the process of destroying Sabina. Only an immediate break could save Sabina from being destroyed by Halm once and for all through betrayal. He knew what it meant to be destroyed by betrayal. Even if we killed those who were destroying us, it wouldn't do any good. Whatever they have destroyed is destroyed. That's what saves their lives, those destroyers. He wouldn't have minded if Elissa had taken a black to bed once in a while if she had told him each time, in advance, to allow him to demonstrate his consent, to regularize it, render it agreeable to all concerned. To betrayal there can be no consent. It shows not one iota of respect for you. Crushes you in the process. Just listen to this.

He pressed a button, starting a tape: Elissa's voice announced that what she was about to say was said at her husband's request. Actually he left her no choice, he was forcing her to describe in detail how she had acquired her extramarital contacts. When, how often, where, how? He wanted to know everything. In future he even wanted to know in advance. Always on this tape. So she would begin with the past.

Rainer stopped the tape. "Do you hear?" he cried. "Did you hear that?" The one who deliberately flouts the law creates the impression—given the possibility of confessing—that she is being victimized. That just shows how insensitive she is. She the perpetrator is the victim. She speaks as if at gunpoint. She hasn't the least idea of the claim that must be made on a relationship for it to be one. That woman stinks in her very soul. You may think differently, but not entirely differently. Or do you want to live day after day in filth, squalor, deceit, treachery, spite? That's the metabolic end product of a betrayed relationship: filth, squalor, deceit, treachery, spite. Day and night. You'll never be able to cope with that. Let Sabina go so you can escape from this miasma of filth. Save Sabina, release her from this joyless marriage. This is your last chance, with you here and Sabina in Sillenbuch. Deceit is also suicide. So don't try. Stay here. Start out so that you no longer have to feel ashamed. He had encouraged Elissa to make those statements on tape so that she no longer need feel ashamed. His tone was awash in alcohol, but every sentence sounded incontrovertible, was based on absolute certainty.

At daybreak Halm walked down the steep, narrow paths of Yosemite Steps and tried to see whether he could spell Yoknapatawpha without having to consult the book. It had stopped raining. Whatever had possessed Rainer to speak like that? Halm could think of nothing that separated him from Sabina. He had to think all his thoughts in harmony with Sabina. He had to twist and turn everything so that it became acceptable to Sabina too. Whatever Sabina couldn't accept he had to reject as soon as it popped up in his thoughts. Such thoughts must exist in him only as rejected, not approved. If he felt something that would hurt Sabina if she knew about it, he must oppose such a feeling. Nevertheless he felt it. But at least he opposed it. So in that case it was no pleasure. Thus he talked himself into a state of balance.

He telephoned Sabina. Between them lay the night, which he had behind him and she still had ahead of her. He longed for an uninhibited chat, but Sabina had just returned from the hospital. Father Gottschalk had now to be tied down to the bed. He has already twice crawled out of the room and fallen down the stairs: two cuts, one on his forehead and one on his chin, requiring stitches. He is now heaping the same abuse on Sabina as on doctors and nurses. He wants to go home. He can no longer eat. He claims the doctors have sewn up his gullet. Sabina, he says, has now deserted him for the doctors. He has tried to spit at Sabina. Sabina sobbed uncontrollably into the phone. After hanging up, Halm was embarrassed at feeling so well. But even if you're embarrassed, he thought, you still feel well.

His little cat friend was avoiding him now. He had to search for a long time, from the spreading, swordlike cactus leaves with their thorny edges to the bamboo thicket and into the laurel hedge and under the lemon tree, until at some point he saw the little pink triangular mouth showing up against the white triangular face. When the wind made the branches groan, the cat flinched, ready for instant flight. She waits until Halm has reached the patio door again before coming up and walking past him at a safe distance, keeping an eye on him to make sure that the one who trod on her isn't coming any closer. As soon as she has finished eating, she scampers off again. So immediate needs can be satisfied without a display of emotion. But can emotion be displayed without concern for needs? Dear cat, this is your assignment. He needs the answer by tomorrow.

Tomorrow is Tuesday. Should he buy a new suit? His clothes were blatantly square. Normally he enjoyed going around in outfits which at the moment looked the most offensive. Things that were no longer being worn and for which there was no immediate prospect of being swept by the so-called wave of nostalgia into a second and this time truly outrageous fashion trend: that was what he enjoyed wearing most. But now he resented his suits making him look fatter, plumper, shorter than he really was. His stomach had shrunk. He couldn't understand why this wobbly thing had never bothered him at home. But to appear in a new suit—that would be overdoing it. His script bore no relationship whatever to buying a suit from here. He had already spent hours walking along the streets looking at suits he would have liked to own. Those he wanted most were the ones he could wear least. Those he could wear he already had. So much for that.

In the afternoon Halm wandered about the campus as if it were some enchanted territory, looking for the Steiner Auditorium. He wanted to be sure of his way tomorrow. The Steiner Auditorium was located even higher up than the Faculty Club. A poster informed him that the students of the music department would be performing Monteverdi that evening. Among the items announced, one was called *Lettera amorosa*. Halm went to that room, although it was a different one. But that would at least give him a certain familiarity with the interior of the building. The auditorium might be as crazily built as Fillmore Hall, about whose labyrinthine Wyoming-Gothic interior long articles had appeared in the *Gazette*.

While Halm was waiting, much too early, for the doors to open for the concert, he could not help watching two girls sitting side by side on a bench in the lobby, turned toward each other and finally exchanging kisses. This couple seemed more cheerful than male/female couples, who often give the impression of mutual suffering. This purely female couple carried out its kissing and stroking with no effort at all. Almost matter-of-fact. He couldn't take his eyes off them. One only gets to see things like that in a music building.

During the concert he followed the text of the *Love Letter* in the program and envied the past its freedoms. Yearning looks, half-suppressed sighs, murmured words. . . . And at the end the hope that this letter will be thrown into the snow and find therein a heart of fire. He would have loved to use such inflated language. Who, after all, has scared us away from the words that say more than can be meant? The art arbiter! Halm had a vision of either Kiderlen or a metropolitan gentleman who wears fur coats in the heat of summer and, to justify this, gobbles down unending quantities of ice cream. Someone who condemns life but enjoys it.

Next morning Halm again carried the food outside barefoot. At first the disreputable old tomcat came dashing up; Halm chased him away and waited for his cat. She came up the steps. Not in wild or even dainty leaps but one paw at a time as if against her will. She manages each footstep only by extending and stretching.

With each advance she takes root again. Yet has to go on. Today she's wearing makeup! A rosy mouth like a signal. Whenever she flings herself down on the next step that fraction of a second before his foot and then rolls on her back to receive his toes with her paws and pull them toward her, toward her mouth, that mouth shines and those paw pads shine with the same rosy red. She bit and pressed and caressed and hugged and rubbed as never before. So must this day begin! The Bay, a glassy dazzle. San Francisco beneath heavy cloud banks. Heroic weather.

The girl didn't turn up for the conversation class. He was aware of how unfair it was to lack all desire to start the ball rolling. Wasn't that tirelessly swinging Gail there? The ever-cheerful Howard? And Art, always silent at the right moment? And Jeff, bravely fighting off his fatigue? And Cynthia, looking across from her dollhouse? And Elaine staring up with fluttering, tangled eyelashes out of her amplitude of bosom? The senate is justified in its antiharassment campaign. Instead of letting yourself be inspired by all of them, you have made yourself dependent on one. Where is she? Will she be there tonight? Didn't she come to your office door on Labor Day just in case you weren't aware of the American holiday? On a fateful day like this, everything looks as if it were happening either for you or against you. That Carol is not on campus is just as it should be. He wouldn't have wanted to be seen by her today. That the Okra stream is foaming along under the humpback bridge is exactly what should be happening today. And the people coming toward him today! And they don't just walk by without noticing him. They look at him. For a few seconds there is a closeness of communication that makes the air crackle. And black couples beyond reproach stroll across the campus grass. The dogs behave as if they knew what is at stake today.

As soon as he was back in the Rinehart house he realized that he wouldn't be able to stand it in these rooms. Never before had he had such problems with Mrs. Rinehart's mirrors. When he sits in the dining room, the dining-room mirror reflects the living-room mirror behind his back. He can't see himself in the first reflection of the living-room mirror in the dining-room mirror. He can only see himself in a reflection of the reflection. He was incapable of thinking it through to the end. And he couldn't read either. From the radio came some highly appropriate music: the triumphal march from Verdi's *Aïda*. By this time San Francisco was lying totally black on the glittering mirror of the Bay. The heat of the sun through the big picture windows was making the Rinehart house so hot that he didn't know where to sit. Professor Rinehart had left instructions that the upholstered furniture was to be protected from the bright shafts of November sunshine by letting down the blinds. Halm couldn't bring himself to forgo the view of San Francisco. Surely the perfect stage setting for *Walküre*.

Toward five he could stand it no longer. He drove into Oakland and walked along the desolate streets of the inner city. There was an excess of light everywhere. Since most of the sky was covered by clouds, the sun had to pour out all its light onto Oakland's bizarre architectural mix. Suddenly Halm found himself in a store. He saw himself buy a suit and put it on immediately plus a shirt to go with it—raspberry red, pure silk, but no tie. The instant Halm stepped out onto the street he realized how appropriate to the moment this suit was. The basic color; a subdued shade of cognac, with a pattern of narrow black rectangles framing yellow lines. Actually it was a suit for Othello Jesús de García from Jamaica. But in this wild sunburst two hours before *Walküre*, he felt he could wear it.

By now everything was towering darkly into the dazzling yellow evening sky where banks of tattered black cloud were slowly drifting by. The world was wearing his suit! The outlines of buildings, palm trees, heavy cables and overloaded poles combined in the brilliant light to form an apocalyptic silhouette. Immediately after closing time the inner city was hellishly empty and hollow. Spellbound by his suit he walked down to the harbor, counting on being murdered. Saw the names *Sea Wolf* and Jack London Square. The wind was now so strong that it drove empty cans along the street.

Slowly and, as it were, happily, Halm drove his borrowed Volvo from that apocalyptic downtown to the green paradise of Oakland Hills. Never before had the façade of the Claremont Hotel, protruding and receding under its turrets and gables, looked so bone white. An opera, too, this hotel. Innumerable tennis courts and sentrylike palm trees separate the mystical façade from the humdrum world. Down by the harbor—that had been the *Flying Dutchman*. In the Claremont Hotel, the Parsifal from Münster had been turned into the Othello from Oakland. Although his Iago is also called Othello. So: through Crocker Gate to *Walküre*.

It was a good thing he knew where to find the Steiner Auditorium since it seemed to be the ambition of each building on this campus to be invisible from the next. Each building here wanted to feel alone. But then he couldn't find Room 98. He hadn't felt it was necessary to look for it yesterday. Instant panic. Fortunately he was, as always, much too early. Once again he hurried along all the corridors. The highest number was 96. And on the second floor the numbers started right away with 100. There was no 98. But perhaps he couldn't find Room 98 simply because it was so important for him to find Room 98. It must exist, otherwise she wouldn't have said Room 98, seven o'clock. True, she hadn't shown up in class this morning. Perhaps any minute now his whole class will come bursting out of one of the doors, laughing and plucking at his cognac-black-yellow suit, and roaring: Brando-Malvolio! So he had made a fool of himself after all. For a third time he poked along the corridors. At last he saw someone, hurried up to him, asked—much too breathlessly—where Room 98 was, had to repeat his question, and was told: "Room 98, no, there's no such room." "What about the Wagner performance?" he asked. "The Wagner performance," said the man, who unfortunately was only about forty and correspondingly uncooperative, "that's in Room 96, at seven o'clock." "Oh, I see," said Halm, "I see, thanks a lot." That was the number of the Sillenbuch house, 96. He knew where 96 was.

He was the first; he walked down the steps from row to row as far as the fifth and sat down. By seven o'clock seven students had turned up: three Japanese girls, one Japanese boy. They all sat down in the first five rows. They opened scores. Then she arrived. She was surprised to see him here. "Well, so you did come, how nice!" she said and introduced her friend Glenn Birdsell. She suggested to Halm and her boyfriend that they move farther forward. Sitting in the middle of the front row, right in front of the screen, she motioned her boyfriend and Halm to the seats right and left of her. It so happened that the boyfriend sat on her right, Halm on her left. She said to Halm that he probably knew this Chéreau production of Wagner's *Ring*. Halm said no, no, he knew nothing. She gaily passed this along to her boyfriend. So Glenn wasn't the only one who didn't know what was in store for him tonight! She hadn't brought a score along so she could follow.

Just then the man Halm had asked about Room 98 appeared in front of the rows of seats; so he was the professor. He wished them a pleasant evening and assumed they were all well prepared, and the guests who weren't in his class would know what to expect, otherwise they wouldn't have come. The lights were dimmed, on the screen the opera began to come to life. The Wälsung siblings Siegmund and Sieglinde find each other. Fran Webb looked more like Sieglinde than Halm looked like Siegmund. Fran's boyfriend looked more like a Siegmund than did the singer. The singer was not as much taller, broader, and stronger than his Sieglinde as Fran's boyfriend was taller, broader, and stronger than Fran. Halm was convinced that the expression in his and Fran's eyes formed a kind of sibling bond between them. But what did an expression in the eyes count for in the frenzy of this Wälsung night! The action on the screen that swiftly mounted to fever pitch failed to fuse him and Fran together; instead it fused the blond giant, the tournament WPP, the All-American boy Glenn Birdsell, and Fran, who was in any case already totally in his thrall. It might be objected that there is no point in a total couple like those two going to an opera; since they are not in danger or at risk, they cannot possibly recognize themselves in an opera, or as victims of fate being drawn in, tormented, and redeemed by an opera. Why do the redeemed bother to go to the opera? Nevertheless: on his right sat the very *incarnation* of the couple that was merely singing on the screen. One must admit, though, that this Mrs. Altmeyer-Sieglinde's singing so completely melted all individuality that each listener could abandon himself wholly to identifying with those emotions. The climactic end to the act was long-drawn-out because it took some time for every emotion to be plumbed; when it finally did come to an end, Halm no longer knew how he would ever carry on as himself again.

But the lights turned painfully bright, and the much too young professor said: "Fifteen-minute break." Fran stood up, stretched, and wiped tears from her eyes without hiding the fact that she needed to. Her boyfriend stood up and smiled. He was wearing a white T-shirt that positively bulged all over with muscles like armor. Around his neck hung the twin to the fine gold chain around Fran's neck. The people in the rows farther back must have all gone, the professor had left, the blond couple stood in front of Halm, Halm sat and didn't know what to do next. He would pretend to be dead. In any case, he wasn't here. That seemed to be the couple's feeling too. The way those two were now standing face to face, although they couldn't possibly have planned it: people can only stand like that when they are alone. And how their movements flowed one into the other! No slow-motion camera could have revealed who began, who followed. Between those two, cause and effect had ceased to exist. Her mouth opened, his mouth was opening as his head came closer, tilting slightly as it inclined. Like a precision tool, his head lowered itself onto her upturned face so that his mouth landed squarely on hers, open as if to receive the Sacrament. Then the mouths munched on each other in such a way that again no slow-motion camera could have revealed more than Halm was seeing from where he sat.

At some point Halm felt he had been watching much too long. He hoped they wouldn't take it amiss. That is, if they had noticed it at all. It must have a terrible effect on so-to-speak free people when someone watches them like that while they kiss. How inhibited he was! How square! A wearer of suspenders! And his palms are sweating! Right, right, right. But not dead. He wasn't dead. He was capable of movement. And how! He didn't have to look at it all. He wasn't a member of the opera class. Light as a feather, that's what he was. Without a sound he was up and away. Without running or stomping or panting, he was outside. Out of doors, in fact. So no one could have noticed him. He hadn't even noticed himself. The way he had escaped Room 96 was how, according to legend, the early Christians had escaped from Roman prisons. Leaving locks and doors intact.

Outside the building he came to himself. Swinging downhill on curving paths. "Chevy—the absolute muscle package," resounded through his head. "The Chevy man can," came the echo. Now he was quite happy to let the slogans dominate him. After all, was he accountable to anybody? Did he have to keep his mind clear of things like slogans? Not at all! In pure bliss he would relish the total devastation of his consciousness by advertising slogans. Now he remembered how he had escaped from Room 96. With a somersault. Glenn Birdsell had been described as a master of the underwater somersault used by swimmers to make their racing turns, or WPP's to free themselves when they have been crowded against the side of the pool. Now *he* had brought off a fantastic somersault! Oh indeed! He had dived deep down and away. That's why he had got away so easily. He had reason to be proud. "Keep your age a secret." Another of those TV slogans.

He went off in the general direction of his Volvo, not paying much heed. These crisscrossing ribbons, these now romantically lit paths were bound to lead downhill. At some point he would arrive down at the bowl. Then he was actually sitting in the Volvo, feeling extraordinarily sheltered. That had something to do with the Volvo and himself being of the same age. One automobile year corresponds to ten human years. The Volvo was ten, he was a hundred. He felt very light now. Absentminded. Unable to concentrate on anything. Beyond what was definite. Your dear lower jaw is a bit slack. Never mind. Something is going around and around in your head. It must be his consciousness, over which he has happily drawn the shades so that only a movement in the dark remains. How pleasant, not having to register anything! And not having to feel anything either. You're the epitome of restlessness. No comments, please, comes a call in the darkness, keep going! And now you've done your driving. Say good-bye to the car! Thanks for the solidarity. You are immediately taken charge of by the television: you can be sure that nothing will be demanded of you that you cannot bear. That is the simply wonderful thing about this American television: it is made to order. It obviously takes into account the experiences you have had. It knows you inside out. It knows you better than you care to know yourself. It recommends Easy-Off spray! And breath deodorant! That's not the most disagreeable of all possible discoveries: there must be millions like you, or it would be impossible to sell this TV. "Life is better on TV than at your front door." So much for that.

If he ever got back to Sillenbuch he would burn his Nietzsche manuscript. Once and for all he would take his place where he belonged, in the consumer society. To disappear—that is the quintessence of redemption. He must hurry up and tear off this cognac suit and this raspberry shirt. Disgusting, this getup. Then he leafed through the programs. With the deep, blissful gulps of a prodigal son, he apologized to the red wine he had been neglecting for so long. A boxing match on TV provided him with what he now needed. In the fourth round, the black boxer leaned his head on Aquino's shoulder and pummeled him a bit. Both would prefer to fall upon each other in a permanent embrace, but they had to go on. They are professionals. In each succeeding round, both faces express more and more clearly sheer overexertion and wretchedness. Steve Hearon, the black, is bleeding. His mouth is open; his mouth guard has slipped and completely fills the opening. "The cut is open and getting larger," says the commentator with obvious relish. "Funny things happen on the way to the championship," he says. Finally Aquino has won. Hardly embarrassed at all, Halm stays up to watch a western. Then the bottle is emptier than he is; he can go to bed.

14

THE CAT ARRIVED. AS soon as she had caressed his feet down onto the patio, she flopped over onto her back, her rosy mouth and the rosy pads of her paws shining up at Halm so that he couldn't help responding fully with his feet. In the same way as she pretended to use teeth and claws, he dug in with his toes. When both find it enjoyable to be mutually dependent, it is enjoyable to be mutually dependent. It was almost a kind of dance that developed from the thrusting, digging, persisting, withdrawing, and advancing of feet. Why should one continue to obey rules laid down during the pastoral age of mankind? They must have had their reasons for husbanding their seed so carefully. Nowhere, it seemed to him, could he rid himself of this tiresome commodity as innocuously as with this little friend. But then he would have to take her into the house. However, in four weeks he would be gone. He mustn't start anything here. So forget about it. And forget about that too. So . . . good-bye, wild one, supple one, furry one. Nothing is as right as what remains undone. At the moment you're not yourself. As soon as you have no wife, you realize what your principal vocation is: procreation. Nothing now remains that doesn't remind you of that. No woman whom you do not look at with that in mind. As long as you fail to carry out Command Number One, you're not free to undertake anything that concerns or interests you personally. The girl is merely the object to be used for the carrying out of this command. The girl is a means to an end. The bait for the sole purpose of driving the baited one mad. Were one to be aware of this each second, one would resist. So the whole rigmarole of approach, the carefully cultivated emotional setup, does have a meaning. It serves a purpose. One goes along with the design. The purpose of the idealization is achieved: one forgets that the idealization has a purpose. The means become the be-all and end-all. But since even the dominant purpose has long since been robbed of its meaning—procreation—idealization serves an illusory purpose; in other words, the illusion serves an illusion. And that is what, day and night, is wasting away your time, your life. An illusory illusion.

Today the students streaming through Crocker Gate seemed to him like troops who have just conquered a city and are now pouring into it. They were all conquerors, all around him. Thrusting their way past him, on both sides. Even the handicapped in their electric wheelchairs were joining in this conquest. No, this was not a city that they were invading. The faces of the invaders of a city reflect the leveling narrow-mindedness of that which they are conquering. These young people were assaulting the future. Something that doesn't exist. The result is a different kind of face. A more beautiful one. An ethereal brightness radiated from every face. A palpable jubilation called Youth.

He had to admit that life, served as it was by all events, was beautiful. He felt like saying: Hölderlin, here we go! But standing in one of the open phone booths next to the newspaper bin was his student Fran Webb, slouched against the wall, one hand holding the receiver, the other the Styrofoam cup of the milk which does a body good. Halm immediately changed direction to avoid crossing her line of vision. She probably wouldn't have seen him at all. The way she was slouching there holding the receiver, she probably saw nothing. That slouching posture showed her up perfectly. It was obvious who she was talking to. Most likely she had had to get up while he was still asleep, now she was calling to say it was almost nine o'clock, was he still in bed, which way was he lying, was he. . . .

Halm paused to look at the monument beside the path just before Coit Hall. To the football players of the class of 1899. Compared with their present-day successors, they wore no armor at all in those days. For weeks he had been walking past this greenish, weathered group without looking at it. Today he had to stop and gaze at the two youths. The scene was not one of battle, let alone victory. One of them was bandaging the injury of the other. When Halm was seated facing his class, he heard himself suggest the theme of suicide, bringing it up as casually as possible. Lucky California, where suicide is not a crime! What better place to live than where, if one felt like it, one could at any time put an end to it all without drawing some weird or drastic punishment down upon one's stone-cold body. Gail was furiously opposed to this law. If she ever went into politics she would see to it that in California suicide was once again made a crime. In her excitement she knocked over one of her crutches. Halm was the first to jump up and prop the crutch against the table beside Gail. Elaine said from the depths of her bosom that a freshman had once climbed up the campanile and threatened to jump off if he didn't get an A. Jeff said that normally anyone who didn't get an A here went to Los Angeles, paid a university fourteen thousand a year, and became a doctor—so much for that. Then he quoted some Camus.

Howard walked to the blackboard and wrote that he had an inflammation of the vocal cords and wasn't allowed to utter a sound. Halm said: "Howard, this is your best contribution so far, and in view of your previous contributions that's really saying something!" That's Howard for you! Inflammation of the vocal cords, but he comes anyway! Halm continued to look fondly at him for some time. Fran Webb was sitting as she always did, one leg at right angles and clasped at the ankle—and following the conversation with slightly delayed turns of her head. She continued to look at the person who had just spoken while the next person was already speaking. This gave her a lethargic quality, a cowlike greatness, almost a kind of divine presence. As soon as Halm saw her mouth, the Wälsung siblings came to mind, how they raved and ranted at the end of the act and then how Fran's head sank to one side and the water polo player's head was lowered like a precision tool onto her tilted profile until their mouths joined and munched away calmly and thoroughly at each other. Sitting across from that angled denim thigh, across from that dazzling specimen of slow motion, it made him feel good to enthuse about hasty suicide preparations, planned panic, and a headlong plunge into unconsciousness as the fatal shot rings out.

Gail said she didn't believe a word. Excellent, he said, she had seen through him, but he didn't feel ashamed, he insisted that there were periods in life that one could only survive intact if one talked constantly about suicide. To be able to end it all at any moment—that's the only thing that saves one from having to end it all. Gail said that those were unwholesome frivolities. Unfair toward life. To live was supreme. Under any circumstances. There was no either/or. There was only life, nothing else. Gail's eyes were moist. The others pounded their approval on the table. Halm contributed by saying, when all was quiet again: "An A-plus for Gail!" Everyone laughed.

Now for the first time Cynthia spoke up: without turning her body toward him she merely moved her head, but even her face was turned so slightly that her eyes could barely look at him, the way Carol sometimes stood—turned away and looking across at one as if to look across was an effort. Cynthia said she had known someone who had wanted to commit suicide because he had run out of energy, but she had spoken encouragingly to him, and that had helped. "I suppose he was quite young," said Halm. "No, not at all," replied Cynthia, "he was almost forty." "Really!" said Halm. Since he couldn't simply run away, he fled to the example of Hemingway, who had shot himself because age had deprived him of something. "Praiseworthy Hemingway," said Halm. And stood up. "If a person can no longer get something he can't do without . . . I'm sorry, Gail, but what is that person supposed to do?" "There's always some sport," said Gail, picking up her crutches and at the same time exposing her wired teeth. He had survived the lesson. Halm opened the door for Gail, but in the corridor he passed her as if hurrying to his next appointment. He rushed off.

Today there was no catching up with him. The creek was foaming under the humpback bridge. Halm flopped onto the chair beside Carol's desk as if it were a sanctuary. Fortunately Carol was in a great panic because tomorrow Rainer was flying to Houston for the poetry and music conference but hadn't yet brought her a single line to copy. The situation had all the earmarks of a disaster. She knew Rainer. He wasn't one to fly there and appear without a manuscript. When Rainer lectured, he always stood behind his manuscript as if behind a rampart. At first it looked as if he merely wanted to hide, but then as the lecture progressed he would raise his head more and more often, accompanying his phrases with ever more gallant gestures directed from his manuscript toward the audience. His expression growing more and more crafty. Don't trust these phrases was what his gestures and mimicry conveyed. Don't be misled by the ostensible profundity and elaborate reasoning inherent in my meticulous presentation. All water under the bridge by this time, ladies and gentlemen. The only true thing now is myself, the speaker, who can no longer subscribe to a lecture he wrote some time or other in the past. Let me tell you, said Carol, there isn't a lecturer between here and Boston who can put on such a complicated show and yet be as persuasive as Rainer Mersjohann. But, because he worked more thoroughly than anyone else he refused nine out of ten invitations. So far she had copied out each of his lectures at least three times before he considered them fit for presentation. And tomorrow morning at 9:45 via United to Houston. And Rainer, who carries his responsibilities the way a mother carries her embryo, as if apart from him there were no one else, as if conscientiousness would go down the drain unless he nursed and nourished and nurtured it—that same Rainer hadn't shown her a single line and was answering the phone with yes and no and nothing else. What, she asked, was going to happen?

Halm assumed that Carol was so worried about Rainer that she hadn't had time to quiz Fran about Halm's latest inanities. That was fine with him. Suddenly he felt compelled to tell Carol what had happened last night at the Steiner Auditorium. He would have liked to turn the Wälsung scene into gossip. He would have felt better if he could now have launched into some good gossip. To tell Carol's darkly gleaming eyes that trivial episode until her pouting lips began to part in incipient desire and reveal the attractive gap between her front teeth. . . . But he couldn't get started. He would give Rainer a call, he said importantly.

When he said good-bye, without having sought relief in gossip, he felt pretty pleased with himself. His footsteps resounded along the corridor. Dempewolf was again standing at the bulletin board, pretending with a supercilious expression to be studying the announcements. Probably he had merely been waiting to intercept Halm in order to repeat that he wasn't begging for Halm's visit, since his pride, which he had preserved intact from Silesia via Siberia to Oakland, would not permit that, but a visit from Halm would still be welcome in case Halm had been serious when they'd first met in the poisoned gingerbread house on Euclid Avenue and Halm had shown some interest in a man who preferred isolation to integration. If not, fine, nothing's changed: the Silesian is used to disappointment. Halm called out as he left, thus avoiding any argument, that he would put a note with a suggested date in Dempewolf's box, next week; at the moment he wasn't sure what he had on.

Halm was glad to be sitting in his Volvo. He pulled onto the street and slowly threaded his way home through side streets. Once again the Bay was so dazzling that the city behind it was scarcely visible. He ought to phone Rainer. Maybe he could help him. But how? Anyway he was incapable of going as far as the phone and dialing. And then Rainer of all people! The phase of spreading gloom had begun again. Soon Halm would be feeling as he had before arriving in California. All he had to do was to conform to his situation, then everything would be fine. Harmony with himself—that was all he needed. No contacts, no mobility, no easy back and forth. To sit opaquely. To stare without seeing. Out onto that dazzling bay, for instance. Until his eyes become totally insensitive. At most, perhaps, to stare at the television screen. Everyone has something he must hide, even from himself. The impression that what he must hide surpasses what he can still admit to himself. What you cannot say, warms you. You've learned that here. What remains unsaid, warms. That's how you must see it. The western hero, whom you are watching in total absorption, is driven by the dramaturgy of the genre into hopeless isolation, a situation compared to which your own situation appears pretty harmless. Olivia de Havilland is thrust by the gloating villains into the iron mail car so that she may be burned to death in it together with Errol Flynn and the piles of mail sacks, while the villains leap from the moving train onto horses brought there by accomplices and ride off. Thanks to the presence of a postmaster's rifle in the mail car, Flynn and de Havilland are saved, whereas when the movie was over Halm was still sitting there alone. Phone Sabina? He really should cover up all those mirrors. Especially the ones downstairs in the bedroom and bathroom. He simply couldn't stand the sight of himself anymore.

He ought now to be thinking about that teacher Labove and the girl Eula. Why on earth had she chosen this rapist? And if he had given a firm promise to go to the opera performance, would she have brought along her boyfriend Glenn Birdsell? Enough of that! She would have avoided that total kiss if she'd had even a shred of feeling! If that total kiss isn't enough for you, you're doomed. Unteachable, as they say here. Ah yes, now you're trying to blame Wagner for that total kiss. She couldn't help herself. After that ranting and raving she too had become what is now known on television as a heat-seeking missile. . . . *I*-Halm moved an end to the debate. A debate on this move is refused.

He drinks up his bottle of red wine. He goes to bed without

turning on the light. He lies in bed like a parcel. That's that. In his dream a woman lay naked in the sand, he himself close behind her, embracing her form; nothing ever felt like this body, never had he been so close to anyone, but he wasn't yet lying quite comfortably, and, because there was a female observer behind *his* back, he and the woman who would have cooperated with him must not make the slightest movement, not the slightest. On waking up he seemed to feel "flawed" and thought, This is how a foreign language penetrates and takes possession of you. The word "somersault" occurred to him. That underwater-racing turn. Once you have been in such a situation, you never forget the word that applies to it.

It was time to get up. Don't turn on the light, and don't look in any of the mirrors. Since he was now drinking a bottle of cabernet sauvignon every night, his nose must show up in his face like a billowing red sail. The cat was already sitting on the top step, right by the door; she immediately slipped between his feet, pleasured them and obtained pleasure from them, going down step by step and across the patio and again down to the lawn. She never wanted to go into the wet grass, so she turned around, jumped up the steps to her bowl and plate, and had her breakfast.

In class he suggested that each of them describe his or her dream of the previous night, but he begged not to have to be the first; his dreams, he said, were embarrassing even for him, how much more so must they be for others. Now they all wanted to hear *his* dream. He made it clear that he hadn't mentioned the embarrassing nature of his dreams in order to be urged to reveal them. So let's hear it, who had a dream last night? He no longer glanced toward Fran Webb. It made him feel good to glance across to Elaine, Cynthia, and Gail. He assured them all that he had no intention of translating their dreams into fact-finding language. If you wished to understand dreams, you must not translate them. There was no second language for a dream. He promised to prove with each dream they told that dreams are intelligible per se, much more intelligible than if their contents were regarded as a disguise that must be removed.

Fran Webb raised her hand. It was the end of November and this was the first time Fran Webb asked to be heard. She sat, as always, with one denim thigh at an angle, her right hand clasping the ankle while with her left hand, apparently because her temerity embarrassed her, she swept her green-gold hair from one side to the other; but then she recounted her dream, hesitatingly, cautiously, as if she didn't want her words to cause any damage. In her dream she is walking across the wide patio of her parents' home. The house is full of people. Inside it looks and sounds like a television studio. She is determined to go inside, but the patio floor is made of down, bottomless, the more firmly she treads on it the deeper she sinks. She can hear her mother singing inside the house. Her second mother. She is singing a raucous hit tune. Her singing sounds very unpleasant. Suddenly men are standing between Fran and the house, they are looking at her like catchers, leaning forward, their hands spread wide apart, ready to grab her. There are also some handcuffs; this gives Fran great satisfaction. She hasn't deserved handcuffs. An injustice is being done her right here on her parents' patio, where she can't move forward, fortunately can't move forward, or she would run straight into the widespread hands of those dreadful men. All she really wants is to go into the house. She has to tell her mother to stop that ridiculous, unpleasant singing. Just then, from among the men Marlon Brando moves effortlessly toward Fran. Instantly the colored dots, that so far had appeared only randomly, are multiplied. Everything is now full of colored dots. Most of all herself, her pale dress and under her pale dress her body. Marlon Brando is now close to her, he grabs her by the shoulders, she sees that it's Professor Mersjohann, but can't help herself, she calls him Marlon Brando. From Professor Mersjohann's expression she realizes the embarrassing and painful impact of her mistake. She can't bear the sight of Professor Mersjohann's devastated expression, and summoning all her strength she desperately turns back again toward the house. But her home is gone, a quite different house is standing there now; she goes inside, a strange family is seated at table, Fran joins in the meal but soon can't stand it any longer, so she runs into the bathroom, lies down in the bathtub; the tub is instantly full, the water is hot and foamy, an opera begins, Wagner, *Walküre*, Act I, she is thrilled but in her excitement she bangs her elbow so hard against the edge of the tub that she wakes up.

Halm felt he would now be better off if he hadn't spoken so cockily about there being no need for dream analysis. It was a good thing nobody had taken him seriously. Almost all of them now proceeded to tear Fran's dream apart, anxious to say what it really meant: colored dots, soft patio floors, men poised to catch, mothers singing tearjerkers, Mersjohann as Brando, home vanished, foam bath with Wälsung love, waking from a pain in the elbow. Halm said no more. He felt sorry for the lovely dream being taken apart by the class as if it were a slaughtered wild animal that had to be gutted, boned, and carved up to prepare it for pot, pan, and stomach. And they were pretty skillful in carving up and identifying. They were all psychologists. Fortunately they couldn't agree. Fran Webb said nothing more. She and Halm sat silently among the dream interpreters, who were led by Howard's partially recovered voice.

After class the girl once again walked along with him as if that were the most natural thing in the world. She said nothing. For the first time he had the courage also to say nothing. They walked toward the bridge. Luckily Rainer was far away in the air or already in Texas. At the highest point of the humpback bridge Halm actually stopped to look down into the eddying Okra Creek. He looked at Fran and she at him. Then they walked on rather quickly. Could she now be thinking of anything but her dream? He hoped she knew that he could also think only of her dream. He didn't know why, but for him the dream, and even more so the fact that she had described it, was an attempt to ask Halm's forgiveness for the *Walküre* scene. Or was he unteachable?

As they stood at the side entrance to Fillmore Hall, he said: "That was an A-plus." She shifted her closed lips. The gray-blue-green, close-set eyes always held a questioning look; in addition, the girl always held her head a shade higher than was necessary.

She was shy, she had said three months ago at the cafeteria table when they had been translating the panther poem together. At the time a hot, gusty wind had come up from the Bay, tugging at everything in its effort to carry it off. Today heavy clouds drifted overhead, but around them there was silence. She told him she thought the way the others had treated her dream was dumb. Halm said: "It's some kind of compulsion, evidently. Instead of experiencing, people want to know." He didn't tell her that, while the class was dismembering her dream, he had been waiting nervously and greedily for someone to discover him, Halm, in some part of the dream. Surely Jeff should have mentioned Halm in connection with Marlon Brando? It would have embarrassed Halm very much, yet he had been hoping for it. Jeff had been doodling and saying less than anyone, merely commenting that he considered dream interpretation to be an exerting of priestly influence and hence contemptible.

Oh, it just occurred to her: might she hand him her essay on her favorite hero, Labove, by the end of next week? But of course! By that time he will have finished reading the Faulkner book. That was also something he preferred to read without understanding it, he said, but he had to admit that the urge to understand kept reasserting itself. After all, one can't help being curious. Oh yes, and then she'd like to invite him too, in case he didn't know yet where he would be having his Thanksgiving turkey dinner, he was welcome at her home, she meant her parents'. Also, she'd like to invite him to a farewell party, since he was leaving soon, wasn't he? Maybe the first Saturday in December? Yes, he'd love to come. But for the Thanksgiving dinner he'd already accepted an invitation. Too bad, she said, she always missed the bus. So then at her home at Hill Court, the first Saturday in December? Yes, he'd be looking forward to that!

He hurried off to his office and, confronted by the still unalleviated children's drawings, again wished he had a poster. But no, he was forced to look at that black pile, daubed onto orange-colored paper, from which a black line loomed and ended in black palm leaves, above it all a black blob for the sun and an airplane, seen from above, with three windows, showing three figures that seemed to be hugely enjoying themselves. He now admitted to himself that he had often looked at this picture. He had immediately seen Sabina, Lena, and himself on their homeward flight. An unbearably drastic infantile depiction. Even he didn't grin like that. And certainly not on his homeward flight.

He heard the sound, a blend of metal and broom, from which by this time he had come to recognize Elisha, the black with Chinese features. Whenever Elisha entered, Halm looked up at him; Elisha never returned his look. His skin was as black as it was yellow. Somehow he looks dusty, thought Halm. But if he were a dentist, one would never think of such a thing.

When Halm entered Carol's office, she merely nodded. Halm said: "So he caught his plane?" Yes, but any moment now she was expecting some grotesque message from Houston. At the latest by tomorrow afternoon, when he's supposed to give his talk. Funny how disagreeably tense life becomes when one can no longer imagine how it's supposed to continue. It was simply unthinkable for that mighty master of order to appear without a manuscript before a conference of delegates from all over America. But appear he must. Yet he didn't have a manuscript. So what did Halm suppose that master of order, whose whole pride was centered in his reliability, was going to do? Can you tell me, please? Halm couldn't tell her. He was glad she didn't ask him whether he'd called Rainer before he left. She invited him for Thanksgiving dinner. Sorry, he'd already accepted. She understood. She realized she'd left it a bit late. But this coming Saturday, was he still free? Oh yes, this Saturday would be fine, next Saturday would be more difficult. Saturday, then.

But on Friday evening Lena phoned to say that Elissa had just had a call from Houston that on Friday morning her husband had been found dead on his bed in Room 411 of the University Hotel. Halm groaned. Lena said: "Hello?" Halm said: "Yes." Lena said: "Are you still there?" Halm said: "Yes." Lena said Elissa had decided to stay here. As soon as Jamey learned of his father's death he would come home right away, she was sure of that. Halm opened a bottle of red wine. "Tears of the mountain." Any reaction seemed justified. He felt the kind of compulsion to laugh that he feels at funerals, which was why he didn't like going to funerals. Nowhere did he feel so incapable of conforming to custom as at funerals. So this was a major event. Washington University of Oakland is apparently justly famous for its events. Dear Rainer Mersjohann, you've topped them all. So now one will be sitting here day and night because of you. Rigid yet softened up. And somewhat cramped. Hemmed in. As far as personal freedom and all that is concerned. Insufficiently oneself, one goes on sitting. Besieged by your windy spirits of the dead. Want to see moist eyes, don't you! "Stop pawing me, you old headless horseman Ichabod Crane!"

"Ah, it's you, Lena—you're back?" She'd been ringing the doorbell for at least fifteen minutes, she said. And she's brought along two bulging suitcases. Elissa had stuffed one of them with presents, apparently to get rid of her in a hurry. Elissa was terribly upset and said she had to be alone now. No witnesses. They'd meet again soon. Only not now. She was feeling fine, never felt better, she felt like someone who'd been sentenced to death and suddenly reprieved. It was simply that she had to be alone to adjust to her new condition. Quite alone. Halm nodded. Caught himself at what he found the most ludicrous thing in the world: comparing grief. Ice-cold Elissa isn't as acutely grief-stricken as you think she should be, is she?

Elrod phoned. Halm mustn't think he could get out of Saturday night. Nothing was more shameful than using the death of others as an excuse. And Honeybunch needed some distraction which he, old man that he was, couldn't supply. If one could bleed to death from tears, she'd already be dead. As Halm was driving along Shattuck Avenue to buy some flowers for the Elrods, the windshield wiper conked out. Since by this time the dense, misty rain had started again, Halm had to pull over immediately. He got out and hurried along the sidewalk looking for one of those boxes that supply a newspaper for a quarter. He found one but didn't have a quarter, so he ran into a store—it happened to be a radio store—bought some batteries, made sure the change contained quarters, dashed back to the newspaper box, got himself a paper, wiped the windshield, and drove slowly on, stopping every few yards to wipe the windshield. When he came back to the car with the bunch of roses, which had cost $17.00, he found an enormous black man standing beside the car door mumbling something. He wanted money. Halm gave him the 70 cents change he found in his pocket. "Gimme a dollar," said the black. Halm thought of the $17.00. They still hurt. Seventeen dollars for a bunch of flowers, it was crazy. He said he wasn't rich, pointing to his old Volvo. The black looked fixedly at the big bunch of roses plumped up with greenery in its plastic covering. "Gimme a dollar," repeated the man, as if saying it for the first time. Halm fished feverishly for a dollar bill in his breast pocket and was relieved that what he pulled out wasn't a five or even a twenty. He handed the man the dollar bill, trying as he did so to express that he felt he was being robbed. The black took the dollar with an expression of utter disdain and walked off without thanking him. Halm felt as if he had been spat upon. He got into the car. Suddenly the wipers were working again. Halm was sure the wipers wouldn't have worked if he hadn't given that man the dollar.

When he came back to the Rinehart house, Lena was listening to the record that Rainer had brought them. *Death and the Maiden.* The title alone bothered him. And the music was too drastic for his taste. Violins at such loggerheads. "Lena!" he said. She didn't hear him. So he called out, almost shouted: "Lena!" She jumped. He gestured at the record. She turned it off at once and asked: "What's the matter?" He didn't want to say what he had in mind, so he said: "Are you coming along to the Elrods?" Lena said: "No." And since she naturally assumed that this question was the sole reason for his having interrupted her listening, she switched on the record again. And from the beginning.

He went downstairs to change. He felt a need to dress as formally as possible. He pulled out everything he had. None of it would do. Except for the garish Caribbean-style cognac-black-and-yellow suit that he had bought in the hellish light of downtown Oakland two hours before *Walküre*. He also put on the raspberry-colored shirt. When he looked in the mirror and saw his own colorlessness—apart from his nose he had lost all color—clothed in such wild colors, he was seized with a compulsion to laugh. "Keep your age a secret." Once again this phrase he had picked up somewhere popped into his mind. And the word "secret" reminded him of "secrets," which made it sound suggestive. He didn't laugh. It was only a kind of belch. Ah yes, Brando-Malvolio.

When Kirk Elrod saw Halm he said: "Good." He had been a little afraid, he said, that Halm would turn up in black. But only a little. "When a maniac abdicates, one should at least wear red," he said. Elrod himself was practically submerged in a dark-red shiny robe with wide sleeves embroidered with Japanese characters in gold thread. The Swiss lady, thought Halm. Carol was all in white. Something clinging. One was relieved for her sake that there was a slit on each side. Her eyes shone as if they were liquid. Her mouth pouted even more. The lower lip thrust forward. The head lowered, averted. As if stricken. It was painful to look at her. Halm told his host he was glad to be permitted to make one last visit to Grizzly Peak Boulevard since he still didn't know who the Swiss lady was! "Only John Frey knows that," said Elrod. Auster said it really was deplorable how casual writers of fiction were about their sources. Everything he said was obviously being directed at his young wife. She had a wild, dark, heavy face but mischievous eyes. Without those eyes the face would seem to dissolve in anguish. Halm was reminded of Beethoven as he looked at that heavyset Rachel. And he looked at her as if at something that required permission to be looked at. After all, she was the only one who was at home in Yoknapatawpha-Yosemite territory. Except when he was eating, Auster constantly held one of his young wife's hands between his own hands. For this, Rachel had to sit very close to him with one hand through his arm so that he could play with that hand. Which he did amply. The contrast between his two hands and hers was as striking as Roy had described it. But how naturally Auster was playing with Rachel's hand! And how she liked it! Halm admired this couple. And he admired Auster more than Rachel. Now he found himself in the company of two such couples.

He complimented Auster on what he had quickly read of his. Auster said: "Rachel, did you hear that? He's complimenting me!" With her free hand Rachel stroked his head as if he were her child. Halm said: "I must congratulate you." Auster said: "Did you hear that? He's congratulating me! Ask him what for." She asked. Halm said: "On your marriage!" "Yes, you may well do so," said Auster, "certainly me." "And me!" said Rachel. Auster said he had once told Halm that a married philosopher was like a bird in a cage. That had been at Rainer's. Standing by P's cage. He wouldn't take it back, but he would have to add that it was much pleasanter in that cage than he had imagined. She stroked him again. "We are happy, and Carol is sad," Auster said sorrowfully. "I'm just woebegone," said Carol, and Halm realized how he missed Rainer, who had always translated unusual words in an undertone into German, as if only for his own benefit. Carol said into the general silence: "He didn't have a mean bone in his body." And after an appropriate interval Kirk Elrod continued the eulogy with: "He was a maniac."

In a tragic voice heavy with pain and praise, Carol recounted the circumstances. He had been lying fully dressed on the bed in the hotel. Beside him the manuscript. A single sheet. On it a single sentence: *At my time of life I ought not to be appearing before you, O men of Athens, in the character of a juvenile orator.* "Oh," said Auster, "that's not Mersjohann, that's a quotation, it's Plato's Socrates, in the Jowett translation." Halm, thinking of Rainer, heard himself saying: "You know too damn much." Auster said: "He's complimenting me again, Rachel, but he's also paraphrasing the deceased, who said to me early in September: 'You write too damn much.' " And he, Auster, had answered: "Publish or perish." Elrod said: "He opted for 'perish'." Auster said: "But I didn't."

From then on, all the talk was of Rainer Mersjohann. If Auster tried to change the subject, Carol would simply say something about Rainer. All she could talk about was Rainer. Suddenly all any of them could talk about was Rainer, nothing else. Rainer really filled the world. At every turn, one came up against him. Halm was rewarded by Carol with approving tragic looks when he mentioned that only the day before Rainer left, he had led a discussion on the subject of suicide in his class. From oneself one can, after all, stand a good deal.

Next time the class met, Jeff proposed that the subject of suicide be discussed again, this time in the light of recent events. They all had memories of Rainer, they all gathered Rainer ornaments like flowers. It was a compulsion. During the regular Sunday telephone call, after Halm had told Sabina the news, she began to stammer. Then she gave up. Halm didn't say anything either. She had nothing more to say about her father. There has probably never been such a long silence during a conversation between Europe and California. He would neither disconnect nor say anything. Finally Sabina said in a shrill voice: "He was such a decent man!" Halm thought: Maybe so. All the more so because Sabina had used a word that was important to Rainer himself. If one describes a person in his own words, everyone is almost perfect. But to do that implies an achievement. Rainer had achieved that. Wherever one went, Rainer was being honored to the point of tautology. And each person was aware only of what he had lost.

Halm felt that he had arrived too late. The time had been too short. He hadn't been able to make full use of the opportunity. He had missed his chance. Rainer might have become a friend. It had come close to that. If Rainer had never seen him with the girl, if Rainer had not been supplied by Carol with reports on Halm and Fran Webb, if Rainer had not always had that absolute sense of justice, if Rainer in his unverifiable sense of justice had not also demanded that Halm must leave Sabina. . . . Probably that terrible fellow would have been the only friend he could have had. Now he had none. Just like before. So much for that. Don't feel sorry for yourself. Or for him. It was all over.

Most embarrassing of all was the evening at the Tudor house on Euclid. Elissa wanted to say what she hadn't been able to say before. She hadn't been in her right mind when she had asked her father to have Rainer invited to the Claremont Hotel. She had wanted to take revenge on a brute, on a girl-scalp hunter, a Spanish instructor, suave, always dancing attendance, always babbling about death. He could talk about nothing but Nothing. She had fallen for him. When she had turned up with Rainer at the Claremont, how that odious fellow's eyes had bulged! She had been eternally grateful to Rainer. She would never forget that he had enabled her to stage such a scene. And Rainer was good at that, staging a scene. He always spread a certain aura of aloofness. He could fill formality with absurdity. He always adhered to formality, always in excess, and that excess provided the absurdity. For those who could see. And he'd been so crazy at the time, so captivated by her, so capable of adoration, so serious. He had worshiped her, she hadn't known that such a thing could exist. Quite a big fellow, with only one thing in mind, to yield, to yield to her, to cease to exist as himself, to be nothing but love for her. So tender, so bent on self-sacrifice, so devoted. As if he had been waiting for her for a million years, as if he knew from universal experience that apart from her nothing existed that deserved emotion. As if, having had to reject all that had been offered so far, he was on the brink of dying of hunger and thirst. And then she came along, the only nourishment that could possibly exist for him. Now, he had said, he knew why until then he had been living in a state of rejection. Well, for a few months they had lived off his ecstasy, from his store of tenderness. Then she became pregnant. Then right away again. But then finally she had to acknowledge what she had long since known, what she could only put in this way: Someone who doesn't feel love doesn't benefit from being loved. That's a pretty terrible law. A kind of natural justice. And Rainer noticed that and began to lay claim to their mutual promises. Day and night. Apparently he believed that one could lay claim to affection, love, proximity, closeness, fusion. Right was always on his side. And the more clearly he saw that it didn't help him to have right on his side, the more stubbornly did he lay claim to it. So had it been right for him to demand that she record on tape her experiences with other men? Had it been possible, he would have liked to have it on video tape. He became insatiable in his demands for graphic descriptions of her affairs with men. He refused to accept it when she said how little this or that affair meant to her. Of even the most inconsequential night he wanted the most detailed description. For him nothing was irrelevant. And he invariably maintained that he was demanding this for her sake. If she told him *everything,* they could continue to live together. Every suppressed second poisoned their marrage. If he knew *everything,* he could forgive *everything.* It was only what he knew that he could forgive. And so on.

At first, she said, she had in all innocence obeyed, had described everything. But the effect had been terrible. So she had stopped describing everything. When he noticed that, things became even worse. When the Halms arrived in August she had been desperate. Rainer had wanted to kill her, she knew that. He would have regarded it as punishment. He had the gift of regarding everything he thought necessary as also being just. He could do nothing without first authorizing himself by a kind of dispensation of justice. But once he had authorized himself he was apparently capable of anything. Why he had now killed himself instead of her, she found inexplicable. Perhaps she had Lena to thank for this. He had spoken of Lena as being of direct assistance. He even wished to please Lena. As far as Elissa knew, Lena was the only person whom he had, as it were, placed beside him in his unceasing judgments. As an imaginary lay assessor, so to speak. He had made it pretty clear to Elissa that nothing would happen to her as long as he hadn't submitted his intention to Lena and obtained her approval. Maybe that was just the latest variation in his justice game. He always used legal jargon when speaking of their marriage. As far as Elissa was concerned, he was permanently involved in a trial by jury. Since she hadn't known his parents, and since he always revealed his origins in images but never in direct statements, she had no idea where all this came from. It was all alien to her. She wished she could have prevented this disaster.

She had found a parcel in his room addressed to Lena. She gave it to Lena. Lena thanked her. Their parting was almost laconic. They had a common bond yet could do nothing for each other. The last thing she said was that she was expecting her sons now. Halm said that, if Elissa should go to Europe, this was his address. And gave it to her. What pleased him most was that she had called Lena a lay assessor. He must tell Sabina about that. Back at the Rinehart house he opened the parcel addressed to Lena. Lena sat there looking on. Out came a manuscript. Handwritten. A title page:

Rainer Mersjohann
California Fragment
154 Sonnets

A letter for Lena was enclosed. Halm asked Lena to open it. From Lena's expression he could tell that she wasn't keen on any further revelations today, that she had learned enough for one day. He repeated, louder: "Lena!" She looked at him blankly. So he went downstairs into the bedroom and lay down on the big bed without regard for the ornaments thundering against the wall. So far he had never picked up any of the magazines lying on the shelf beside the bed. A pile of *Playboy* and a pile of *Moral Majority Report*. He picked up a *Playboy*. The issue he had in his hands was ten years old and might have been performing its honorable service in this bedroom for the past ten years. An Irish girl from Missouri thrust forward her closed crease. A dark line beneath dark hair. A grove. He remembered the word from Rainer's whimsical guide to the campus. At the top of the grove's crucial area, a sharp concentration of hair. A real little thicket. The caption read that so far this girl had had no more than ten men. But that to count those ten she still needed both hands. He laid the sex rag aside.

Now he had to put out the light. It was an effort. When he

had finally accomplished this and was lying in the dark, he thought about Fran Webb. A kind of kitschy vision foamed up in him: Fran as an opera swan in some Parisian decor of the *belle époque*. But he also thought about Elissa, pale, heavy-breasted, short-haired. Now a widow. He thought about that. Yes, he thought about that. Elissa, alone in the tarantula chapel. He, alone, here. He thought about that. In the morning, standing in the narrow shower stall, he watched the water run down his corpse. He soaped and washed himself with a sense of washing a corpse. Rainer had also had a job washing corpses.

On Friday the girl handed him her essay on Labove, saying: "See you tomorrow," she was looking forward to it. The woman from Cologne was sitting in for Carol so he could drive straight home. Lena was again listening to Rainer's Schubert record. Again Halm found this inappropriate. Too drastic. He closed the door to the study and read Fran's essay. It seemed to him that she was longing for something exceptional, even if it were to be painful, embarrassing, terrible. Had she written all this down because the WPP was too well behaved for her? Hadn't Elissa put Rainer's life on the line to drive a few beads of sweat onto the brow of some overbearing, odious Spanish docent? Your incurable ignorance of a woman's inner life. Or is it plain ignorance, period? Tomorrow evening he'd know a bit more. If he was the only guest there could be no further doubt. Smile, Brando-Malvolio.

He arrived an hour early at the street from which Hill Court branched off. He wanted to play it safe. He parked the car many streets away. Ten minutes after the appointed time, he rang the bell at a noble, solemn, medium-size house. The girl opened the door. The corridor behind her was dimly lit. The sound of many voices. She wore her bold expression as if her name were Leif. He handed her his flowers. She showed polite surprise. "Roses!" she exclaimed. She ushered him inside and down the stairs and around to the left and through a door on the right: her bedroom. Her bed. Almost buried under coats. But one could still see that her bed linen had a pattern of spring colors. Her bed was a kind of Renoir meadow. Would be, without the coats. On the walls, framed opera scenes with Wagnerian characters. In the kitchen the guests helped themselves from casseroles and bowls as well as to wine, beer, and whisky. Students were standing around everywhere and talking. Not only students from his conversation course. Fran led him around, tried to be helpful, persisted until she had found him a seat upstairs in the large living room near the huge fireplace. It was really more of a living hall. A Nordic one, perhaps. The wooden ceiling is supported by beams. The stones on which the beams rest at each end are decorated with batlike figures. And in the middle of the ceiling each of the supporting beams has been branded with curved crosses. The fireplace is itself a piece of architecture. A towering brick gable relief.

He was glad to find Jeff sitting close by. In the light of the open fire, Halm notices for the first time that the tip of Jeff's left ear is bent, almost folded over. Halm finds that very endearing. On the floor by the fireplace, around the wood pile, stands a row of creatures made of narrow strips of iron. Cicadas perhaps. Quite big. They form a screen for the hearth. The light in the room tends to be more dusky than dim. Below the stone supports of the ceiling beams, iron lamps project from the wall, their yellow light so feeble that they seem designed to reinforce the impression of duskiness. The flames in the fireplace bring the dusk to life. Music pounds from invisible loudspeakers. People have to draw close together if they want to carry on a conversation.

Halm knows he has to drink a great deal and very fast. Otherwise he can't stay here. Eat as little as possible, eat nothing at all. Decline food. As if he never ate at all. Fran looks after him. She shows him that she wants to know every few minutes how he is doing. Each student comes up to him in turn, conversation is made in which one mentions that one is making conversation, so one laughs, and Halm says that by this time they have all reached the A-plus level. Tonight Elaine's makeup gives her a look of doll-like rigidity. Art the giant has banged his head in the kitchen and is bleeding. Tonight Howard is saying less than anyone. The level in his glass doesn't change, so he's not drinking at all. Genuine conversation evidently doesn't appeal to him. Gail tells Halm that tomorrow she's driving to Daly City, another of those San Francisco suburbs, to the institution where the pelican tormentor, meanwhile captured, was now confined. She intends to save him. She also intends to visit the rapist before Christmas and persuade him to have himself castrated. She devotes every weekend to some cause or other. Almost all evil could be prevented, she said, if one could only talk to those troubled people in time. She wants to run for governor of California and turn it into the most humane state in the country.

Whenever Fran comes up to him, she asks whether there is anything he needs. He shakes his head. As soon as she is gone he is afraid he may have grinned as he did so. Actually he would like to stare her down so that she can see from his expression that, even when she is merely speaking, she appalls him, as it were. At any rate, the WPP isn't there. Many have brought along their boyfriends or girlfriends. She could just as easily have summoned the WPP. Or is his team playing in San Diego today? If she had wanted him to be present she would have chosen a different evening. So all these guests would gradually be leaving. He can be the last to leave. Or he can stay behind. Whichever. He'll go on drinking now, regardless. He feels an urge to shed all responsibility. Good God, he'd held back long enough! Now, for one evening, surely he could loosen the shackles a bit. And the way Fran keeps coming up to him! He doesn't need to move. He'll go on sitting by the fire, a procession of iron cicadas at his feet. He's determined to drink more than anyone else and pretend to forget to leave. Suddenly she will return alone from the front door, where she has accompanied the last of her guests, and finally sit down with him by the fire. Across from him. Or beside him. Either way. The main thing is, they can talk. For the first time. She had already supplied a good topic to start off with. Labove. Your best essay, Fran, this one about the rapist in the classroom.

Now to his dismay they have begun to dance. But he doesn't want to dance. He can't dance at his age. If he ever could. He could never have danced to this music. As she brings him a second bottle of red wine, Fran says that, now they've talked such a lot to each other, it's time they danced together. "I see," he says. If she puts it like that, of course he will dance with her. But, he says rather grandly, he refuses to take a step before he has finished the second bottle. Finished it! It wasn't all that unusual for one's steps to become more and more confident the less one was aware of executing them. And in his case at least two bottles were needed before he could leave his feet to their own devices. She says he mustn't think he can escape her like that. It's a deal: as soon as the second bottle is empty, he's hers. "Oh yes," he says, "oh yes, Miss Mephistopheles! It's a deal." He is still able to appreciate that, were he capable of sound judgment, he would not like to hear himself talking the way he is talking now. But *his* students are obviously delighted to see their instructor come out of his shell, so to speak. Halm is talking as he hasn't talked for a long time. Perhaps he has never talked like this. Gradually he feels able to say anything. At least he can say something to each and every one. And what he is saying to Elaine and Gail and Cynthia and Jeff and Art and Howard is exactly right. He can feel that. To each he says exactly the right thing. He is speaking only English now. The urge to speak English is unbounded. Just as a singer hears himself only to his own advantage, he now considers his English to be in full bloom. It is the language, too, that dazzles him. How rich one becomes by emigrating! By being away! Something he wishes for. Like this language—that's how he'd like to be. What a nerve! And he raises his glass and calls out that he's drinking to the "extenuating circumstances."

Then the girl comes to claim her dance. Does she intend to lead? He can't permit that. He simply whirls her around a few times, with no idea of whether it fits the music. There is something more important at stake. And because this whirling seems to have made Fran a bit nervous, she leans against him, supporting herself somehow on his arm. This makes him feel he can swing her around as he wants. His strength has increased markedly. There's absolutely nothing to swinging this girl around. She's so light! And gets lighter all the time. And now the others are making room for him. His twirls are sweeping everyone off the dance floor. It's turning into an exhibition. His only embarrassment is on account of Gail. Actually he had intended to stay seated beside her to show her that even those who don't dance don't miss anything. Fran and he look into each other's eyes. As never before. Her eyes are the eyes of his grandmother, are his eyes. For a split second he sees himself as a corpse, a dead burr on that living person. *Death, Bound to,* poor Fran. He calls out to her: "Don't look anywhere or we'll get giddy!" Eye to eye! Then there's no more whirling. We're standing still. The world is revolving around us. Let it. We are one. And beyond the reach of the world revolving around us. He doesn't call this out; he merely thinks it. Fran is no longer frightened, he can see that. Is the music still playing? He doesn't know. There is still some kind of pounding sound. More like surf than music.

Then his foot lands on something that slips from under him. Near the fireplace. Mustn't fall into the fire! He clutches Fran to him. It was one of those iron cicadas. He realizes this as he crashes to the floor. Or she crashes. Both fall over a chair and on top of one another; in any case, they're lying on the floor. Then they are both helped up. He sees Fran's face. Her expression tells him there's something wrong with him. Besides, he can feel blood running down his face. Howard's voice: "I'll drive him to the hospital." Halm is totally passive. As if not there. Car, voices, hospital corridor, a nurse, a stretcher, the nurse does things to his face, then the doctor comes, a Chicano, who also does things to his face. Halm feels nothing, everything is infinite. The doctor tells him he worked for two years in Germany. In Bochum. Compared to an American hospital, he says, a German one is nothing but a barracks. Halm says: "Oh yes." As he is being helped up, he hears the doctor say: "Six stitches." He recognizes Howard. Howard drives him to Contra Costa Avenue. At the very last moment he plucks up enough courage to ask what he has been wanting to ask all along: "How's Fran?" "She's O.K.," says Howard. Fran had only hurt her ankle a bit. "Her ankle," says Halm. "Thank God it's her ankle." And touches his head and encounters bandages everywhere. Only his left eye is uncovered. He says: "Howard, how many more things will I have to thank you for?" When Howard smiles, the smile ends not in his face but in his beard. "Oh, your glasses!" says Howard, and hands Halm an envelope full of broken glass. "You picked up all the pieces, Howard. You really needn't have done that. Oh, Howard. Anyway, Howard, thank you."

Halm gropes his way into the house. He keeps on his undershirt; he doesn't think he can get it over his bandaged head. He lies down on his back and wonders how to tell Sabina without her dying of shock. In the morning he calls up the stairs to Lena, would she please come to the stairwell? When she calls down from above he says: "Please don't be frightened, I had a bit of a fall so there's a bit of a bandage around my head." Only then does he show himself to her. She still gets a shock. At that moment the phone rings. He calls out: "Don't bother, I'll take it." It is sure to be Fran to find out how he is. It is Sabina. Her father is dead. Died this morning. Oh. While I was dancing, he thinks. Sabina says: "Thank God it's all over for him." Halm says: "Thank God it's over for you too." "Come home soon," she says. "Yes," he says, "we'll be coming home soon now." Sabina was glad that Lena was living with Halm again. She'd been afraid that Lena might stay behind in California. "So let me know when I'm to pick you up." "Yes." "See you soon, then." "Keep your chin up." "You too." "Yes. Yes. Yes."

After he had hung up it occurred to him that he hadn't mentioned his split right brow with its six stitches. Poor Father Gottschalk. But Halm was glad he didn't have to go to that cemetery again. And he was glad that his bandaged head could serve as an excuse for not having to attend the interment of Rainer's ashes at Mountain View Cemetery. There was almost nothing he would not put up with to avoid attending a funeral. Nothing more embarrassing than the inevitable comparison at funerals between various displays of grief. Quite apart from the urge to laugh, which he always feared on such occasions.

Halm's appearance with his bandaged head was enough of an issue for a conversation class. Fran didn't show up. But Carol was back behind the desk, so Halm sat down again, forced as usual by the chair to turn his profile toward her. Her face was still stiff with gloom. She looked like someone who doesn't wish to be spoken to. "Copycat!" she said at the sight of Halm's bandaged head. She told him Fran had a cracked ankle bone and would be coming back tomorrow. A thick ankle and a fat head: that proclaimed Halm's intentions. Halm said: "At least you can make jokes again, Carol." "Far from it," she said.

On Tuesday Fran turned up again. So now there were two girls at the table with crutches. Gail seemed displeased. Apparently there is no limit to rivalry. Gail took no part whatever in the conversation about the evening at the Hill Court house. Halm told them that those who had been attending his course for the sake of their grades could take the rest of the week off since he was handing in his grades to the computer today. But the next morning they were all there again, and so it was until Friday. On Thursday Halm's bandage was removed. His right eye was totally invisible behind an enormous blue-black swelling. *Severe bruises*: that was now part of his vocabulary.

The split brow is healing well. He will be able to have the stitches removed next week in Stuttgart. In spite of the severe bruises, the eye itself was almost certainly undamaged. Lena was in for another shock when Halm came back with only a light dressing but with that huge blue-black swelling. Carol got a shock too. Roy laughed and said he must take a picture of Halm for Sally. His students laughed and congratulated him. No professor had ever achieved such a horror mask. The girls laughed a little less loudly. They were biting their lips. Fran. . . . He avoided looking in her direction. From her he expected more than a mere facial expression.

After class he walked slowly beside her to the fountain plaza, stood with her, discussed with her what she had written about Labove. And he said how very sorry he was that she had been so badly injured through his carelessness. She thought it was quite neat to walk on crutches for a change, she said. Nevertheless, he said, he knew how important running and swimming were to her. She was now exercising with crutches, she said, that was quite interesting. But not very pleasant, he said. But neat, she said. And in a few weeks she would make up for all she was now missing. He insisted that he was carrying an almost intolerable burden of guilt. Not at all, she said. His eye was much worse than her foot. Not worse, just not as neat, he said. No, she said, it was neat too, his eye, they were a neat couple now, with her foot and his eye. He said he didn't know why, but these injuries reminded him of Benedick and Beatrice. However, the fact that he was to blame for the injuries diminished his pleasure in this notion. If he had the eye, and she perhaps a sprained hand, but for her to be on crutches, no, no, no. . . . She would have none of his regrets, turned away, and swung herself along the sloping path, quickly and confidently and striving for a kind of grace.

On Friday Halm said good-bye to them all and told them how wonderful it had been and how much he regretted having to leave this sunny land to crawl back under a permanent cloud cover, into a tree-darkened house on a north slope that had very little light anyway. He begged them all to appreciate the privilege of living in a sunny land. This would be his final contribution to the conversation, in which it was appropriate for a departing guest to express his gratitude to his host in the form of highly flattering remarks. This, of course, was easy to do when there was some sincere feeling behind it all. Nothing had ever come more easily to him than this expression of gratitude to his California hosts.

After moist-eyed handshakes all around, he went off toward Crocker Gate. He walked slowly, hoping the girl would catch up with him. She did, with Jeff. The three of them walked as far as the fountain plaza. Jeff promised—as Howard had done too—to visit Halm in Sillenbuch. Jeff is planning to begin his philosophy studies as soon as possible in Berlin, but right now he didn't want to impose upon the two disabled victims of life any longer. He swung himself onto his ten-speed bike and disappeared downhill under the trees. On the path along which within a few minutes the girl would disappear too. The young brother was gone. The young sister was still standing there. He noticed that she stood very lightly between her two crutches. She said: "This is good-bye, Professor." "Right," he said. "Well then," she said. "I still feel guilty," he said gesturing at her crutches. She really was enjoying her crutches, he must believe her, she said. So in this way for a few weeks she'd have something that would remind her tangibly and pleasantly of him and of this enjoyable semester. "Conversation A-plus," he said. "Thanks to you," she said. "Well then, dear girl," he said. "Well then, Professor," she said. They shook hands. As always, he stood and watched her go. But this time, before disappearing under the trees, she stopped, turned around, and waved to him with her right crutch. Then she went on, didn't stop again, disappeared. She must have always known that when she left he would stand there watching her, otherwise she wouldn't have turned around again.

Halm and Lena put the house and all its contents into a state in which it had not been when they arrived. There was one more phone call from Kirk Elrod. Was Honeybunch at Halm's? No. Then she must be out exchanging something. She always shopped too hastily, and then she would discover she had bought the wrong thing and have to go back again to exchange it. Honeybunch spent ten times as long exchanging as buying. She had driven off at ten that morning, now it was close to six o'clock. Unfortunately there were no fixed store hours here as there were in Europe, so there were no limits to exchanging. Ah well, then he'd just wait till Honeybunch came home. From exchanging. But if she should turn up at Halm's he might mention that her husband had called. And once more he wished him a safe journey. Halm had the feeling that Elrod hadn't believed that Carol wasn't with him. Evidently Elrod regarded all that exchanging as an excuse. Then Sabina phoned. Was everything going according to plan? Yes, said Halm, but she mustn't be shocked, he would be arriving with a small dressing above one eye. He'd had a bit of a fall. The eye was already beginning to open a little. He'd explain it all to her. But don't be frightened, please.

On the last morning, Halm kept on the slippers with the hard soles that had once hurt the cat. She understood at once. She ran down from the top step without waiting for his feet. But on the patio she flung herself on her back, her rosy mouth and pads shining up from the white fur. He bent down, performed everything today with his hands which otherwise he had done with his feet, filled her bowl and plate as never before, waved across to the blind pug dog, and said to his little friend: "Good-bye for now." He picked a hibiscus blossom and three lemons, then closed the patio door as it were forever.

Roy was more punctual in picking up the two Halms than Rainer had been in picking up the three Halms. Roy wasn't a maniac. He was acting chairman until Rainer's successor was appointed. Sally said she had come along because Roy had been raving about Helmut's bruise. Halm said that the last thing he would see of California would be Sally: how was anyone supposed to tear himself away! Carol was planning to come too. "She's probably still busy exchanging," said Roy. "Now he's always holding his hand over his rainbow-hued eye," Sally said, "he wants to deprive me of the pleasure." "He learned that from Leslie," said Roy. "But his eye," said Sally, "isn't blind." "Oh, is Leslie blind in that eye?" asked Halm. "Didn't you know?" said Roy. That was why Leslie had cut short his athletic career and become a scientist. "Why d'you suppose he always holds his hand over it!" "I took it for a kind of leitmotiv," said Halm. Sally said: "How sweet."

Carol approached them across the departure hall, walking with dragging footsteps. Her expression explained why she didn't greet them. As soon as she was there, the conversation turned entirely to Rainer. It was she who was really the widow, who said the least. "He spared himself a lot through his death," said Sally. Carol looked away as deliberately as if she had just been called from somewhere. "He was unable to live," said Roy. "He had such strange demands," said Sally. "You know how she means that," said Roy. Carol didn't indicate whether she did or not.

It was time for Halm and Lena to go through the gate. Carol took a slip of paper from her handbag. This was another of those

Chinese fortune cookies he liked so much. He put it in his pocket, thanked her, and said he'd read it on the plane. Dear Sally, dear Roy, deardear Carol, many, many thanks, good-bye. In her sadness Carol looked more like a romantic sheep than like Lord Byron. Halm could feel this touching sheeplike grieving trying to hold him back. Perhaps that shining black eye-power could hypnotize. He simply wanted to stay. He belonged now to Carol. Rainer and Carol: to be with them suddenly seemed so wonderful that he had no desire to move. He said, looking straight at her: "But now I have to go." That unlocked her mouth. "Give my regards to Tee-Aitch," she said. He'd be glad to if he ran into him, said Halm. Her mouth hadn't quite closed again. A little of the intriguing gap between her front teeth remained visible. While here he had really done everything wrong that could be done wrong. Oh, Carol. Well then. Halm made an exaggerated gesture of tearing himself away and immediately felt like a ham actor. But then this walking off into the airplane is like ancient Greek theater. It is not merely the insubstantial Christian soul that is taking off: the whole body lifts itself off. On the plane he read Carol's fortune cookie: *Redecorating will be in your plans.* Oh, Carol, there's no one in California whose language I understand as well as I do yours. With this casual little phrase, Carol had at the very end recovered her light tone. Nothing is as appropriate to a heavy heart as a light tone.

He had one more look down onto the land as it sank away, then buried himself in the *San Francisco Chronicle.* He read it as if it were his newspaper and his city, as if he were taking a short flight somewhere and would soon be back again. Some of the topics were familiar to him. For example, that the rapist had been offered a choice between thirty years in jail and castration. Some choice! Gail will have visited him. Glorious Gail. With crutches and orthodontic braces, an indomitable helper. He gingerly felt around his swollen eye. Probably his departure was made easier by the drama of that little accident.

In Brussels they landed between ice and snow and in Stuttgart were met on Platform 16 by Sabina who, before saying anything, pulled her husband's hand from his right eye and let out a scream. Not loud but piercing. Halm shook his head, claimed that his vision was as good as ever, that he'd merely acquired it to impress. He thought it would be nice to come home as a damaged Odysseus and to be engulfed for a few moments in Penelope's tender shriek of alarm. "All right, let's go, take us to the car, shiksa!" Sabina said nothing. Not until she was driving out of the parking lot was she able to speak. She told them, as if she had to apologize for something, that it had only been snowing and freezing in Stuttgart for the past two days, before that the weather had been better, but now Lena and he must watch out that they didn't slip on the icy garden path at home and break something. An ankle, he thought. Although she had sanded the path, it was still slippery, she said. "And where's Otto?" asked Halm. "Oh, Otto," said Sabina, "he's been very quiet the last few days." "The winter weather," said Halm. "Maybe," said Sabina. "And you, Lena, let's hope you're a little bit glad to be home again." Lena said: "Let's hope so."

15 IN THE OBSCURE LIGHT

of the January afternoon, Sabina and Halm were sitting in the living room. Was it right for Kugel the baker to have the living room face south even when the south was nothing but a steep slope above which from November until the end of February the sun can scarcely lift itself? Halm didn't realize just how dark it was here until he returned from the land of the Pacific. Sitting in this room is like a punishment. They didn't sit across from one another. Or side by side. Sabina was sitting on the uncomfortable, nondescript sofa, Halm in one of the two armchairs belonging to the set. A quarter of a century ago, when they were buying this and other furniture all in one afternoon, Halm had thought that at some time or other he would make enough money to buy some decent furniture. For years now he had been making enough money to have afforded new furniture. But it seemed they had become used to what they had. For the first time it occurred to him that one shouldn't spend one's whole life with this kind of furniture. On the other hand, by now it was almost too late. They had spent their lives with this furniture.

Since coming home, whenever he sat with Sabina over a cup

of coffee he wondered whether he shouldn't ask her how she felt about some new furniture. He said: "The fact is, it's cold in this house." Sabina said it was overheated. He said he felt chilly. Ever since getting back he'd been feeling cold. No matter how warm the rooms were, he could feel the chill in all the warmth. He thought he could feel how cold the air had been before being heated up. "Maybe it's the light," he said. "A sort of lightlessness comes through the windows that defeats all lighting." On the other hand, the natural lightlessness of these days, unimpaired by lighting, felt agreeable. He didn't want to see anything, he said. Whatever emerged from one's efforts to dispel this daily gloom with electric light was downright painful to him. "Despite the lack of light, one still sees much too much," he said, pointing to the window. "Everything bare, stiff, hard, cold." Sabina said this all sounded as if aimed at her. She would leave him to himself now, perhaps that would make him feel better. And if he really couldn't stand it here any longer, O.K., she'd like to remind him that at Father's funeral Elmar had made it quite clear that he wasn't going to put up much longer with the way things were being handled around here. Elmar had meanwhile found out a thing or two: what was going up next door was an eight-unit apartment building. The time for idle talk was past, Elmar had said. He was going to get them some offers from construction companies. Perhaps Helmut could include that in his gloomy contemplations. She had to go into town with Lena and buy some clothes for her because Lena was leaving the next day. After a few minutes she came back and put the mail on the table, saying: "The mail." She suggested they go out into the garden with Otto for a bit, that would do them both good.

He felt better as soon as he was alone. Not that I've anything against you, Sabina, he mentally called out after her. As soon as he was alone the compulsion of having to justify himself was less palpable. As soon as he was alone he could be what he was. Even if he was impossible. When you're alone it doesn't matter if you're impossible. As soon as Sabina was in the room it embarrassed him that he was as impossible as he was. He was indecisive, unwilling, unkind. He was not here, not there. He felt he mustn't find it bearable here. But it was bearable here. He would be able to bear it here. Everything was fine. All he had to do was relax and find everything as fine as it was. He found this easier to do when he was alone. As soon as Sabina was in the room, he kidded himself that Sabina was to blame for his being here and not there. As if he could have been there. As if something would have been possible there. As if the absolute worst wouldn't have happened if something had been possible there. Unthinkable, what would have happened if Miss Webb had said: Come! But even this if/then scenario was superfluous. There was nothing. There is nothing. There will be nothing. There will have been nothing. And that's far from being a disaster. The opposite would have been a disaster. But like this everything's fine.

When he was alone he felt reasonably sure of all this. Of course, what he most wanted was to sit there in the gloom of these murky days and drivel to himself: If you're not with me, I'm not with myself either. . . . Nothing seemed more appealing than to imagine her first letter. She was bound to write. Perhaps in writing they could. . . . *What* could they in writing? Nothing. Naturally Rainer had to get into the act too. Rainer, that maniac. Yes, it requires a special talent to develop a highly sensitive system of justice that works solely to one's own advantage. He didn't have that talent. Maybe because he was really not as good as Rainer.

He had never felt as embarrassed with Sabina as he did now. Mentally he was begging all the time for a postponement. Everything is as it was. It's just that at the moment one can't say so. When Sabina went into raptures over Rainer, making him out to be the supreme human being, he nodded. He could agree. For different reasons. But he could also curse Rainer. Rainer wouldn't have killed himself, Sabina, if you or I or anyone else had meant something to him. He was through with all of us. That's what I blame him for, if you don't mind. And forever. Makes Lena a gift of his hundred and fifty-four love sonnets to Elissa! Yet they are nothing but love poems to himself. Advertising leaflets for the benefit of poor Rainer addressed to the cruel uncomprehending one. It's her business to love him. It's her duty. And if she doesn't, he'll tell the whole world, *then* she'll see! As if there were such a thing as a claim to love! As if one could demand to be liked. No registrar's office could make Halm feel that he had a claim to Miss Webb. So stop it. But since he could no longer abuse, beat up, or stroke Rainer, no amount of arguing would help. He who thinks of the dead thinks of himself. Halm savored moments. The way Rainer could look at one over the top of his glasses, uplift his Saint John's hands, and so on. Now he had reached such and such an age and still hadn't learned to cope with death. Death had snatched Rainer away from him. Just as a grown-up takes away a toy from a child without explanation, so death had taken Rainer away from him. Yes, because you weren't watching out. You let him be snatched away from you. You behaved as if there were ten Rainers. Now there is none. If only you'd phoned him. You knew that he had no lecture and that he couldn't bear that. You could have foreseen all that and then prevented what was to come. You could have prevented it. So O.K. What do you say, Otto? The two of us, right?

Why hadn't Sabina handed him the mail? He saw the mail lying on the table. Newspapers, letters. Perhaps a letter from her. He would spend all afternoon sitting there without moving. He would prove to himself that he thought nothing was possible. He needed no one. Except Sabina. When Sabina came home with Lena, she was to find the mail just where she had put it. That would prove to her that he wasn't curious about anything from the outside. Besides, it was in his nature not to move. After managing for almost four months to suppress any embarrassing confession, he wasn't about to write a letter now and blab it all out. She would read the letter to Carol. And meanwhile Carol had had a second phone conversation with Kiderlen, so. . . . But even without the vision of such extreme embarrassment, he simply would not write. And if there was a letter from her today, he didn't know whether he would open it. Of course he would open it at once. As soon as Sabina was no longer in the room. But he would not reply. Of course he would reply at once. But one thing is sure: he wouldn't write a single word more than he had said.

Suddenly he stood up, walked toward the mail, past it, got himself a bottle of wine and, carrying bottle and glass, walked once again past the mail, set bottle and glass on the low marble table, and devoted himself to Otto. He pushed the cushions under Otto so he could sit upright and breathe more easily. Sabina and Lena wanted to consult a vet. Juliane wrote angry letters from Berlin. That was no way to treat old age! Take him to the vet immediately! she wrote. Halm had relented. The appointment was for tomorrow. "Oh, Otto," said Halm as he opened his bottle of Bordeaux. And Otto said, without looking up, for he was so weak that he could only look straight ahead and so only mutter to himself: *Why, what's the matter, that you have such a February face, so full of frost, of storm, and cloudiness?* "Oh, Otto, fancy your knowing that my name is Benedick!" Otto made no reply. He was breathing laboriously. Hard work, every breath. Halm kneeled down in front of Otto and tried to catch his eye. "Otto, listen, Sabina thinks we should go into the garden. Or would you rather go up into the woods, our favorite walk, Otto? Or along Eselsweg down to Rohracker, to those pious Communists? Tell me what you'd like, Otto. I'd rather follow you than anyone else. Maybe toward Frauenkopf? Is there another Hohenzollern scion you'd like to show me who's moved in somewhere around there? Or do you want to bite one of those developers next door? Come on now, tell me!" The painful, labored breathing was Otto's only reply. "Otto, listen to me—don't leave me so soon! One more summer, Otto, just so you can see that we won't leave you all alone like last year in August! Never again, Otto! Otto, there's so much I still have to tell you about California. Dogs go out alone there, they really do, Otto, they go into town, call on friends, everybody respects them on the sidewalk, they wait for the green light, then cross the street."

When Halm noticed that Otto was no longer listening the way

he used to, he sat down again in the armchair and stared out into the garden that stared back. Unimaginable that on Monday he would be going back to school. If he were to go back to school—which he couldn't yet imagine—then without a tie. That was the only thing he was sure about. And he wouldn't feel like a servile Kiderlen-imitator. Perhaps on some hot, sultry July day he would even put on his Caribbean-Oakland suit and the raspberry-colored shirt. On seeing that suit Sabina had cried Oooh! The girl and her boyfriend must have thought he looked ludicrous in that suit. On their way home from the Steiner Auditorium they must have laughed. Each trying to outdo the other. What's Malvolio compared to that, she had exclaimed! Watch out, he had said, you'll be hitting a tree! One can never be as naked, as exposed, in the flesh as one becomes in the mind. He wanted to tell himself the uttermost. The most important. You know it, but you're keeping it from yourself. Don't behave as if you had died in California of an emotional heart attack and were staggering around here as a ghost! Applaud your stance that forbade you to permit a class photo to be taken. You were on the right track, for you didn't need that girl for a single second. You were pretending. A touch of inevitability had to be present. It is only true love when you have no choice. Love is the most highly valued disease that is identified by the symptom of You-can't-help-it. You wanted to be as heartbroken as a younger man. Scream like a thirty-year-old. Rage, persist, sweat, hit out, race, climb, fall, get up again, race on, like a thirty-year-old. Relentlessly. That one and no other. Let the whole world bear witness. . . . An Asra presumption, that's what it was. But presumption it was. For you're still alive. You have not had the guts to admit to yourself what it was during these weeks that determined your actions: that you have absolutely no need of her. You can survive splendidly without her. You are already so shorn of feeling that you can walk past even a girl like that without turning a hair. It's just that you can't admit yet to yourself that you haven't turned a hair. You have to pretend to have caught a horrendous disease, put on an act to avoid admitting to yourself that all is over. Everything. Just an act, that's all.

Was he divided again? Was it *He*-Halm speaking? Revenge for being gagged? No, Halm was no longer divided. NEW BALANCE was stamped on the running shoes he had worn while jogging in Tilden Park's eucalyptus forest and redwood groves. When he unpacked his running shorts, something rustled in the zipper pocket: the stuff he had picked from the bushes that covered all the hills he had run through. Rosemary, Sabina had said, and added the words which, as he was picking the leaves, he had imagined her saying—that apart from snowdrops he didn't know one plant from another, did he!

He was only able to move again when Sabina and Lena returned. Lena hadn't felt she needed either a new coat or anything else. Her mother had thought differently and had prevailed. Halm jumped up and asked Lena to put on what had been bought. With gentle persuasion and combined efforts they forced Lena into the new purchases. They looked nice, and fitted. Now it was also necessary to persuade her to admit that she had needed this force and was glad it had been applied. Children must be forced to admit everything one wants them to admit.

Halm sat down again and asked for the mail. He wanted to receive it from Sabina's hands alone. Probably he had subconsciously noticed that the letters included one from America. That kind of large buff envelope was used only in America. "From Washington University of Oakland!" he said. "Ah, from our dear Carol!" he went on. "I wonder what our dear Carol has to tell us!" She had written: "I've slipped back into my routine, others were not so lucky, as you can see from this." That was the entire letter. The envelope also contained a Chinese fortune-cookie strip and a newspaper clipping. The newspaper report:

Coed Dies in 300-foot Plunge

Two young people in a BMW bounced down a cliff Friday night near Daly City's Mussel Rock Beach. One of them, Glenn Birdsell, was plucked from the steep cliff in a dramatic rescue by a Coast Guard helicopter. Fran Webb, who was Birdsell's girlfriend, died in the car, which she owned. The vehicle went off the cliff from a parking lot, the ground giving way at the edge of the cliff as a result of a landslide caused by the season's heavy rainfall. Birdsell survived by being thrown unconscious out of the car before it plowed into the beach sand and ended up in the stormy surf. "It seemed like it took five minutes going down the cliff," 22-year-old Birdsell said yesterday through swollen lips from his bed at Kaiser Hospital in South San Francisco. "We were so shocked, we went kind of silent as we hurtled and bounced down the cliff face," he said.

Birdsell, an outstanding water polo player, suffered a broken collarbone, chipped teeth, and other injuries, including possible damage to his right eye, which was closed by severe bruises. Fran Webb, hampered by crutches due to a broken ankle she suffered three weeks earlier, was trapped as the surging surf of the incoming tide washed over her demolished BMW 528. She was already dead when she was removed from the car.

In the margin, a note in Carol's writing to say that the memorial service had been held on January 3 at Grace Cathedral in San Francisco.

This time Halm couldn't let it rest at mere understanding: He had to translate the contents word for word. What had sometimes so appealed to him over there—to leave everything pleasantly vague—was now unthinkable. He wanted to be absolutely sure of every detail. First, so as not to lose it, he stuck the fortune-cookie strip (*Optimism, versatility, all your strengths*) onto the newspaper clipping.

There was also a letter from Juliane. Sabina was waiting impatiently to read it to him. Juliane's letters were usually written in the evening. She always wrote when she had to get something off her chest. This time it was Mr. and Mrs. Kempinski who had made a letter necessary. Through Juliane's letters the Halms had long been familiar with all the inmates of the retirement home.

Mr. Kempinski is the one who has forgotten, five minutes after his breakfast, that he has had his breakfast, and who then spends all morning writing angry letters to the administration claiming that he had not been given any breakfast. Every day he orders his wife to take his complaint across to the administration office before lunch. His wife always throws these letters in the same paper basket in the corridor of the administration building. On her return she finds her husband chewing. He tries to hide this from her. In his locker he has a cache of food that he wants to keep entirely to himself. But this time, because of his haste, an unchewed bit of zwieback had found its way into his windpipe, and a tracheotomy had been necessary. Mr. Kempinski, eighty-four, was saved, but Juliane had to put up with serious reproaches from the administration because she had admitted to having known about Mr. Kempinski's food cache. Now she was furious with the Kempinskis. "Poor child," said Halm. Sabina said she was at least glad that in this letter Juliane had said nothing about Brazil. Perhaps she's having second thoughts.

"What's the news from California?" asked Sabina casually. "Rather sad news, I'm afraid. A girl who was in my conversation course drove to the sea with her boyfriend. You'll remember how close the cars stood to the coast, at the very edge of the cliffs. You remember how people drive up as far as they can, then they sit in the car holding a can of beer or soda and looking out over the ocean. Remember? Apparently there have been all kinds of landslides from all that rain. That must have happened there too. They slid down, in their car, tumbling from rock to rock, about three hundred feet down the cliff till the car came to rest on the beach, in the surf."

"And then?" asked Sabina. "On the way down, the boyfriend was flung out of the car onto a rock, where he lay until he was picked up by a helicopter, severe bruises but alive." "And the girl?" asked Sabina. "She wasn't flung out. She had crutches beside her from a recent accident. The crutches may have prevented her from being tossed out of the car. By the time they pulled her out of the car, it was too late. She had drowned. The breakers. Those winter storms. Ah well." "Poor girl," said Sabina.

Lena said: "Good night," and went upstairs. Sabina said she found Lena more mature. Amazing how Lena had managed to turn those scars into a part of her expression, said Halm. "They've simply ceased to be scars," he said. She simply looks more determined than before. Sabina said she must admit that she felt California had done Lena a lot of good. In any case she was now beyond the reach of that self-idolater Traugott. "But why Bochum, of all places?" said Sabina. "It had to be an automobile city, she told me," said Halm. "But she wants to go into the used-car business," said Sabina. "What a crazy idea, the used-car business, and in Bochum of all places—can you understand that?" Bochum, he thought, the doctor with the six stitches had been in Bochum. "Helmut, I asked you something! If you don't want to talk to me anymore, just tell me and I'll shut up."

Halm said he'd go out for some fresh air with Otto; he was sorry he'd missed his chance during the afternoon. Just a few steps toward the woods. Otto was reluctant, but Halm insisted. As soon as they were outdoors he took pity on him. Every two or three steps he let him rest. Only when they were up onto the road did Halm walk ahead as if he didn't care whether Otto followed him or not. Otto followed him. Some memory of previous walks animated him. Halm walked as far as the woods and into the woods. For the first time since being back he enjoyed the sensation of cold. Otto suddenly sat down. "All right," said Halm, "we'll go back now." Again Halm led the way. At the sound of a car, he stopped at the side of the road and looked back. Otto was walking along the middle of the narrow road, oblivious. Although the driver couldn't fail to see him, since his headlamps were on high beam, Halm called out: "Otto!" But it was too late. The old red Volkswagen—the last time Halm had seen one like that was in that movie in which a prostitute and marine biology student was in love with her teacher—ran over Otto and, if Halm hadn't forced it to stop, probably would have driven straight on.

Halm rushed over to Otto, but before he reached him Otto got up, made a few little jumps, managed to reach the construction site, ran up against a pile of bricks, fell, and lay still. His eyes were open. But he was no longer moving. The driver had run after Halm. He smelled of beer. When he saw what had happened, he let out a howl. "How could I have run over a wee doggie? Oh no, how could I run over a wee doggie—if I tell 'em about that at home, what d'you think they'll do to me? They'll kill me, I tell you, they'll kill me. And a spaniel, too, it's a spaniel, isn't it, I can't tell 'em that, a spaniel, oh no!" The tears were running down his red cheeks. He had just come from two PTA meetings, in two different schools, he had two daughters, he said none of the teachers had shown the slightest understanding, they'd been as hard as rock, so neither of the girls would be promoted, that's it, amen, so he needed a drink, and now this, run over a wee doggie, such a dear little doggie, a spaniel, oh no! . . .

The man was yelling his head off. Halm had no choice but to calm him down. Halm asked whether he had an old blanket in his car. Yes, he did, no blanket was too good for such a dear wee doggie. They laid Otto on the blanket and carried him down to the garden. So from now on, whenever he goes through the garden gate and sees the house number 96 he will have to think of Act I of *Walküre* in the Steiner Auditorium, Room 96. It seems that, as time goes on, reality looks more and more like a conspiracy. They laid Otto under a fir tree in the garden. The man was determined to leave the blanket there, but Halm pressed it upon him. Then Halm accompanied the man back to his car and urged him to drive home slowly. The man merely nodded and sniffed noisily through his wine-plugged nose. Halm went back to Otto: Oh, Otto, who am I going to talk to now. . . .

Halm went indoors and brought Sabina out. She said they couldn't leave Otto lying there like that in the open! Probably he was only unconscious. Sabina brought out a sheet in which they carried Otto into the basement. Sabina wanted to examine him in the light. Blood was now coming from Otto's mouth. Halm said that if Lena didn't ask about Otto tomorrow morning, they shouldn't tell her anything. Sabina burst our angrily, tearfully: "Always this secrecy, why in God's name?" Halm said: "Just when she's leaving, something like this—must we?" Sabina shrugged.

While he had been out with Otto, Kiderlen had phoned, Sabina told him. He was looking forward to working with Halm. He'd phone again tomorrow, perhaps even drop by. He really made an effort. "You mean, he bent over backward to please you," said Halm. That evening Halm spoke only English. When Sabina became irritated, he yelled at her. Then apologized. But in English. It was only when Sabina put on her mother's slippers in the bedroom that he gave up his English. In German he said: "How much longer do you intend wearing those things?" "Oh, welcome back!" Sabina said in English. "Ah, Sabina," he said, "all I can do now is look forward to school. To Kiderlen! I must admit that suddenly Kiderlen seems to me to be no problem at all." Halm opened the closet door and took out the suit from Oakland. No, he'd never wear that one again. That garish cognac shade with the black and yellow rectangles! What must the light have been like! He said: "D'you remember, Sabina, those evenings, the Bay with its strings of lights, beyond it the city with its gold-green patches rising one above the other? As if by Klee." He fell silent. The girl had had gold-green hair. Depending on the surroundings. When she lay on the grave, for instance. O Virgil.

Sabina said that, if it were up to her, Lena wouldn't be going to Bochum tomorrow. Halm said nothing. Sabina went on: "Why Bochum! Can you tell me that?" Halm said: "No." "And the other one to Brazil," said Sabina. "Can you understand that? And now Otto, too." After a while Sabina continued: "It feels as if he has taken with him all the years he was here." Then: "But Bochum! Why Bochum?" Halm produced a sound from which Sabina was supposed to infer that Halm was just falling asleep or had already fallen asleep. In case Sabina wasn't yet through with her struggling, he could pretend to wake up again and share in the back and forth of the parental script. But he hoped he would fall asleep before that.

The little warm, dark space of his bed protected him. He felt for his eye, no longer swollen but still bluish, and put his hand over it like Leslie Ackerman. So Glenn also had something the matter with his eye, it was closed from "severe bruises," perhaps permanently damaged. Strictly speaking, one of those iron cicadas standing around on the floor in front of the hearth was to blame. His foot had landed on one of those iron objects, it had slipped from under him, he had slipped, the whirling was cut short, the fall began. He could remember nothing of that fall. The whirling he still remembered. That had been something solid. Then that slipping and falling. They had "hurtled and bounced down the cliff face," into the surf. Drowned in "the surging surf." That wonderful wife of the Scandinavian scholar wanted the Valkyries to rise from the breakers. . . .

He could hear that Sabina, instead of relaxing, was becoming more and more restless. That heavy breathing and turning and groaning meant that she knew he was listening. She was putting it on. He responded with the regular breathing of the sleeper. Let's see whether he couldn't convince her. She said she couldn't stand it any longer. What was the matter, he asked? That was what she was asking him, she said. "I'm always supposed to do the reassuring around here," he said. She didn't bother to reply. He breathed again like someone falling asleep.

Tomorrow he'd listen to the record they'd been given by Rainer. When such things happen, such drastic things, one simply can't fight back. When he used inflated language, at least he always knew that he was using inflated language. This knowledge alone made him feel justified. But when such drastic things really happened. . . . Elissa's fireplace decoration, one could think about that. A skull with all its teeth, and a female one too, supposedly, and the tarantula skeleton and the naked female figure on the wood pile. That's how it should be. Decorative! Joyce Ackerman with her ever-open rectangular mouth, her glasses reaching from braid to braid—a death's-head. And a pretty death's-head at that. A beautiful death's-head. The girl also had some resemblance to a death's-head. Nonsense. But she did! Yes, she did. Everyone does. O Virgil! The much-too-soft bag over her shoulder. And as she put her hand into this bag she looked at him. He had told her more than once that he was to blame for her now needing crutches. She wouldn't accept that. He had repeated that he was to blame. She had waved to him with one crutch. Why aren't you coming, Professor? But in that case why had she turned away? Because he hadn't made a move. . . .

Sabina tossed aside the quilt, jumped out of bed, and ran out of the room. He hurried after her. She was already sitting downstairs, in the armchair. She was absolutely rigid. He kneeled down beside her, in front of her on the floor, but she kept turning away. He said: "Forgive me, please, Sabina. Please, Sabina, forgive me. You are right. Please, forgive me." He drew her up gently out of the armchair. As her tension subsided, he tried to lead her upstairs. She wanted to go down to the basement, to Otto. He said: "You'll catch cold," but he went with her. They stood beside Otto. His paws lay slightly bent, as if he were asleep. But his eyes were open, and there was blood coming from his mouth. Halm drew Sabina away. He led her back to her bed, tucked her in, went to his bed but lay down as close as possible to her. "Well then," he said. He reached one hand across. She seemed calmer now. That made him also feel calmer. He fell asleep.

When he woke up again it was still dark. He had been dreaming. Some students had besieged the house. It was Christmas Eve. They were shouting, throwing rocks against the shutters, rattling at the doors, the house creaked and groaned. They shouted that they had no place to go, and it was freezing cold. They were claiming their rights, they had been promised lodging here. He couldn't move a muscle. Sabina had dashed out in her nightgown, and silence had immediately descended outside. Sabina had come back, the silence had persisted, but Halm hadn't been able to breathe for fear that the racket would start up again. That had woken him up.

Halm now slipped cautiously across into Sabina's bed and let her warmth enfold him. Her sleep soon sent him off to sleep again, but he awoke once more. Again from a dream. This time it was a matriculation dream. He had to correct a matric essay. While he had to do his correcting, he was sitting on a stage. On the stage a play was being performed. The hall was full of people. The essay he had to correct was his own matriculation essay, dealing with a Shakespeare play. The play his essay dealt with was being performed on the stage on which he had to correct his essay in full view of the public. Everyone in the audience could tell from his manner that he found his essay unsatisfactory. Everyone would notice that he was trying not to let anyone see how unsatisfactory he found his own essay. Just as he was about to give himself a better mark then he deserved, the actors bent over his papers. Concealment was now out of the question. The disgrace would immediately be revealed on the stage in theatrical exaggeration. When embarrassment became unbearable, Otto bit his hand. The pen, filled with red ink, sprayed red ink over the sheet of paper and fell to the floor. Halm clutched the hand that was bleeding from Otto's bite, and awoke. His arm was hurting. The way he had been lying on it must have cut off the circulation. He slowly pushed himself back into his own bed. He wasn't keen to fall asleep again right away. First he wanted his dream to fade. In his mind he followed the course of the dream, wanting the dream simply to unwind again in his consciousness. With dreams that were so drastic that they tormented and then wakened him, he always found it best to let them unwind in his mind again. In the repetition they lost their power over him. He positively enjoyed having a second look at a so-to-speak tamed dream-content that had just been so painful. Without wincing he could now observe himself sitting on the stage in front of all those people, trying to fake a successful essay out of an unsuccessful one. Even Otto's bite didn't hurt anymore. Or had it been his little friend, the California cat? And without having seen any red ink in his dream, he had known at once that what sprayed over the paper after the bite was red ink. It is always a mystery how in a dream one knows everything so quickly and so precisely. How much one knows, and how quickly! One arrives at a thorough and instant assessment of the highest potentials in any given situation. The bite came from Otto as well as from the California cat. And from the girl. No problem for the dream. The girl had Halm's eyes, which were his grandmother's eyes, which had come more and more to resemble those of a cat. . . . But he now remembered that, before Otto as the California cat, and the cat in turn as the girl, had bitten him, he had tried to prevent something painful, which was why he leaped up and called out to the audience, now sitting in the lecture room of the Faculty Club: I invite you for a state visit! Then the bite. In his dream he had known that he had been addressing everyone in the audience but had meant only one: the girl. It pleased him that in a dream one turns oneself into a statesman who can invite a person who is beyond one's reach. What wonderful help there is in dreams, he thought. Exactly the kind of help one needs. It was true, of course, that the girl was no longer alive. Not even a state visit could bring her back. That information hadn't yet reached the source area of his dreams. During the next few nights it will supply him with dreams that are up-to-date. Always that compulsion to laugh. Closely allied to the compulsion to weep.

His dream had now outworn its effect. Couldn't he now feel more comfortable? Wasn't his weight more evenly distributed? He was no longer bearing down heavily on one point. Sabina's breathing, that moved in and out like the softest strokes of a violin bow, assured him that she was fast asleep. What he felt as he listened to her was familiar. Everything came together and persuaded him to admit that he now felt at home. Since it's so dark, he thought, I can even nod. What one doesn't do for a quiet sleep! But he didn't dare fall asleep again right away. What dream would he have to face if he fell asleep now? He'd rather stay awake for a while and think. He preferred being unmasked by thoughts to being exposed by dreams. Now he was afraid of his dreams. He said, so softly that only he could hear it: "Sabina." Sabina said at once and too loud: "Yes!" He said he must tell her something. Sabina said:

"Yes." "Well then," he said. "Well then," she said. By means of this back and forth they had reached the sound level that was right for both of them. Now he could begin. He began with the second day of school vacation when he had stood facing the bathroom mirror. He had finished shaving but couldn't stop contemplating his face with an indissoluble blend of dislike and satisfaction.